R.F.Outcault's The YELLOW KID

Author's dedication

The world's only complete print file of the Outcault Yellow Kid pages on which this book is based (now in the San Francisco Academy of Comic Art) was peserved through the serendipitious activities of

ERNIE MCGEE   and   JACK HERBERT

to whom this book is dedicated with great thanks and appreciation.

—BILL BLACKBEARD

Publisher's acknowledgment

This year, as the Centennial of the Comic Strip is celebrated in the United States and throughout the world, Kitchen Sink Press marks the anniversary with this volume reprinting the first comic strip. The realization of the work has been made possible through the cooperation of many individuals and institutions. For their generous assistance, the publisher offers sincere thanks to William Randolph Hearst III for his eloquent foreword, and to Bill Blackbeard, Director of the San Francisco Academy of Comic Art, for his comprehensive introduction, and to him and the Academy for providing the rare color pages as well as most of the black and white illustrations. Images were also generously provided by Craig Koste, Bob Cook, Richard Olson, and Jerry Muller. Further generous assistance and advice were lent by: Dean Mullaney and Catherine Yronwode of Eclipse Press; Dr. Eileen Boris, Howard University; Dr. Richard Olson, University of New Orleans; Dr. Lucy Caswell, Director of the Cartoon, Graphic, and Photographic Arts Research Library, Ohio State University; Professor Tom De Haven, Virginia Commonwealth University; Sarah Mekrut, Archivist, and James Driscoll, Historian, Queens Historical Society; Robert Friedricks, Queens Public Library; and Sandy Northrop, Northrop Productions. Assistance in photographic research was generously provided by Martina Fahrner, Museum of the City of New York; Carol Butler, Brown Brothers; Wendy Haynes, The New-York Historical Society; Gwen Allen, Smith College Museum of Art, and M. Richard Fish, Photographer, Smith College. For Kitchen Sink Press: N. C. Christopher Couch, editor; Tamara Sibert and Amie Brockway, art directors; Leslie Cabarga and Tamara Sibert, cover designers; Tamara Sibert, designer; Jacquelyn H. Southern, consulting editor; Kate Carey and Allison Smith, editorial assistants; Doug Bantz, Denise Clark, Kevin Lison, Brendan Stephens, Lisa Stone, production and design.

Library of Congress Cataloging-in-Publication Data

Outcault, Richard Felton, 1863-1928
      The Yellow Kid : a centennial celebration of the kid who started the comics / R.F. Outcault.
          p.   cm.
      Includes bibliographical references.
      ISBN 0-87816-380-8. -- Isbn 0-87816-379-4 (pbk.)
      I. Title.
PN6727.098Y45 1995   95-20552
741.5'973--dc20   CIP

First Printing: July 1995

5 4 3 2 1

PRINTED IN HONG KONG

R.F. Outcault's the Yellow Kid

**A Centennial Celebration
of the Kid Who Started
the Comics**

KITCHEN SINK PRESS®

NORTHAMPTON, MASSACHUSETTS

Contents

List of Illustrations

Figures

Plates

22. RICHARD F. OUTCAULT, *Hogan's Alley,* "First Grand Coaching Parade of the Season in Hogan's Alley," June 7, 1896 (*New York World*).

23. RICHARD F. OUTCAULT, *Hogan's Alley,* "The Bicycle Meet in Hogan's Alley," June 21, 1896 (*New York World*).

24. RICHARD F. OUTCAULT, *Hogan's Alley,* "Hogan's Alley Folk Sailing Boats in Central Park," June 28, 1896 (*New York World*).

25. RICHARD F. OUTCAULT, *Hogan's Alley,* "An Old-Fashioned Fourth of July in Hogan's Alley," July 5, 1896 (*New York World*).

26. RICHARD F. OUTCAULT, *Hogan's Alley,* "A Hot Political Convention in Hogan's Alley," July 12, 1896 (*New York World*).

27. RICHARD F. OUTCAULT, *Hogan's Alley,* "Hogan's Alley Children Spend a Day in the Country," July 19, 1896 (*New York World*).

28. RICHARD F. OUTCAULT, *Hogan's Alley,* "The Opening of the Hogan's Alley Roof Garden," July 26, 1896 (*New York World*).

29. RICHARD F. OUTCAULT, *Hogan's Alley,* "A Wild Political Fight in Hogan's Alley—Silver Against Gold," August 2, 1896 and GEORGE B. LUKS, "Red-Hot Energy of the Populists" (*New York World*).

30. RICHARD F. OUTCAULT, *Hogan's Alley,* "Hogan's Alley Folk Have a Wild Trolley Party in Brooklyn," August 9, 1896 (*New York World*).

31. RICHARD F. OUTCAULT, *Hogan's Alley,* "Hogan's Alley Folk Discover the North Pole," August 16, 1896 (*New York World*).

32. RICHARD F. OUTCAULT, *Hogan's Alley,* "The Great Lawn Tennis Tournement in Hogan's Alley," August 30, 1896 (*New York World*).

33. RICHARD F. OUTCAULT, *Hogan's Alley,* "The Great Bull Fight in Hogan's Alley," August 23, 1896 (*New York World*).

34. RICHARD F. OUTCAULT, *Hogan's Alley,* "Li Hung Chang Visits Hogan's Alley," September 6, 1896 (*New York World*).

35. RICHARD F. OUTCAULT, "The Yellow Dugan Kid," September 7, 1896, ink, pencil, watercolor and blue pencil on paper.

36. RICHARD F. OUTCAULT, *Hogan's Alley,* "A Secret Society Initiation in Hogan's Alley," September 13, 1896 (*New York World*).

37. RICHARD F. OUTCAULT, *Hogan's Alley,* "What They Did to the Dogcatcher in Hogan's Alley," September 20, 1896 (*New York World*).

38. RICHARD F. OUTCAULT and GEORGE B. LUKS, *Hogan's Alley,* "Opening of the Hogan's Alley Athletic Club," September 27, 1896 (*New York World*).

39. RICHARD F. OUTCAULT, *Hogan's Alley,* "The Amateur Dime Museum in Hogan's Alley," October 4, 1896 (*New York World*).

40. RICHARD F. OUTCAULT, *McFadden's Row of Flats,* October 18, 1896 (*New York Journal*).

41. RICHARD F. OUTCAULT, *McFadden's Row of Flats,* October 25, 1896 (*New York Journal*).

42. RICHARD F. OUTCAULT, *The Yellow Kid,* "The Yellow Kid and His New Phonograph," October 25, 1896 (*New York Journal*).

43. ARCHIE GUNN and RICHARD F. OUTCAULT, cover for *American Humorist,* November 1, 1896 (*New York Journal*).

44. RICHARD F. OUTCAULT, *McFadden's Row of Flats,* "Receiving the Returns in McFadden's Row on Election Night," November 1, 1896 (*New York Journal*).

45. RICHARD F. OUTCAULT, *McFadden's Row of Flats,* "The Season Opens with the Horse Show in McFadden's Row of Flats," November 8, 1896 (*New York Journal*).

46. WILLIAM H. FRIDAY, JR. and HOMER TOURJEE, "The Yellow Kid, the Latest and the Greatest," sheet music with drawings by RICHARD F. OUTCAULT (*New York Journal,* November 8, 1896).

47. RICHARD F. OUTCAULT and ARCHIE GUNN, cover for *American Humorist,* November 15, 1896 (*New York Journal*).

48. RICHARD F. OUTCAULT, *McFadden's Row of Flats,* "Inauguration of the Football Season in McFadden's Row," November 15, 1896 (*New York Journal*).

49. RICHARD F. OUTCAULT, *McFadden's Row of Flats,* "A Turkey Raffle in Which the Yellow Kid Exhibits Skill With the Dice," November 22, 1896 (*New York Journal*).

50. RICHARD F. OUTCAULT, *The Yellow Kid,* "A Few Things the Versatile Yellow Kid Might Do For a Living," November 22, 1896 (*New York Journal*).

51. RICHARD F. OUTCAULT, *McFadden's Row of Flats,* "The Yellow Kid Introduces a Monk, Who Enlivens the Pool Tournement in McFadden's Flats," November 29, 1896 (*New York Journal*).

52. RICHARD F. OUTCAULT, *The Yellow Kid,* "The Yellow Kid Indulges in a Cockfight—A Waterloo," November 29, 1896 (*New York Journal*).

53. RICHARD F. OUTCAULT and ARCHIE GUNN, cover for *American Humorist,* December 6, 1896 (*New York Journal*).

54. RICHARD F. OUTCAULT, *The Yellow Kid,* "A Three-Cornered Fight in McFadden's Flats," December 6, 1896 (*New York Journal*).

55. RICHARD F. OUTCAULT, *McFadden's Row of Flats,* "McFaddens's Flatters Skating and Tobagganing Expedition," December 6, 1896 (*New York Journal*).

56. RICHARD F. OUTCAULT, *The Yellow Kid,* "Dark Secret; or How the Yellow Kid Took a Picture," December 13, 1896 (*New York Journal*).

57. RICHARD F. OUTCAULT, *McFadden's Row of Flats,* "A Merry Christmas in McFadden's Flats," December 13, 1896 (*New York Journal*).

58. RICHARD F. OUTCAULT, *The Yellow Kid,* "The Yellow Kid's Great Fight," December 20, 1896 (*New York Journal*).

59. RICHARD F. OUTCAULT, *McFadden's Row of Flats,* "The Opening Night in Kelly's Bowling Alley," December 20, 1896 (*New York Journal*).

60. RICHARD F. OUTCAULT, *The Yellow Kid,* "The Yellow Kid Wrestles with the Tobacco Habit," December 27, 1896 (*New York Journal*).

61. RICHARD F. OUTCAULT, *McFadden's Row of Flats,* "The New Year's Fancy Dress Ball in McFadden's Flats," December 27, 1896 (*New York Journal*).

62. RICHARD F. OUTCAULT, *The Yellow Kid,* "How the Yellow Kid Planted a Seed and the Result," January 3, 1897 (*New York Journal*).

63. RICHARD F. OUTCAULT, *McFadden's Row of Flats*, "The Studio Party in McFadden's Flats," January 3, 1897 (*New York Journal*).

64. RICHARD F. OUTCAULT, *McFadden's Row of Flats*, "The Yaller Kid's Mother Goose Vaudeville, Co., Ltd.," January 10, 1897 (*New York Journal*).

65. RICHARD F. OUTCAULT, *Around the World With the Yellow Kid*, "Off To Europe—Where They Won't Do a Thing to the Effete Monarchies," January 17, 1897 (*New York Journal*).

66. RICHARD F. OUTCAULT, *Around the World With the Yellow Kid*, January 24, 1897 (*New York Journal*).

67. RICHARD F. OUTCAULT, *The Yellow Kid*, "The Yellow Kid Goes Hunting Becomes a Dead Game Sport," January 24, 1897 (*New York Journal*).

68. RICHARD F. OUTCAULT, *Around the World With the Yellow Kid*, "Mickey and His Friends Hobnob with Royalty," January 31, 1897 (*New York Journal*).

69. RICHARD F. OUTCAULT, *The Yellow Kid*, "The Yellow Kid Studies Music and Tries it on the Dog—And Others," February 7, 1897 (*New York Journal*).

70. RICHARD F. OUTCAULT, *Around the World With the Yellow Kid*, "At Balmoral Castle—a Lawn Party in the Kid's Honor," February 7, 1897 (*New York Journal*).

71. RICHARD F. OUTCAULT, *Around the World With the Yellow Kid*, February 14, 1897 (*New York Journal*).

72. RICHARD F. OUTCAULT, *The Yellow Kid*, "The Yellow Kid's New Phonograph Clock," February 14, 1897 (*New York Journal*).

73. RICHARD F. OUTCAULT, *Around the World With the Yellow Kid*, "High Life in Paris—The Yellow Kid (L'Enfant Jaune) Takes an Airing," February 21, 1897 (*New York Journal*).

74. RICHARD F. OUTCAULT, *Around the World With the Yellow Kid*, "In the Louvre—The Yellow Kid Takes in the Masterpieces of Art," February 28, 1897 (*New York Journal*).

75. RICHARD F. OUTCAULT, *Around the World With the Yellow Kid*, "Fortune Smiles Upon the Yellow Kid at Monte Carlo," March 7, 1897 (*New York Journal*).

76. RICHARD F. OUTCAULT, *Around the World With the Yellow Kid*, "The Yellow Kid Shakes His Trotters in Old Madrid," March 14, 1897 (*New York Journal*).

77. RICHARD F. OUTCAULT, *Around the World With the Yellow Kid*, "A Bull Fight in Honor of the Yellow Kid," March 21, 1897 (*New York Journal*).

78. RICHARD F. OUTCAULT, *Around the World With the Yellow Kid*, "Mickey and His Friends Climb the Alps," March 28, 1897 (*New York Journal*).

79. RICHARD F. OUTCAULT, *Around the World With the Yellow Kid*, "The Yellow Kid Afloat on the Grand Canal," April 18, 1897 (*New York Journal*).

80. RICHARD F. OUTCAULT, *Around the World With the Yellow Kid*, "The Yellow Kid Invades Germany," April 4, 1897 (*New York Journal*).

81. RICHARD F. OUTCAULT, *Around the World With the Yellow Kid*, "The Yellow Kid's Soliloquy," May 2, 1897 (*New York Journal*).

82. RICHARD F. OUTCAULT, *Around the World With the Yellow Kid*, "The Yellow Kid in Cairo," May 9, 1897 (*New York Journal*).

83. RICHARD F. OUTCAULT, *Around the World With the Yellow Kid*, "An Eruption in Honor of the Yellow Kid," May 16, 1897 (*New York Journal*).

84. RICHARD F. OUTCAULT, *The Yellow Kid*, "The Yellow Kid Makes a Century Record," May 23, 1897 (*New York Journal*).

85. RICHARD F. OUTCAULT, *Around the World With the Yellow Kid*, "The Yellow Kid Returns," May 30, 1897 (*New York Journal*).

86. RICHARD F. OUTCAULT et al., cover for *American Humorist*, October 3, 1897 (*New York Journal*).

87. RICHARD F. OUTCAULT, *The Yellow Kid*, "The Yellow Kid Stakes a Claim at Klondyke," September 25, 1897 (*New York Journal*).

88. RICHARD F. OUTCAULT, *The Yellow Kid*, "The Yellow Kid Inspects the Streets of New York," October 10, 1897 (*New York Journal*).

89. RICHARD F. OUTCAULT, *The Yellow Kid*, "The Yellow Kid Treats the Crowd to a Horseless Carriage Ride," October 17, 1897 (*New York Journal*).

90. RICHARD F. OUTCAULT, *The Yellow Kid*, "The Yellow Kid Takes a Hand at Golf," October 24, 1897 (*New York Journal*).

91. RICHARD F. OUTCAULT, *The Yellow Kid*, "The Yellow Kid Loses Some of His Yellow," October 31, 1897 (*New York Journal*).

92. RICHARD F. OUTCAULT, *The Yellow Kid*, "How the Goat Got 'Kilt Entirely,'" November 14, 1897 (*New York Journal*).

93. RICHARD F. OUTCAULT, *Ryan's Arcade*, "The Crowd Gets Up a Bonfire and the Yellow Kid Plays Nero," November 7, 1897 (*New York Journal*).

94. RICHARD F. OUTCAULT, *Ryan's Alley*, "Thanksgiving Day in Ryan's Alley," November 21, 1897 (*New York Journal*).

95. RICHARD F. OUTCAULT, *Ryan's Arcade*, "Grand Opera in Ryan's Arcade," November 28, 1897 (*New York Journal*).

96. RICHARD F. OUTCAULT, *Ryan's Arcade*, "A Christmas Festival in Ryan's Arcade," December 5, 1897 (*New York Journal*).

97. RICHARD F. OUTCAULT, *Ryan's Arcade*, "The Ryan's Arcade Gang Go Sleighing," December 12, 1897 (*New York Journal*).

98. RICHARD F. OUTCAULT, *Ryan's Arcade*, "Scene in Ryan's Arcade on the Morning of New Year's Day," December 26, 1897 (*New York Journal*).

99. RICHARD F. OUTCAULT, *The Yellow Kid*, "Signs of Snow," January 2, 1898 (*New York Journal*).

100. RICHARD F. OUTCAULT, *The Yellow Kid*, "The Yellow Kid's R-R-R-Revenge; Or How the Painer's Son Got Fresh," January 9, 1898 (*New York Journal*).

101. RICHARD F. OUTCAULT, *Ryan's Arcade*, "The Yellow Kid Gives a Show in Ryan's Arcade," January 16, 1898 (*New York Journal*).

102. RICHARD F. OUTCAULT, *The Yellow Kid*, "The Yellow Kid Experiments With the Wonderful Hair Tonic," January 23, 1898 (*New York Journal*).

103. RICHARD F. OUTCAULT, "The Casey Corner Kids' Dime Museum," May 1, 1898 (*New York World*).

104. WILLIAM H. FRIDAY and HOMER TOURJEE, "The Dugan Kid Who Lives in Hogan's Alley," sheet music with drawing by or after RICHARD F. OUTCAULT (1896).

105. RICHARD F. OUTCAULT, poster for the *New York Journal, American Humorist,* late 1896.

106. RICHARD F. OUTCAULT and ARCHIE GUNN, poster for the *New York Journal, American Humorist,* October 1896.

107. RICHARD F. OUTCAULT and ARCHIE GUNN, poster for the *New York Journal, American Humorist,* November 8, 1896.

108. RICHARD F. OUTCAULT, poster for the *New York Journal, Around the World With the Yellow Kid,* January 18, 1897.

109. RICHARD F. OUTCAULT, poster for the *New York Journal, American Humorist,* February 1897.

110. GEORGE LUKS, "Hogan's Alley Attacked by the Hoboken Pretzel Club," May 31, 1896 (*New York World*).

111. GEORGE B. LUKS, *Hogan's Alley,* "Training for the Football Championship Game in Hogan's Alley," October 11, 1896 (*New York World*).

112. ANONYMOUS, *The Yellow Kid,* "Yellow Kids of All Nations," February 2, 1898 (*New York Journal*).

113. RUDOLPH DIRKS, "First, the Anti-cartoon Bill. Then, Perhaps This," February 20, 1898 (*New York Journal*).

114. RUDOLPH DIRKS, cover for *American Humorist,* March 27, 1898 (*New York Journal*).

115. CARL ANDERSON, "The Bill Poster and the Kid," January 24, 1897 (*New York Journal*).

116. RICHARD F. OUTCAULT, box lid for McFadden's Row of Flats "Yellow Kid" Puzzle, ca. 1897.

117. RICHARD F. OUTCAULT?, cover for *The Yellow Kid in McFadden's Flats,* by E. W. Townsend and R. F. Outcault (New York: G. W. Dillingham Co., 1898).

118. RICHARD F. OUTCAULT, *Buster Brown,* "The Yellow Kid Meets Tige and Mary Jane and," July 7, 1907 (*American Examiner*).

119. RICHARD F. OUTCAULT, *Buster Brown,* "Strange Things Do Happen to," November 3, 1907 (*American Examiner*).

120. RICHARD F. OUTCAULT, *Buster Brown,* "So This Then is the Yellow Kid's Cousin," March 27, 1910 (*American Examiner*).

121. RICHARD F. OUTCAULT, *Buster Brown,* "When Shall We Four Meet Again?," April 3, 1910 (*American Examiner*).

122. RICHARD F. OUTCAULT, *The Yellow Kid,* pen and ink with watercolor wash, signed and dated May 12 1907.

Illustration credits

FIGURES: Unless otherwise noted, figures are taken from the New York Public Library's microfilm of the *New York Journal* and the *New York World,* provided by the San Francisco Academy of Comic Art and Eclipse Books. Courtesy of the Museum of the City of New York: 1, 7, 13, 25, 44, 47, 51, 52, 53, 62, 63. Courtesy of the New-York Historical Society: 30. Courtesy of Brown Brothers: 38, 45, 65, 67. From the Tappan Collection, Smith College Museum of Art, Northampton, Massachusetts. Purchased with the Hillyer-Mather-Tryon Fund, with funds given in memory of Nancy Newhall, and with funds given in honor of Ruth Wedgwood Kennedy: 54-61. Courtesy of Richard Olson: 15, 16, 17. Courtesy of the Craig Koste Collection: 64, 66, 79.

PLATES: Courtesy of the San Francisco Academy of Comic Art: 1-34, 36-104, 110-122. Courtesy of the Cartoon, Graphic, and Photographic Arts Research Library Ohio State University, Columbus, Ohio: 109. Courtesy of the Bob Cook Collection: 105, 107. Courtesy of the Craig Koste Collection: 106. Courtesy of the Library of Congress, Prints and Photographs Division: 35. Courtesy of Jerry Muller: 108.

Foreword

In some ways, publishing the *San Francisco Examiner* was like being captain of a ship at sea. Newspapers are self-contained societies. Under one roof you start with curiosity, then commission stories, go out and report the news, lay out pages, write headlines, set type, run a printing press, coordinate a fleet of trucks, sell advertising, and try to deliver the product, reputation intact, for twenty-five cents a day. And just when things seem calm, all hell breaks loose. For when the big story breaks, like a storm on the ocean, the whole system finds a new, instant top priority. If that doesn't get your blood pumping, you're doing it wrong.

Part of the extra satisfaction of working for the *Examiner* was the daily realization that this was the paper my grandfather had published. He had, in a way, walked the same halls, looked at the pages, wrestled with the same issues, and tried to capture the readers of the same city.

Part of my education was learning from the past. In 1987, the *Examiner* celebrated its hundredth birthday from the date W. R. Hearst took over the helm of the paper. As part of our centennial project, we dove into the archives of the paper and tried to discover what had remained the same and what had changed about newspapering from two eras separated by 100 years. We found to our amazement that an incredible wealth of visual art had graced the pages of the old *Examiner*.

It's a common assumption—and wrong—that only with the arrival of cold type did newspapers start to explore the whole world of graphic design. If you want to see really energetic page design, epic layouts, and imaginative use of type and illustration, look to the hot metal newspapers of the late 1890s and early decades of this century. The work those craftspeople did was harder to do, and they did more of it. But far and away the most dazzling difference was the role played by illustrators and cartoonists in that era. Photography for deadline was still some years away. The only technique to *show* readers was to make engravings and use drawings.

The power of the image is still with us today. I have answered the phone many days to find an irate reader complaining about a cartoon or comic. Not because of bad taste or language. They simply wanted to know why this infernal opinion was permitted to exist in their newspaper. I began to realize that readers will skip over a columnist they don't like or turn the page if a story doesn't seem appealing, but nobody can ignore the pictures. You notice. You can't look away. That's why it has never surprised me that the kind of newspapering practiced in that era was named after a cartoon. For it was the Yellow Kid who supplied the image for the phrase "Yellow Journalism." Not an editor, reporter or proprietor, but a cartoon names this phenomenon.

Sensationalism has all but disappeared from daily newspapers today—although sometimes I think television has recently discovered its ability to attract public attention. In fact, some of the old newspaper stories strike me as more devoted to hero worship than sensationalism. All events were larger than life. Fires were conflagrations. Shipwrecks were disasters. Out of ordinary life heroes and villains sprang from the pages daily. This was the era when mass communication was born. And the public, not always educated, understood those devices. Newspapers were both entertainment and news, laughter and parody. And the cartoonist more than any other creative talent could humble the mighty, puncture the pompous, and still be understood by all.

For good or ill, the same goes on today in fields like music, television, motion pictures and publishing where the key re-source is talent. For it is talent that holds the audience, that has the ability to tell a story and define a character. In all those businesses, whether global media companies or start-ups, the key strategy is to identify, attract, and nourish talented people.

The owners of newspapers in that golden era fought for the talent of the "Yellow Kid." They fought for readers every day. And capturing talent was the device for building audience. None of that has changed. The battle for the Kid became the symbol of those early pioneering days.

WILLIAM RANDOLPH HEARST III

1. JACOB RIIS.
   Mullen's Alley,
   Cherry Hill
   (1888).

One

Laughing on the Outside:
The Slum Kids of M. A. Woolf (1893–1896)

At the turn of the century, expensive weekly comic magazines such as *Life, Judge,* and *Puck* featured often viciously caricatured immigrants and African Americans, symbolizing the extreme economic and social divide between the impoverished and upper classes in the Gilded Age city. These magazines were for the entertainment of the city's elite and, in addition to cartoons about the disadvantaged, they featured comic drawings about the pastimes and social rituals of the wealthy and socially prominent. The divisions of the city were enacted and reinforced on a weekly basis in their pages, in the drawings as well as in the text and commentary that accompanied them.

The public display of street kids in cartoon magazines served as something of a safety valve for an upper-class urban populace in much more direct contact with immigrant thugs—as they saw them—than is the case today. In the 1880s (and, in fact, well into the 1940s), the neighborhoods of the poor crowded into exclusive neighborhoods. Hell's Kitchen jostled costly mansions leading onto Park Avenue; Five Points leaned against expensive homes fronting the East River (a location that served as the setting for Henry Kingsley's *Dead End* play and movie of the 1930s). The better-off felt that they had to wade through noisy avenues of the impoverished, and they didn't care much for it. Cartoons aimed to show the essential color and comedy of the daily metropolitan social scene, reflecting the prejudices of their readers with the leavening of humor.

So long as they were funny, no obstacles were placed in the way of publishing more sympathetic cartoons. Michael Angelo Woolf, a cartoonist possessed of an exquisite graphic dexterity and an eye at once perceptive and witty, began to submit black and white line cartoons to *Life* in the mid-l880s. Born in 1837 to English immigrants, Woolf came to cartooning relatively late in life. His first career had been the stage, an experience that affected both the subject matter of his cartoons, which sometimes showed children in outsized costumes rehearsing back-yard plays, and the cadences in the dialogue captions he wrote for them. He had also studied painting in Munich and Paris. Woolf had an elfin comic imagination coupled with heartfelt compassion for New York's street children. His work met with ready checks and public interest and, by the late 1880s, he was averaging one drawing per week in *Life*. By the early 1890s, his work appeared in virtually every comic weekly in distribution.

2. MICHAEL ANGELO WOOLF. Self-portrait with cartoons, from *Life*.

OUR READERS WILL BE PLEASED TO LEARN THAT THE JUVENILE BAL MASQUE HELD IN THE HALL OF THE BROTHERHOOD OF UNITED BRICKLAYERS WAS A DECIDED SUCCESS.

A QUESTION OF SOME IMPORT.

SAY, JACKSON, DOES YER TISK DER PUP IS TOO WICIOUS TER KEEP IN LER ROOM, AN' DAT SANTY CLAUS 'LL BE SKEERED OFF FROM COMIN' DOWN DER CHIMLEY?

3. MICHAEL ANGELO WOOLF.
Cartoon from *Life*
(March 16, 1893).

4. MICHAEL ANGELO WOOLF.
Cartoon from *Life*
(December 23, 1896).

Woolf's cartoons sensitively depicted their subjects as individuals, whatever their race or ethnicity. A Christmas 1896 cartoon for *Life* concerned two African-American children who worried that their tiny pup might prevent what already was a highly unlikely visit from Saint Nick. Characteristically, Woolf's rendering was devoid of racial stereotypes; one kid's name and some darkening lines for the face were all he found necessary to identify them as African American. For Woolf, whose sympathies were with the poor, race was incidental.

In the 1880s and 1890s, about half New York City's population lived in tenements, many in the wretched conditions so movingly described by reformer and journalist Jacob Riis in *How the Other Half Lives*. Irish Americans, among the city's largest ethnic groups, controlled the Democratic Party; in 1888, Hugh J. Grant became the first Irish American mayor of New York. Although Irish Americans were moving into skilled and professional employment, many Irish neighborhoods suffered from poverty, unemployment, and high rates of infant mortality. Political organizations like Tammany Hall helped to open opportunities and ameliorate the conditions in which they lived. The well-to-do, of course, denounced their vote-getting activities as municipal corruption which, in the case of machines like Tammany Hall, was often true. In his captions, Woolf gave most kids Irish monikers and, in another 1896 *Life* cartoon, he echoed the then-common "Shantytown" for his lightly caricatured Irish ghetto (a precursor of the more colorful "Hogan's Alley" and "Casey's Corner" of a later cartoonist).

It is impossible to look at Woolf's art without feeling that it testifies to a deeply felt concern for children. Perhaps editors published his work in order to attract women readers to the humor magazines aimed primarily at men. However, while the conscientious reader may have understood and sympathized with Woolf's point of view and its implicit pathos, the general public probably saw only the same obnoxious, troublesome kids who populated other cartoons—more effectively drawn, less rambunctious, but essentially identical.

Was Woolf, as the saying goes, laughing on the outside while crying on the inside? In the end, there is no way to be certain of his personal views. Turn-of-the-century cartoonists regarded themselves primarily as popular entertainers. When interviewed by the press, they told anecdotes, praised favored fellows, and gave practical tips to newcomers to the art, but revealed little or nothing about their personal convictions. Further, political cartoonists almost always worked for hire, dutifully slinging barbs to order. We do not even know whether Woolf supported the church or urban charities.

What is certain is that his gentler images did not supplant the naive brutality of most cartoons based on immigrant themes. For every Woolf drawing of a slum kid looking wistfully at the single lump of coal found on a winter morning, there were a dozen others depicting raucous gangs raising hell with each other and respectable citizens.

Nevertheless, imitators appeared as Woolf's popularity grew. Young cartoonists striving to break into the competitive market of New York's cartoon magazines began to show up in editors' offices with portfolios "just like" Woolf's (but cheaper). Two of them did good work in this vein at the close of the 1880s. The young Charles Dana Gibson was a competent Woolf imitator before he went on to become creator of the Gibson Girl, a genteel, pen and ink pin-up appealing to fraternity boys and the men they grew into. (Its succcess led to his rise to the editorship of the old *Life*, the leading cartoon magazine of the day.) Another successful imitator was Frank "Chip" Bellew, Jr. His attractive work—shorn of the heavily sketched detail typical of his contemporaries—stood out on the page, though it resembled Woolf's more in delicacy and wit than in subject.

In England, a brilliant cartoonist whose career and themes formed a rough parallel to Woolf's also emerged in the late 1880s. Phil May, the great graphic poet of cockney kids' slum life, had seen little if any of Woolf's early work, but his deft line work and keen eye for the streets attracted the same attention in London that Woolf's did in New York. Then as now, comic art tended to be insular and, though May's work appeared regularly throughout the 1890s in such magazines as the *Daily Sketch*, British *Punch*, and *Pall Mall*, he remained as little known to the American comic-magazine reader as Woolf did to the British.

Artists who chose poor urban children as subjects needed to sense the furious heartbeat of determined life in such kids; the vibrant, daily excitement of being alive and young; and the refusal in their play to succumb to poverty, instead raucously thumbing the community nose at both the wealthy and the "do-gooders" sent into tenement streets by the wealthy and the churches. Charles Dickens had shocked readers of *Bleak House* by making devastating fun of the social-worker likes of Mrs. Jellyby and Mrs. Pardiggle. He understood that communities hated even the hint of dependence on outsiders, however often circumstances forced them into it, and he drew out the spirit of mocking gaiety and "vulgar" behavior that so shocked the poor's devoted helpers.

A cartoonist who seemed at first to be just another Woolf imitator was soon to bring to American comic art just that Dickensian awareness of the cock-a-snook, us-against-them truth of city kids' lives. With it, he brought one of the great comic figures of all time. The cartoonist was named Richard Felton Outcault, and he was a sockdolager.

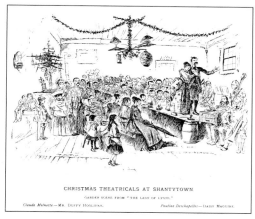

CHRISTMAS THEATRICALS AT SHANTYTOWN

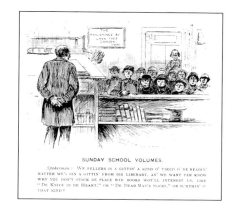

SUNDAY SCHOOL VOLUMES.

5. MICHAEL ANGELO WOOLF.
Cartoon from *Life*
(December 23, 1896).

6. MICHAEL ANGELO WOOLF.
Cartoon from *Life*
(February 16, 1893).

7. Jacob Riis.
Tenement Baby
(1880s–1890s).

Two

Coming Events:

R. F. Outcault and the First Newspaper Comics
(1892–1895)

Richard Felton Outcault was a Midwesterner, born January 14, 1863, in Lancaster, Ohio. He studied art at McMicken University in Cincinnati and, after several years as a professional artist in Ohio, was hired by Edison Laboratories as a scientific and technical illustrator. In 1890, he began working for *Electrical World* magazine; he married Mary Jane Martin on Christmas Day of that year. By 1892, they had settled in Flushing, Queens; from there, Outcault would have taken the Long Island Railroad and a ferry across the East River to publishers' offices in Manhattan.

Outcault quickly became a successful free-lance artist, supporting himself and his wife on illustrations and advertising work. He was fascinated by New York's street life, and it was during 1892 that he completed a series of open-air sketches of the crowded city streets. It was in this series that he first sketched a baldheaded, nightshirted urchin standing among the tenement kids.

Outcault was not the only artist attracted by the life of the streets in America's cities. Stephen Crane, who would win his greatest fame as author of *The Red Badge of Courage,* began his career with *Maggie: A Girl of the Streets* (1893), set in the same New York neighborhoods where Outcault drew. The artists who would form the nucleus of the Ash Can School and lead the first successful revolution in twentieth-century American painting with their searing images of the city and its people were already at work drawing the subjects they later would paint. Jacob Riis, who had published *How the Other Half Lives* in 1890, had been taking his camera into the streets and tenements to document the lives of the oppressed and disadvantaged. In addition to their fascination with urban life, these artists had another common bond: all were working journalists. Riis was a police reporter, first for the *New York Tribune,* then the *Evening Sun.* Future Ash Can artists George Luks, William Glackens, and John Sloan were artist-reporters for Philadelphia newspapers. Crane had reported for the *Herald,* and would later write for both the *New York Journal* and the *New York World.*

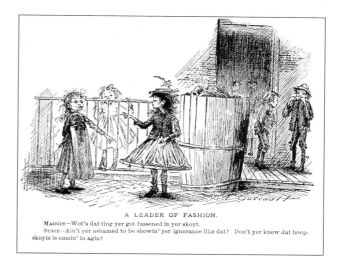

A LEADER OF FASHION.

MAGGIE—Wot's dat ting yer got fassened in yer skoyt.
SUSIE—Ain't yer ashamed to be showin' yer ignorance like dat? Don't yer know dat hoop-skoyts is comin' in agin?

8. RICHARD F. OUTCAULT.
    Cartoon from *Truth*
    (March 4, 1893).

9. RICHARD F. OUTCAULT.
   Cartoon from the
   New York World
   (September 16, 1894).

10. RICHARD F. OUTCAULT.
    Cartoon from the
    New York World
    (November 18, 1894).

Outcault, too, soon would be employed by a newspaper, but his fascination with New York's lower classes was to lead him in a very different direction. Early in 1893, he took a portfolio of cartoons based in part on his street sketches to *Truth,* a weekly cartoon magazine. Launched in 1886, *Truth* ranked a poor fourth in national circulation and was edited out of inexpensive offices at Nineteenth Street and Fourth Avenue. The three top-selling humor weeklies—*Puck*, *Judge*, and *Life*—each had circulations much larger than *Truth*'s while an odd title from the south, *Texas Siftings,* came in a low fifth.

Puck was founded in March 1877 by Joseph Keppler, a German immigrant who, like Joseph Pulitzer, had begun his publishing career in St. Louis with a German-language version of the magazine. *Judge* followed when James Wales, one of Keppler's artists, struck out on his own. *Puck* and *Judge* specialized in political cartoons, *Puck* generally favoring the Democratic Party while *Life* was a Republican organ. Their cartoons influenced national politics, sometimes setting the themes for presidential contests. These cartoons, many published in color, were often crowded, detailed drawings filled with recognizable political figures.

Outcault, who had good business sense, had worked his street sketches into cartoons that closely reflected the style and tone of Woolf's ubiquitous work. Scanning the cartoon-magazine market, he chose the low-paying but ambitious *Truth* as a likely outlet. A charming talker, he had little trouble convincing *Truth's* editor that since he could not afford Woolf, Outcault was the next best alternative.

After an initial graphic bow on March 4, 1893 (with a drawing of a slum girl sporting a hoop skirt made from a real hoop), Outcault's art proliferated in the magazine's weekly issues over the next two years. *Truth's* circulation rose in fits and gasps, spurred by the work of rising stars like George Luks as well as Outcault's kid cartoons. In the late summer of 1895, *Truth* finally was able to purchase its first Woolf cartoon, thereafter publishing both Woolf's and Outcault's work well into 1896. Ordinarily, Outcault's well-received work in *Truth* should have led to work for the better-paying big three weeklies, but in 1893, a more remunerative market opened when Joseph Pulitzer's *New York World* began buying original cartoons for its new Sunday supplement.

The *World*, which had the highest newspaper circulation in Manhattan, published the nation's first comic supplement in color newsprint on May 21, 1893. The effect on the public was electric. For the first time, color cartoons, long the exclusive province of the glossy weekly magazines sold for a dime, could be had for a mere nickel every week in a Sunday newspaper. The cartoons in the first supplement were first-rate. The cover drawing was by *World* political cartoonist Walt MacDougall, a veteran of *Punch* and the illustrated newspaper *Daily Graphic*. (His *World* cartoon "The Royal Feast of Belshazzar," attacking Republican presidential candidate James G. Blaine, appeared on campaign posters and was credited with winning New York and thus the 1884 election for Grover Cleveland.) The inside pages, in black and white, reprinted choice cartoons from *Judge, Life,* and *Puck.*

During its first years, the Sunday supplement varied in format, dropping to tabloid size for a while, and the editor's selection of art and humor was uneven. The first Woolf reprint did not appear until Sunday, May 6, 1894, almost a year after the supplement was launched, and much of the new work published in 1893 and 1894 was inferior to that in the major cartoon magazines.

However, the *World* did have one edge over the magazines: its coffers, continually filled by the huge readership. The fees paid by the *World* were so high that the cartoon magazines could not afford to deny second (reprint) rights to their new competitor. The rates for original work were several times higher than those the big three offered newcomers and nearly equal to those paid Woolf and Gibson, but space

ARISTOCRACY OF THE FOURTH WARD.

Madeline McSwat—You'se might tink from his look 'at he wuz a slob, but he belongs to de most aristocratic fambly in de fourt' ward. Last week he had his picture took, and day before ylsterday his mudder gived a pale pink tea. How's dat?

11. RICHARD F. OUTCAULT. Cartoon from the *New York World* (January 13, 1895).

12. PHIL MAY.
"Peg-top"
(1896).

for original cartoons remained limited due to extensive use of reprints. As a result, cartoonists competed fiercely for sales to the *World.*

Outcault's first original cartoon in the *World,* a six-panel captioned narrative, was published September 16, 1894. Outcault had not done panel-story layouts before and his experiment with the form must have been part of his effort to sell to the *World,* which ran many multipanel continuity cartoons. (In fact, two similar panel-story layouts appeared on the page alongside Outcault's.)

Similarly, Outcault's first full-color cartoon for the *World* was a multipanel narrative. Titled "Origin of Species," it featured his first continuing character, an unfunny-looking clown whose dog is eaten by a boa constrictor. Repulsive to modern eyes, it apparently tickled the odd fancy of the *World's* editor, and the clown appeared in two more six-panel color sequences in December 1894.

Outcault's single-panel kid cartoons also appeared in the *World* even as they continued to be published in *Truth.* (Out of loyalty, he may have favored *Truth* with first bid on his kid gags.) New York's tough, precocious street kids continued to fascinate Outcault, who developed his street sketches in *World* cartoons. On January 13, 1895, in the upper right-hand corner of a jam-packed, black and white Sunday page, there appeared a kid with a shaved head wearing a checked man's shirt buttoned up the back and falling to the youngster's shoes.

Baldheaded kids were not uncommon in the Manhattan slums of that decade, when shaving a child's head was the fastest and cheapest way to get rid of head lice. For economy's sake, young children often were sent into the streets to play in cut-down nightshirts or older sisters' dresses. The combination of dress and shaved head apparently amused Outcault. The same sort of image later caught the restless eye of Phil May on a London street corner in 1896, and was included in a drawing of two kids spinning tops.

The 1895 *World* cartoon may have been the newsprint debut of the figure Outcault said he first sketched in the Manhattan slums in 1892. The diminutive bald figure was the prototype of the newspaper gamin who was to outrage and delight New Yorkers of the 1890s. He was not yet, however, the authentic article.

Three

Nightshirts In Stasis:

Outcault's Kid Is Created But Ignored (1894–1895)

On February 9, 1895, *Truth* printed a special issue, the "Art Number," for which all regular contributors were asked to submit a representative drawing. To emphasize the motif of an art gallery, each cartoon was placed in a drawn frame and accompanied by a photograph of the artist.

Outcault's contribution, "Fourth Ward Brownies," alluded to Palmer Cox's impish Brownies, but showed kids in a tough Manhattan slum. Round-eyed and potbellied, Cox's Brownies had first appeared in

FOURTH WARD BROWNIES.
MICKEY, THE ARTIST (*adding a finishing touch*)—
Dere, Chimmy! If Palmer Cox wuz t' see yer, he'd
git yer copyrighted in a minute.

FEUDAL PRIDE IN HOGAN'S ALLEY.
LITTLE ROSELIA McGRAW—No; we won't come and play with youz, Delia Costigan.
Our rejuced means may temporary necessitate our residin' in a rear tenement, but
we're jist as exclusive as when we lived on the first floor front and papa had charge
of the pound in the Department of Canine Captivity!

A FAIR CHAMPION.
LORREENA LAFFERTY (*as a parting shot*)—Remember dis, Izzy Silberman may be a
mozer. But de day will come when as a millionaire banker, an' me his bride, de dust
his carriage wheels makes t'roo Forsythe street will not be able den to blind youz to
his good qualities.

14. RICHARD F. OUTCAULT.
Cartoon from *Truth*
(February 9, 1895);
reprinted in the *New York World*
(February 17, 1895).

15. RICHARD F. OUTCAULT.
Cartoon from *Truth*
(June 2, 1894).

16. RICHARD F. OUTCAULT.
Cartoon from *Truth*
(July 14, 1894).

Life and *St. Nicholas* in the early 1880s. As their popularity grew, their hyperactive droves filled dozens of books with drawings captioned in rhyme. Look-alike stuffed dolls and ceramic figures could be found on toy shelves everywhere.

In Outcault's drawing, a kid in a battered derby is meticulously painting round Brownie-type eyes on the face of a tubby child wearing a Brownie pillbox cap, to the amusement of a juvenile audience. "Dere, Chimmy!" says the kid with the brush. "If Palmer Cox wuz t' see yer, he'd git yer copyrighted in a minute."

Behind him, holding a dead cat by the tail, stands the same basic kid figure—big ears, bald head, nightshirt and all—that Outcault had drawn in the January *World* cartoon, but there is a world of difference between the two. The deceased cat, the expression of mischievous delight as he watches the fat kid get painted, and a smeared, dirty hand print on his nightshirt render this kid totally at variance with the demure child of the earlier newspaper cartoon. (If Outcault had guessed then what his pen had unleashed, he might have had *his* creation "copyrighted in a minute." In fact, he did so a year later when public response made clear to him what he had invented.)

The editor of the *World's* comic supplement reprinted "Fourth Ward Brownies" in the February 17 issue. The Hogan's Alley charmer to be known as the Yellow Kid was thus given newsprint birth. The "Brownies" cartoon is important because the nightshirted kid among the spectators anticipates so closely the final character design and personality Outcault would create for the Yellow Kid. Reprinted in the *World,* it becomes the first newspaper comic appearance of the character. Three cartoons published in *Truth* in 1894 show a bald, nightshirted kid; these were never reprinted in the *World,* but show Outcault working toward the lively presence of the "Brownies" cartoon. "Feudal Pride in Hogan's Alley" (June 2, 1894) shows a child clutching his sister's hand, standing under a street sign reading "Hogan's Alley" and "Ryan's Arcade." The forced perspective of the building and its stairs emphasizes the misfortune of the children, whose family has been made to move to a rear tenement apartment. "A Fair Champion" (July 15, 1894) shows the child among a group of spectators; "Going by Precept" (September 15, 1894) depicts him crying as his mother prepares dinner.

In 1895, when the Yellow Kid-to-be appears in the *World,* he bears little resemblance to the grinning goblin of the Brownies cartoon. There are nightshirted kids in two original black and white cartoons in the *World:* "The Fate of the Glutton" (March 10) and "An Approaching Event" (May 5), where he bawls his head off over some fancied slight.

On May 5, the *World* ran the first original kid cartoon in color, "At the Circus in Hogan's Alley." The nightshirted kid acquires a second dirty hand print on his bright blue gown, but loses the unholy glee that had transfigured his face in the Brownies cartoon. In "The New Restaurant in Casey's Alley" (May 19), we see only the back of the purple-clad kid, who studies a posted French menu. In the black and white "Emulation on the East Side" (May 25), there are two kids in nightshirts: one facing the viewer from the pool-hall doorway, the other seen from the back. One is shod, the other barefoot, so that he seems to appear twice in the same drawing.

In "The Day After 'The Glorious Fourth' Down in Hogan's Alley" (July 7), the kid again is doubled and can be seen well to the back in a panorama of Hogan's Alley. An unusually sharp social commentary, the cartoon deplores street kids' use of dangerous explosives in fireworks. A black wreath hangs on a door and a sign on a balcony reads, "Pleeze keep quiet fur Mickey is durn near ded." One of the two kid figures, in blue, has an arm in a sling; the other, farther to the rear on the right, wears an apron and sports a black eye.

In "The Great Cup Race on Reilly's Pond" (September 22), *three* prototypes of the Kid appear. One, to the far left in a blue gown, sits asleep on the sand; a second, in a yellow sunbonnet and yellow skirt to the far right, stands holding his sister's hand; the third, on a grassy bank to the right, stands shouting and waving a flag.

In a Woolf-like color drawing of "The Great Social Event of the Year in Shantytown" (November 10), kids mimic all the ceremony of a costly wedding. The topical inspiration for the cartoon was the expensive and widely reported wedding of heiress Anna Gould to the Marquis de Castellane, which had taken place the previous March (see the parrot's sage comments at upper left). The only remotely familiar image is the farther of the two small kids standing before the bridesmaids. Instead, the drawing's chief interest lies in its tongue-in-cheek, rear-view self-portrait of Outcault as "the *World's* artist," seated to the far left on a "Press" box.

In "The Horse Show as Reproduced at Shantytown" (November 17), a kid in a gray nightshirt sits with his back to "McStabb's Private Box." In a much smaller drawing called "An Untimely Death" (November 24), a seated kid in an orange nightshirt watches impassively as his sister gabs with another kid on the porch.

The 1895 color series in the *World* ended with "Merry Xmas Morning in Hogan's Alley" (December 15). Again there are two nightshirted kids in the same drawing: one dressed in yellow (smudged hand print and all) and another, more ebullient kid clad in a checked red nightshirt and blowing a celebratory horn. The first kid wears a green

17. RICHARD F. OUTCAULT.
Cartoon from *Truth*
(September 15, 1894).

18. RICHARD F. OUTCAULT.
Cartoon from the *New York World*
(March 10, 1895).

19. RICHARD F. OUTCAULT.
Cartoon from the *New York World*
(December 22, 1895).

20. RICHARD F. OUTCAULT.
Cartoon from the
New York World
(July 5, 1896).

21. RICHARD F. OUTCAULT.
Cartoon from *Truth*
(December 28, 1895);
reprinted in the *New York World*
(January 5, 1896).

cap; from its fit it would appear that there is nothing under it but a bald pate. Woolf is referenced by name as the illustrator of *Alice in Blunderland*, carried by a schoolgirl to the far right (predating an actual *Alice in Blunderland* parody written by John Kendrick Bangs and illustrated by Albert Bevering, published in 1907 by Doubleday).

Finally, in his last 1895 drawing for *Truth*, Outcault returns to the nightshirted kid with the dirty hand print for the first time since February 9. This kid, frowning rather fiercely at Miss Charlotte Van Tassell McStab's dramatic reading, suggests more feeling than the noncommittal figure in most of the *World* cartoons. Again he is accompanied by the dog seen in "Fourth Ward Brownies," which had been absent from the *World* cartoons. However, this is the kid's last bow—or leer or frown—in *Truth*. From 1896 on, he becomes wholly a creature of the newspapers.

Also in 1895, slum kids attracted another major cartoonist in Eugene "Zim" Zimmerman, who built a series around a "Shantytown" for *Judge*. Although Zim's treatment was genial enough, his kids were a much rougher and more brutalized lot than those of Woolf and Outcault. The *World* reprinted one of Zim's cartoons, but otherwise left its pages to Woolf reprints and Outcault's increasingly featured originals.

Outcault, who later christened his nightshirted kid Mickey Dugan, wrote and illustrated a text in dialect for the *World* which was

TRUTH

A LITERARY SOCIETY.

MISS CHARLOTTE VAN TASSELL MCSTAB (*reading aloud*)—It were between the hours of midnight, de darkness hung in big chunks, and slobs from de Prussian blue-sky. Suddently a screech rent der air—
SWIPE MCSORLEY—Say, who paid de rent?
CHORUS—Aw, shut up! Go chase yerself.
MISS VAN TASSELL (*again*)—Hurried feetsteps wus heard hurrying toward der spot—den dere were sounds of a struggle an' muffled sware words was heard as dough de gent had overshoes on his voice and wen de cops got dere dey found wot is gettin' to be a too common ting in a great city—it was a poor mistreated husband a-tryin' to coax his drunken wife an her bloomers ter come home.

signed by a different kid, also named Mickey. First seen in the Brownies cartoon, this Mickey returned on April 14 as author of an illustrated recital review signed Mickey der Kid.

Outcault captioned his cartoons extensively with pronouncements or dialogue by the principals. His drawings are so arresting that we may be inclined to gloss over the captions with their tight, small print and seemingly endless loquaciousness, but they are often amusing in their own right, revealing an ear for slang at least as sharp as Woolf's. The flowery and wonderfully preposterous speech of Sissy McMahon in "An Approaching Event" (May 5) is a delightful case in point, while Irene O'Shaugnessy's speech in "Emulation on the East Side" (May 26), is gorgeously a-crackle with Irish dialect.

The longest captions in Outcault's *World* cartoons appear below the smallest cartoons, where he perpetuated the format of his work in *Truth*. The page size of the *World* offered the chance to draw cartoons far larger than any he had done before. As he drew more cartoons in this new and larger format—cartoons designed to fill half of a bedsheet newspaper page, his captions became less extensive.

For the cartoons, the captions usually included both title and dialogue. With a limited number of figures, it was simple to indicate who was speaking. In the large cartoons with a multitude of characters distributed across half the page, this was more difficult, and the lively perorations often disappear altogether. The large cartoons usually have only titles, with added information provided by words within the drawing consisting of signs, broadsides or newspaper pages, and graffiti. There had been little room for in-panel texts in the small cartoons, but the vast canvas of the *World* cartoons afforded Outcault ample space to experiment with new ways of combining words and images.

It was not until 1896, in the Sunday color pages, that Outcault attained the final balance of text and image, at last joining signs and captions on the Yellow Kid's gabby nightshirt itself. It was then that Outcault's character, in his full majesty as the Yellow Kid—the awesome Mickey Dugan, became the sole property of William Randolph Hearst and his *World*-whipping *New York Journal*.

22. Eugene "Zim" Zimmerman.
Cartoon from *Judge*;
reprinted in the *New York World*
(April 7, 1895).

23. Richard F. Outcault.
Cartoon from the *New York World*
(May 5, 1895).

24. Richard F. Outcault.
Cartoon from the *New York World*
(May 26, 1895).

25. ALBERT E. HAHN.
Park Row.
The *New York World*
building is at left
(1936).

Four

Death of a Legend:

The Great Yellow Ink Hogwash in M'Googan Avenue
(1892–1896)

Without his yellow nightshirt, the Yellow Kid never would have received
the name by which he is best known. How he came to be dressed in this
golden-hued garment, which in some way seemed to encapsulate the
high life and the low of New York in the Gilded Age, has never received
satisfactory explanation.

One chestnut, deep-dyed in ochre, has been favored in the pages
of comic histories. Its most elaborate presentation appears in Coulton
Waugh's *The Comics*, an entertaining but misleading account of comic-
strip development in the United States. Waugh's colorful reconstruction

of the choice of yellow for the Kid's grimy gown begins with an imaginary conversation in the pressroom of the *World*.

"Yellow? Why yellow? The yellow jumps out at you—jumps right out of the pages. I'm an artist, I understand color." The speaker, a lean man with handlebar mustaches and tight trousers checked in green and brown, was bent in a concentrated S over his drawing board, scowling at a proof before him. "Take my advice, Charlie. Color shouldn't startle, it should soothe. Now, a soft green..."

"You don't understand, Art," Charles W. Saalburgh, leaning over the drawing board, broke in. "This isn't a matter of good or bad color. I want you to color the kid in this drawing yellow because I've got to find a way to prevent that yellow ink from running and sliding around. I've solved the problem with all the other colors. Now I think I've found the answer for the yellow—to apply a drier made with tallow. I want a good test area which will be printed in yellow, so that I can easily check on the results when the color section is printed.

Art picked up a brush. He was whistling softly, "After the Ball is Over." "O.K., Charlie, I'll make a yellow kid. A yellow kid! One thing—it's going to be something new!"

The speakers were identified by Waugh as an artist, invented for the occasion, and Charles W. Saalburgh, "foreman of the *New York World's* tint-laying Ben Day machines." The cartoon was "The Great Dog Show in M'Googan Avenue" (February 16, 1896), and Waugh went on to imagine the delight this new creation brought New Yorkers. He characterized the Yellow Kid as an intermediary between viewer and image, a figure that was "always looking toward the reader, interpreting events for him, becoming the reader's man." The drama and assurance of Waugh's account made it easy to accept while lack of documentation made it difficult to disprove.

Waugh's fictionalized account and its many variations in histories of comic art are incorrect and unsubstantiated. Although the *New York World* did have problems printing yellow in its color supplement, these were solved months before the Yellow Kid appeared in its definitive form. The first cartoon to feature the standard design for the Yellow Kid, as well as the intermediary posture Waugh so clearly describes, was "Golf—the Great Society Game as Played in Hogan's Alley" (January 5, 1896), not "The Great Dog Show in M'Googan Avenue" (February 16, 1896). The decision to color the character's nightshirt yellow may have been Saalburgh's, but there is no evidence on this point. In an article published in the *World* on May 1, 1898, Outcault indicated that the decision was not his: "I don't remember who did the coloring—I know

26. THOMAS NAST.
Cartoon from the
Daily Inter Ocean
(October 22, 1892).

I didn't—but whoever it was colored Micky Dugan's dress yellow, a bright, glaring, golden, gleaming, gorgeous yellow!" Examination of color cartoons in the years preceding "The Great Dog Show in M'Googan Avenue" demonstrates that newspaper presses were capable of printing a "golden, gleaming" yellow long before it was applied to the Yellow Kid.

The printing of color cartoons in newspapers was not initiated by the *World*. The *Chicago Inter-Ocean* published Sunday and Wednesday color tabloid supplements during the Chicago World's Fair of 1892 and 1893. The technology to print color on rotary presses, which could produce the high volume in short periods necessary for newspapers, was developed in France and England in the late 1880s. H. H. Kohhlsaat, publisher of the *Inter-Ocean*, was the first to construct a rotary press with this new capability in the United States. In its design, yellow was to be the first primary color rolled from the plates onto the newsprint, followed by red and blue. There seems to have been difficulty in printing yellow during the first few months the supplement was published. The supplement began in June, 1892, and the first dozen or so issues contained only red and blue. On October 22, 1892, a bright, stable yellow was printed for the first time.

The addition of yellow enabled the printers to enlarge their palette to include green and other hues. "Rip Van Winkle Dazzled by the World's Fair," a drawing by Thomas Nast, the cartoonist who had skewered Tammany Hall's Boss Tweed in New York in the 1870s, featured strong yellows and greens. From that point, the *Inter-Ocean* press appears to have had no problems printing yellow.

Although it was neither the first newspaper to publish cartoons in color nor the first to incorporate supplements in its Sunday edition, the *New York World* played a key role in the development of both. Much of the success of the *World* was based on the use of illustrations, which grew ever more numerous as other papers began to compete with Pulitzer in this area. By 1890, forty percent of New York's population was foreign-born, and the pictures and increasingly large headlines appealed especially to readers who were still learning English. When the *New York Recorder* contracted with R. Hoe and Company for a four-color rotary press, Pulitzer ordered one as well.

The *New York World*'s press was introduced to Gotham readers with a special Sunday edition on May 7, 1893, commemorating the tenth anniversary of Pulitzer's ownership. The paper totaled a record-breaking one hundred pages (forty-eight was the maximum until that time) and sold 400,000 copies. The supplement was printed on heavy stock, and its only colors were red and blue.

The *World*'s Sunday supplement was modeled on illustrated monthly magazines such as *Harper's Monthly,* the *Century Magazine,* and

Scribner's. These magazines, featuring prominent American and English writers, were expensive and appealed to an upper-class audience. The same readers purchased the humor magazines *Life, Puck,* and *Judge,* which published political cartoons and other comic drawings. With the success of the Sunday supplement, it must have seemed a logical next step to adapt the humor magazine format for the newspaper and the comic supplement was added to the Sunday *World* on May 21, 1893. Its first cover, by *World* political cartoonist Walt MacDougall, was a topical cartoon on the dangers of cable cars, a mode of public transportation proving to be ill-suited to New York's streets. The most prominent color on the cover was yellow, and the *World*'s printers seem to have had no trouble running it. In the second weekly supplement, the same strong yellow appeared on the coat of a tiger and the gown of the visiting Spanish Infanta Eulalia.

Both the Sunday and the comic supplement were successful. The popularity of the Sunday supplement increased further when Morrill Goddard moved from the city desk to be its editor in 1894. Goddard filled its pages with illustrated stories on crime, society, and popular science which were derided by the press, but were hugely entertaining to the *World*'s readers. (Outcault's black and white cartoon, "A Geographical Goat" (February 23, 1896), parodied the supplement's stories about freaks of nature.)

The comic supplement's popularity apparently did not suffer from a printing problem with yellow that developed shortly after it began. Yellow first faded to hues barely discernible from white, then disappeared almost entirely from the *World*'s color pages while red and blue continued to appear. The reason yellow left the *World*— whether technical or economic, related to press or ink, is unknown. Several of the rare attempts to use yellow and green during this time involved Outcault's cartoons. Areas of pale yellow and green occur in "The Invisible Wire: or, the Secret of Young Sandow Explained" (December 16, 1894), "An Adverse Criticism" (April 7, 1895), and "At the Circus in Hogan's Alley" (May 5, 1895).

Unlike Hearst, who was deeply involved in choosing the contents of the Sunday and comic supplements of his own papers and who personally supervised the construction of his presses, often contributing innovative ideas to their design, Pulitzer was forced to leave editing to his editors and presses to his pressmen. By 1890, Pulitzer was hampered by grave health problems, losing his eyesight to diabetes, while suffering from asthma and an extraordinary sensitivity to noise that left him unable to occupy the magnificent publisher's office at the top of his gold-domed building on Park Row. Perhaps this explains why the deficiencies of the *World*'s color presses went uncorrected between mid-1893 and

27. RICHARD F. OUTCAULT.
Cartoon from the
New York World
(February 23, 1896).

28. RICHARD F. OUTCAULT.
Cartoon from the
New York World
(April 7, 1895).

THE ONLY SURE BAROMETER AS INDICATED BY FARMER OATCAKE'S RHEUMATISM.

Southerly winds.   Changeable weather.   Westerly winds—Clear and fair.   Easterly winds with showers.

Warmer.   Colder weather with local rains.   Warmer weather—Rain or snow.   Thaw.

29. LADENDORF.
Cartoon from the
New York World
(July 28, 1895).

mid-1895; Pulitzer was most likely unaware of them.

Finally, on July 28, 1895, a strong, saturated yellow appeared once more in the cartoons of the comic supplement. It is most clearly seen in "The Only Sure Barometer as Indicated by Farmer Oatcake's Rheumatism," a cartoon showing the facial contortions of a suffering farmer in eight vignettes. The *World's* printers seem to have selected it to test either an improved yellow ink or an improved press delivery of that hue. Each vignette was filled with a bright yellow background. On the same page, a three-panel cartoon included landscapes of fine green grass. A sports cartoon on the same page featured a strong green formed with this yellow. Afterwards, yellows and greens appeared more frequently in the *World's* cartoons. One seaside drawing by Outcault (August 18, 1895) showed middle-class children playing on bright yellow sand; another, "The Pace That Kills" (October 13, 1895), included a girl in a bright yellow dress in the foreground.

Yellow and green also appeared more prominently in the large *Hogan's Alley* cartoons. "The Great Cup Race on Reilly's Pond" (September 22, 1895), for example, shows a kid in a yellow hat and nightshirt in a green park. "The Horse Show as Reproduced at Shantytown" (November 17, 1895) includes many areas of yellow. A yellow-garbed kid appears with a red-gowned one in "Merry Xmas Morning in Hogan's Alley" (December 15, 1895). Finally, "Golf—The Great Society Sport as Played in Hogan's Alley" (January 5, 1896) features the Yellow Kid in the foreground and a second kid in a yellow gown tumbling headfirst down a stoop at rear. Although Waugh and others consider "The Great Dog Show in M'Googan Avenue" (February 16, 1896) to be the test for the printers' "improved yellow ink," an effective yellow had been installed on the *World* press long before its publication.

With the Yellow Kid becoming an increasingly important figure in Outcault's drawings of tenement children, the bright new yellow in the *World's* palette may have seemed a good color to help him stand out. Unlike red, green, or blue, it was sufficiently transparent to permit reading text on the nightshirt.

It is easy to see how the story that the Kid's nightshirt was used to test the ink gained credibility. It makes for a far more engaging and colorful yarn than Farmer Oatcake's faces. But the legend of the Yellow Kid's nightgown as a proving ground for a new yellow ink just ain't so.

30. ANONYMOUS.
    Joseph Pulitzer (ca. 1896).
    Collection of the New York
    Historical Society.

Five

Barbaric Yawp:
The Yellow Kid and the Menace of the Comics
(1895–1896)

Kicked into effective life for the first time in "Golf—the Great Society Sport as Played in Hogan's Alley" (January 5, 1896), the Yellow Kid—with his sharply caricatured face and bright yellow gown—was clearly meant to catch the amused eye of the *New York World*'s readers. The graphic burst of ochre energy may have provoked reader demand for the curious kid, as comic historians suggest. Certainly, Outcault himself recognized his creation's potential, which he proceeded to develop with vigor and imagination.

SUNDAY, DECEMBER 22, 1895.
THE GREAT FOOTBALL MATCH DOWN IN CASEY'S ALLEY.

31. RICHARD F. OUTCAULT.
Cartoon from the
New York World
(December 22, 1895).

Throughout most of 1895, Outcault's first year of cartooning for the *World,* his tenement gangs were relatively static, his characters gentle in demeanor. Outcault's work (and indeed, all the *New York World*'s cartoon art) was a subdued reflection of the national cartoon papers. However, at the end of 1895 and in the first months of 1896, Outcault's work began to change. He began gradually to develop the elements that would lead to his great success with *Hogan's Alley* and the Yellow Kid. Although the acme of his success, and the full development of the Yellow Kid character, came in the large weekly color panels, the innovations often appeared first in his smaller cartoons.

It was in the black and white cartoons that Outcault first introduced a kind of graphic, almost surreal violence rarely, if ever found in the cartoons of the sedate comic weeklies produced for an upper class Victorian audience. This new comic violence first explodes in "The Great Football Match Down in Casey's Alley" (December 22, 1895). The nightshirted figure who would become the Yellow Kid is nowhere to be found in this cartoon, but its composition and setting anticipate the series in which he will become the star. With its tremendous swatch of flowing blood on the field and bricks, cans, and bodies flying through the air, this gridiron encounter served as prelude to increasingly violent escapades by the Hogan's Alley gang. Succeeding cartoons emphasized knockabout brutalities of all sorts. In short order, this violence drew the attention of self-appointed guardians of media propriety, who waged a campaign of denunciation that was not to ebb for many years.

The incendiary nature of the new, violent imagery can be seen by comparing Outcault's Independence Day cartoons of 1895 and 1896. The former, "The Day After the Glorious Fourth—Down in Hogan's Alley" (July 7, 1895), shows a quiet, sorrowful tableau in the aftermath of an injurious celebration. In the latter, "An Old-Fashioned Fourth of July in Hogan's Alley" (July 5, 1896), Outcault draws the gloriously exploding horror of the day in full flash, with a grandly excited Yellow Kid pointing to his own dog as it gets blown off its feet. In the foreground, delighted kids shoot off fireworks while behind them, fleeing residents escape the tenement that has been set ablaze. It is hard to imagine that this marvelously celebratory image would have deterred any child from setting off stacks of fireworks.

Another important innovation is a decreasing reliance on printed dialogue captions. Perhaps not surprisingly, no dialogue appears below the battling tenement athletes in the black and white cartoon, "The Great Football Match Down in Casey's Alley" (December 22, 1895). Lively scenes like this do not require conversation. Shortly after the appearance of this cartoon, below-panel dialogue captions disappear permanently from the large Sunday panels.

The black and white cartoons also include instances where Outcault begins to develop two features that would be key to the Yellow Kid's success: a continuing title for the feature, and recognizable named characters. Outcault had begun to use "Hogan's Alley" after the first color panel with a nightshirted kid, "At the Circus in Hogan's Alley" (May 5, 1895), but he did not use the title consistently.

In a satirical black and white cartoon, "A Crying Need of the Day is a Few More Popular Songs" (April 5, 1896), Outcault mocks the products of songwriters who produced popular songs for the sheet music publishing industry. In this cartoon, he associates the figure that would become the Yellow Kid with what soon would be established as the permanent title of the series, one so valuable that the *World* would retain title to it when Outcault was hired away by the *Journal*. The nightshirted kid is shown warbling a forgettable tune called "Hogan's Alley," the first time the figure and the title are so closely associated.

Three weeks later, the last large color panel that did not use "Hogan's Alley" in the title appeared. After "Amateur Circus: The Smallest Show on Earth" (April 25, 1896), all cartoons were clearly designated as part of the *Hogan's Alley* series.

The Yellow Kid is named for the first time in "Two Geniuses" (March 29, 1896), a small black and white cartoon. The memorable cognomen, Castillo McFinnerty, appears only here, in what would prove to be Outcault's last dialogue caption. Outcault gave the Kid an appropriately brief and punchy moniker when his importance as a continuing character dictated a permanent name. In August 1896, he received the name Mickey Dugan, not in one of the large panels, but in a small cartoon like "Two Geniuses," containing only two figures.

In place of dialogue, Outcault began to use signs and placards. The first outburst appears in "The War Scare in Hogan's Alley" (March 15, 1896), where four-sided placards proclaim, "Down Wit Ingland" and "Down Wit Spane." The Yellow Kid has not begun to emote on his nightgown-cum-word balloon, but a single word, "Artillery," is lettered just below the hand smears on his skirt.

The "war scare" of the cartoon's title refers to the aggressive revival of the Monroe Doctrine by Richard Olney, secretary of state under Democratic president Grover Cleveland. In a prelude to the expansionist policies of the United States after the Spanish-American War of 1898, the Cleveland administration warned Great Britain that it would take an active interest in the settlement of a dispute over a boundary that crossed gold-bearing territory between Venezuela and British Guiana. The British submitted the dispute to arbitration, and Olney's

32. RICHARD F. OUTCAULT.
Cartoon from the
New York World
(April 5, 1896).

33. RICHARD F. OUTCAULT.
Cartoon from the
New York World
(March 29, 1896).

aggressive diplomacy put the European imperial powers on notice that henceforce the United States would consider the western hemisphere its sphere of influence. The placards in the cartoon denounce English presumptions, while a window from which someone has hung a sign reading "Hurrah for Old England" has been bombarded to ruins by the kids. This violent act refers to both the threat of war and the antipathy towards the English that would be expected in an Irish neighborhood. The Hogan's Alley troops stand at attention with their wooden-stick guns before a sword-wielding general who is ready to unleash the "dogs of war" chained to his midriff. This is the first Yellow Kid cartoon to comment on a political issue; many more will follow.

In "First Championship Game of the Hogan's Alley Baseball Team" (April 12, 1896), the Yellow Kid proclaims his first words from his nightshirt. On a cloth panel pinned to its front, the Kid boasts, "Wait till my strike. SAY! I won't hardly do a thing to 'em." It is as though one of the signs and placards that have replaced the dialogue captions has migrated to the Yellow Kid's clothing. The chalked "Announcement" on the bulletin board behind the backstop reads: "YESTERDAY wuz to bin de opening game but Casey's goat swallered de ball while Mickey Dugan wuz makin' a home run in de first inning so de game wuz postponed till Sunday to give de management time to get another ball. NOTISS Dat goat is ded."

For the first time, a full page of the comic supplement was devoted to Outcault's work in an unusual double-header combining two half-page color cartoons (April 26, 1896). In the upper cartoon, "The Racing Season Opens in Hogan's Alley," kids on a fence cheer jockeys riding a motley collection of mounts, including goats, dogs, and a stick horse. The Yellow Kid sports a jockey's cap and his nightshirt is free of hand prints, but his smiling demeanor has been replaced by an expression of distress as he nearly bounces off his canine mount's back. In the mayhem, incidental comic touches in the bleachers may escape notice: the pair of bottles used as binoculars by a kid at the far left, and the lucky horseshoe on Kitty Dugan's broad green bonnet at center. A recurring presence in the series, a horrified adult looking on in dismay, appears here as a woman who throws up her hands, helpless to stop the kids' antics.

The blackboard carries the "Book Meckers" odds for such entries as "Chevalier," "Trilby McSwat," "Buckwheat Cakes," "Neverwin," "Yvelte," "Tony Past Her," and finally "Bill Goat," who has been scratched (perhaps Outcault's first reference to a preceding cartoon, recalling the deceased animal who ate the baseball). Most of the names refer to figures from the music halls and vaudeville houses that were the primary entertainment of the working and middle classes of the city. Albert Chevalier was a singer and monologuist from England who portrayed working-class English characters in his one-man shows. Tony Pastor, whose theater occupied part of the building that served as headquarters of Tammany Hall, was the foremost vaudeville showman of the 1880s and 1890s. *Trilby* was George Du Maurier's popular novel about an artist's model in Paris, adapted as a successful play with music in 1895.

In the lower cartoon, "Amateur Circus; the Smallest Show on Earth," some rich kids have secured the services of "two celebrated clowns from Hogan's Alley" to put on a show in the music room of a Manhattan mansion. One clown is the Yellow Kid, holding a ringmaster's whip and wearing torn, folded newspapers as his clown costume. "Little Nipper," lettered on his hat, may refer to a theatrical or circus performer of the time. The outfit of the second clown, a nameless spread-armed kid, more nearly resembles a Japanese theatrical costume than a European pierrot (perhaps as a result of Outcault's having served as an artist for Edison in Paris during an international exposition in 1893, when *japonisme* was sweeping Parisian artistic circles).

The other children, progeny of Park Avenue scions, have been stimulated to somewhat wild but harmless behavior. The only lasting damage to the elaborate Victorian interior seems to have been wrought by the artist who drew on the wall to the right, leaving an upended paint bucket and fallen brush in the foreground. The trapeze-hung chandelier looks none the worse for wear while the cat, though anguished, appears in no danger of losing even one of its nine lives. The "management," author of wall signs in standard English that tout the "Big Show," may well be the dismayed boy in the right foreground with a painted face and feather-duster tail. He seems to look in horror at the spilled paint as his mother arrives home in the background.

"Moving Day in Hogan's Alley" (May 3, 1896) shows an obnoxious family named Dugan leaving their "3rd Floor Back" tenement apartment. A delighted Yellow Kid calls attention to their exit, indicating that Outcault had not yet decided, as he would only six weeks later, that the Kid himself would be a Dugan. The Lower East Side was the most densely populated area in the nation, and landlords rented every square inch of their tenements, including the lightless, airless cellars and windowless interior rooms. Housing was the most costly item in a working family's budget and, while evictions were common enough, landlords were often seen as exploiters. "Jumping the rent" by people who otherwise paid their debts was not considered dishonorable. In a tenement

A MATERIAL DEMONSTRATION.
(From Truth.)

Maggie Hill—Say, Sloppy Slocum, does you believe in spiritualism?
Sloppy Slocum—Well, yer kin jist bet I does. Say, me fadder goes down to de
gin mill every night ter one o' dem seances, an den comes home bringin' der
spirits along, and if ye could see me mudder's face ye'd know der was some
lively rappings and goings on of der spirits.

HIS WAY OUT OF IT.

34. RICHARD F. OUTCAULT.
Cartoon from *Truth*;
reprinted in the
New York World
(July 28, 1895).

district, moving under either of these circumstances was more likely to evoke sympathy than the neighborhood condemnation shown in Outcault's cartoon.

"Hogan's Alley Preparing for the Convention" (May 17, 1896) is the first of several cartoons marking major events of the political season. The election of 1896 was among the hardest fought and most bitter in U.S. history, with an electorate riven by differences over economic policy. Although the rallying cry of "Free Silver" is best remembered, deeper issues included farm prices and the concentration of political and economic power in the trusts. In June 1896, the Republican convention nominated William McKinley as the party's presidential candidate. Backed by magnate Marcus Hanna, McKinley championed continued use of the gold standard for U.S. currency. The *New York World* ultimately endorsed the Republican ticket.

This cartoon, timed to coincide with the Republican National Convention, shows Hogan's Alley denizens on their way to the convention. At the time, most Manhattan slum dwellers were ardent Democrats, but Outcault sends the Yellow Kid and his pals to pack the G.O.P. rally in far-off "St. Loous" in support of the Republican minority. The Kid's saucy nightshirt reference to "de Maine guy" refers to Stephan Sontagg, a G.O.P. delegate from Maine and leader of the Free Silver minority who endorsed the end of the gold standard and free coinage of silver. Attentive sign readers will find jibes at politicians for buying votes and altering platform planks to suit the candidates' personal predilections. One sardonic sign, equating free silver with free lunch, hints that appeals to voter venality lay behind the controversy over national monetary policy.

Coney Island had attracted New York City residents seeking seaside recreation since the early years of the nineteenth century. By the 1880s, its hotels and amusements catered to all social classes, and steamboat and rail lines made it increasingly accessible. Its first enclosed amusement parks were built in 1895 and 1896. Coney Island offered a variety of diversions including rides, shows, games, saloons and, of course, the ocean. Offering inexpensive recreation to urbanites, it was an obvious subject for a *Hogan's Alley* cartoon.

In "The Residents of Hogan's Alley Visit Coney Island" (May 24, 1896), Outcault's rendition seems a little flat. The Yellow Kid himself is decidedly shorter than in preceding cartoons, suggesting that Outcault was essentially reinventing the Yellow Kid from drawing to drawing (assuming, perhaps, that his readers had thrown away the last color supplement by the time they read the next one). At this point, the Yellow Kid is more a focusing device for the action than a consistent character.

The ubiquitous advertisements and exaggerated claims of posters touting Coney Island's sideshow attractions are wittily guyed in this cartoon. Slipped in among the sideshow placards is an aside aimed at *Judge, Puck, Life,* and *Truth:* "The Combined Circulation of the New York Weekly Comic Papers Can Plainly be Seen by Means of a Powerful Microscope." (The *New York World* called its own comic section a "colored supplement.")

Outcault's witticism may be read in context as a counterattack in a war of the comics. The old-guard comic papers had begun to attack the *World*'s colored supplement, no doubt for the reason indicated in Outcault's crowing placard—they were being left in the circulation dust. They equated the *World*'s broad circulation with lowbrow readers, implying that no cultured person would care to associate with the great unwashed. Almost every issue of *Life* included an attack on Pulitzer or his newspaper. A mocking, anti-Semitic profile published March 12, 1896, described the publisher as "noted for his extreme modesty, fine, discriminating taste, his love of the beautiful, and the wonderful purity of his mind. . . . Will do his worst work on Sunday." The *World* and its readers were targeted in this attack from the February 13 issue: "It used to be so that one could tell a man by the newspaper he read; but now it is by the newspaper that he doesn't read." Clearly, the cartoon magazines wanted it understood, the sight of the *World* in proper, upper-class sitting rooms would be valid cause for ostracism.

Elements of the clergy echoed this campaign. The *New York World*'s Sunday supplement featured articles on pseudoscientific topics and sensationalistic illustrations. These were easily branded as un- or anti-Christian in a period when the ideas of Darwin and Huxley were only just appearing in the popular media. Politicians maneuvering for re-election contributions from the "better" people also joined in the fray.

Apparently, the well-to-do and professional classes largely accepted the comic papers' argument. The *World* became a pariah not only in the sacrosanct homes of the favored few, but in many public libraries and schools. Although no demographic studies of its circulation base exist, the large circulation and content of the *World*'s advertising suggest that it appealed to tens of thousands of young, reasonably well-paid, white-collar, home-owning families. The *World* successfully held advertisers oriented towards a mass consumer public, leaving the paper unaffected financially by its stigma among the elite.

35. RICHARD F. OUTCAULT.
Cartoon from the
New York World
(October 13, 1895).

36. RICHARD F. OUTCAULT.
Cartoon from *Truth*;
reprinted in the
New York World,
(July 21, 1895).

37. KEMBLE.
Cartoon from *Life*
(June 4, 1896).

The campaign against the *World* was also aimed at the artists. Undoubtedly it made the assured market of the comic papers seem far more stable than the new, if moneyed operation of the color supplement, which might disappear overnight. Thus, one motivation behind the comic weeklies' attacks was a desire to keep their major cartoonists—Woolf, Gibson, Opper, Chip—from being tempted away by the *World*'s higher rates of payment. On the one side, the comic weeklies sold second rights to the *World,* pocketing the considerable fees while the artists never received a cent. On the other, many cartoonists saw their growing incomes as keys to higher status, which could be threatened by either blackballing by the major papers or association with lowbrow culture. Virtually all the regular cartoonists for the elite weeklies were persuaded to stay with their existing outlets, while their rates of pay were grudgingly raised as a precautionary measure.

With the top cartoonists holding firm at the big three weeklies, many of the *World*'s cartoonists were new or marginal artists. The comic supplement's graphic success was based on the work of the paper's own staff cartoonists and that of artists like Outcault, who had published in the next-tier weekly, *Truth*. Although the *World* tried to bind some of its artists and writers with exclusive contracts, these were virtually unenforceable in the freewheeling legal world of the time. Most of the *Truth* free-lancers continued to work for both papers.

Among them was George B. Luks, a twenty-nine-year-old artist from Pennsylvania who had formed a fast friendship with Outcault during their years with *Truth*. On that basis, Luks drew the first published parody of Outcault's *Hogan's Alley* series for the *World*, "Hogan's Alley Attacked by the Hoboken Pretzel Club" (May 31, 1896). Hoboken, New Jersey, had a large German population, and weekend ferry trips to visit its beer gardens grew popular, especially after New York enacted laws prohibiting the sale of liquor by the drink on Sunday. In this cartoon, Luks did not attempt to duplicate Outcault's style. (Later that year, when Outcault had taken his character to the *New York Journal*'s competing comic supplement and Luks was assigned to continue *Hogan's Alley* for the *World,* he followed this precedent and worked in his own style.) In light of later developments, perhaps the most striking element of the cartoon is that Luks picked up the crucial innovation of the Yellow Kid's nightshirt comments, which Outcault had used only twice.

Also as in Outcault's cartoons, the crowd debarking from the Hoboken Ferry carries signs. One reads "Viva Cuba Libre," echoing the *World*'s outspoken support for the Cuban rebels fighting Spain, support that in time would lend itself to direct U.S. involvement in that war. Thus, two coming events cast their highly colored shadows before them in this cartoon: the short Spanish-American War of April through August 1898, and the rather longer Great Yellow Kid Newspaper War of 1896–1898.

38. BROWN BROTHERS.
   William Randolph Hearst
   (circa 1900).

Six

The World, the Kid, and William Randolph Hearst:

Practical Philanthropy on Newspaper Row (1895–1896)

Newly arrived in New York in mid-l895, William Randolph Hearst, the thirty-two-year-old editor and publisher of the highly successful *San Francisco Examiner*, was looking for a local newspaper to buy. Hearst was an ardent admirer of the *New York World*. A few years earlier he had worked at the *World* to get a feel for how such a spectacularly popular newspaper operated. He had put what he learned there into practice at the *Examiner* and made it the most popular newspaper in San Francisco. Now his deepest ambition was to outdo the *World* on its own terms by

GEORGE B. LUKS.
As R. F. Outcault sees him.

RICHARD F. OUTCAULT.
As G. B. Luks sees him.

39. George B. Luks and
Richard F. Outcault,
portraits from the
New York World
(July 19, 1896).

editing and publishing the best-selling paper in New York. He considered purchasing the nearly moribund *New York Times*, but decided that so doggedly dull a paper could never be remade in the *World*'s image. Hearst instead purchased a lively but underdeveloped paper with a readership of only 77,000, the *New York Journal*. Already full of reprint cartoons and gags and with a reputation as a gossip sheet, the *Journal* must have seemed a promising candidate to be recast in the mold that had been so successful at the *Examiner*.

Hearst published the first issue of the *Journal* under his name on November 8, 1895. He began his competition with the *New York World* by lowering the *Journal*'s price from two cents to a penny and by mounting a citywide advertising campaign. His massive poster and placard assault on hoardings from Far Rockaway to Staten Island announced to New Yorkers that they could buy a paper equal to or better than the *World* at half the price. The *New York Journal* soon included all the features that had made the *World* successful: illustrated daily news columns, serial fiction, reprint cartoons, and lively coverage of all the ongoing urban scandal and crime. The sales of the revived *Journal* promptly soared to just over 100,000, a remarkable increase but still minuscule compared to the *World*'s towering circulation of one-half million. The *World* remained blithely indifferent to its new self-styled competitor.

While publishing the *Examiner,* Hearst had hired Eastern reporters and editors to help him create the kind of newspaper he wanted. He had transformed the San Francisco paper from a dull organ of the Democratic Party into a lively paper with extensive coverage of metropolitan and Western news. Hearst's California reporters were usually first at the scenes of disasters and crimes, and the paper itself became important in California politics, particularly in its long fight with the Southern Pacific Railroad. In New York, Hearst modeled the *Journal* on the *World,* but lacking a staff of editors and reporters of the caliber he had assembled in California, his paper without substance. Although the *Journal* followed the *World*'s format, particularly in its Sunday edition, it also lacked a color press and could not compete effectively with the Sunday *World* until it acquired one.

In a daring move that went beyond anything he had done at the *Examiner,* Hearst simply hired the men he needed en masse from the *World*. He approached Morrill Goddard, the *World*'s gifted editorial entrepreneur, and brought him and his entire editorial staff to the *Journal* in January 1896. Goddard spent the rest of his career in the

Hearst organization, serving as publisher of Hearst's famed *American Weekly* Sunday magazine well into the 1940s. After acquiring Goddard and his staff, Hearst temporarily refrained from further attempts to snag the *World's* top talent. At the time he was still in the process of paying for construction of his own color press, and he was not yet ready to offer Outcault an appropriate venue for publication of his cartoons. That would come about in October.

Joseph Pulitzer was furious over the loss of his staff, who had jumped ship for salaries he would never consider paying. As noted above, contracts meant little in the freewheeling environment of late nineteenth-century, unbridled capitalism. They seem chiefly to have obligated the employer rather than the employee, leaving Goddard and staff free to join Hearst without legal reprisals. To replace Goddard, Pulitzer turned to Arthur Brisbane, a reporter who had gained a reputation as a fresh and brilliant writer while covering the Jack the Ripper murders in London and the prize fights of John L. Sullivan. With the talented Brisbane at the *World's* helm, readers noted no particular loss of verve or sensation in their preferred paper. He was adept at creating many of the same sorts of features, from scandal to popular science, that Goddard had pioneered for Pulitzer. Brisbane, too, would later work for Hearst, becoming one of his closest associates and the editor who supplied subjects for Winsor McCay's conservative political cartoons.

Pulitzer responded to the competition rashly by cutting the price of the *New York World* to a penny. Advertisers rebelled at Pulitzer's attempts to make up lost revenue by raising their base rates and cut their advertising expenditures accordingly. From this point on, the *World* was locked in mortal combat with the *Journal*, a rivalry that continued until the *World* merged with the *Tribune* at the start of the Depression in 1931.

None of this was apparent to readers of the Sunday *World* in mid-1896. The paper had a diverse readership attracted by its lively writing, wealth of illustrations and, of course, the Sunday comic supplement. European immigrants with limited English were attracted by the *World's* illustrations and were ready and able to laugh at the excitingly detailed rampages of the Yellow Kid. Multitudes of young white- and blue-collar workers with regular jobs and brand-new families found news, cartoons, and advertising for the stores where they bought their clothes, appliances, and furniture. A populist and Democratic newspaper, the *World* found a readership in the city's poorest neighborhoods, while adventurous readers among New York's upper classes read it as well. Its readers eagerly anticipated the weekly capers of the Yellow Kid and his Hogan's Alley compatriots, purchasing tens of thousands of copies off the racks of the newsdealers. The comic supplement was

A ROOF GARDEN AT THE NORTH POLE.

40. RICHARD F. OUTCAULT.
Cartoon from the
New York World
(August 25, 1895).

wrapped around each copy of the Sunday *World*, and the colorful cartoon characters on its cover seemed to saunter in their duplicate tens of thousands down every street of the city, as the papers were carried home under the arms of their purchasers.

The city's multitudes also snapped up the growing numbers of Yellow Kid toys, games, cigars, chewing gum, candy, and comic pins to be found in novelty stores, tobacco shops, street carnival booths, and other outlets in 1896. The burgeoning thousands of manufactured Yellow Kid images in metal, glass, and wood might offend the Park Avenue swells and the literary-tea crowd, but the *World's* diverse readers loved them. Outcault profited handsomely from the royalties.

The *Hogan's Alley* pages of June through October, 1896, marked the apogee of Outcault's work in the *World*. The Yellow Kid and his gang rocked disastrously and gaily through social events, holidays, and festive outings. In June, the Kid and his cronies hitched every animal in creation for a "coaching parade"; got half-drowned in the Coney Island surf, where the drenched Yellow Kid's nightshirt compared Republican presidential aspirant McKinley's campaign to his own plight; shook, rattled, and rolled through a bicycle race past back-fence signs mocking Yellow Kid sheet music, cheap fiction, and the shocking sight of female bicyclists' bloomers; and wrapped up the month with an idyllic visit to Manhattan's Central Park where the kids raced homemade boats.

July began explosively with the vigorous and exhilarating fireworks extravaganza, "An Old-Fashioned Fourth of July in Hogan's Alley" (July 5, 1896). In "A Hot Political Convention in Hogan's Alley" (July 12, 1896), Outcault paid more or less serious attention to the 1896 Democratic convention. In this cartoon, the Yellow Kid declares himself a nonpartisan mugwump, his disaffection emphasized by a satirical background of sloganeering signs, including one on a barn demanding "pensions for artists and humorists." The *New York World*, previously a solidly Democratic paper, was reluctant to endorse candidate William Jennings Bryan, and the tone of this cartoon reflects the paper's wavering editorial stance.

After this rather somber political page, Outcault returned to humorous action in "Hogan's Alley Children Spend a Day in the Country" (July 19, 1896), a lively roll in the hay with the gang enjoying the pleasures of the countryside. The Yellow Kid is moved to poetry by the rural idyll, although some of his less fortunate companions tumble from the trees they have climbed. In the same Sunday supplement, the

World lauded the accomplishments of the two cartoonists the paper had lured from the comic weeklies in a pair of portraits in which Luks drew Outcault and Outcault depicted his friend Luks.

"The Opening of the Hogan's Alley Roof Garden" (July 26, 1896) finds the Yellow Kid ably filling the role of master of ceremonies for the evening's entertainment. Roof gardens, open-air places of amusement that offered dining and dancing to those who could afford them, first opened atop hotels and other commercial buildings in the 1880s. The 1890s marked the peak of their popularity when the most fashionable and successful, like that above Madison Square Garden, attracted well-heeled crowds with shows featuring vaudeville entertainers. In this cartoon, the thespian extravaganza includes the first formal introduction of Mickey Dugan's "regular" girl, Liz, who appears in a blue gingham dress at his rear. More than previous work, this drawing depends for its humor on the presentation of children in social roles and situations ordinarily associated with adults. While situations in which children innocently ape adult dress and behavior were staple humor, large numbers of teen-agers alone in their own company for an evening's night-club entertainment were not generally seen until the 1900s. Outcault's cartoon, however comic, probably tended to confirm middle-class notions about the widely believed but, of course, largely mythical "loose" social life of the young in the slums.

Corruption is the theme of Outcault's representation of urban politics in "A Wild Political Fight in Hogan's Alley—Silver Against Gold" (August 2, 1896). This bombastic panel finds the Yellow Kid resplendent in jewelry and a "new piece," a strip of cloth sewn to the bottom of his gown, which became a running gag played out over several weeks. The glass gewgaws and "new piece" were apparently sufficient to persuade the Yellow Kid to abandon his earlier neutral stance and rousingly endorse Bryan, the Democratic presidential candidate. Further political venality is evident in the notice fastened to the door of the "Campaign Head-quarters" at far left: "Heelers an hustlers lookin fer dough must call between de hours of 1:55 an 2 o'clock—votes will be bought an sold at regular market prices." As in "A Hot Political Convention in Hogan's Alley" (July 12, 1896), the artist's cynical view of the kinds of issues that sway voters is reinforced by the mélange of placards behind the

41. RICHARD F. OUTCAULT. Cartoon from the *New York World* (August 2, 1896).

TREMENDOUS ENTHUSIASM OF THE GOLD TEMPERANCE PARTY.
(FROM THE POINT OF VIEW OF R. F. OUTCAULT.)

Yellow Kid, while the huge fight between Republicans and Democrats over the merits of maintaining the gold standard versus permitting the free coinage of silver surges in the background.

As in Outcault's earlier cartoon on the Republican National Convention, "Hogan's Alley Preparing for the Convention" (May 17, 1896), part of the comic effect lies in the very preposterousness of the action. Since Hogan's Alley was in the middle of an Irish Catholic district where the populace was solidly for the "Dimmycrats," the likelihood of any Republican daring to identify himself as such, let alone round up enough fellow Republicans for a fight, was virtually nil. The Yellow Kid seems to be preparing for his own political future. A baffled-looking child, to the lower left of the Kid's platform, seems just to have found a Yellow Kid emblem attached by parties unknown to his shirt.

Two related political cartoons accompany this riotous Yellow Kid panel. In one, Luks parodied the Populists while in the other, Outcault took on the Prohibitionists. The Populists, a powerful third party that nominated Bryan and fought for economic reform, were stereotyped by their opponents as unsophisticated farmers and violent anarchists. Luks combines both these elements in his cartoon. Outcault mocks a combined "gold temperance" ticket.

"Hogan's Alley Folk Have a Wild Trolley Party in Brooklyn" (August 9, 1896) celebrates an outing for the gang. The Yellow Kid sports a cigar-filled pocket on his nightshirt. His well-heeled look is emphasized by proclamations on his nightshirt referring to Luks's earlier parody, "Hogan's Alley Attacked by the Hoboken Pretzel Club" (May 31, 1896), but informing the reader that "Dis time I'm de real ting." Electric trolleys had largely replaced slower horsecars and attracted "pleasure riders" who exchanged their nickels for the diversion and cooling breezes. This inexpensive pastime attracted family parties from the Lower East Side of Manhattan, and was especially popular in Brooklyn and outlying towns. Before electric street lights were installed in these areas, nighttime parties in brightly lit trolleys provided summer entertainment.

The next week, as Manhattan pavements baked, *World* readers could find cool sanctuary in a Hogan's Alley panel set at the North Pole—a visual gag dating back at least to Cruikshank. The good ship *Liz* of New York, named for the Yellow Kid's girl, has brought the gang to the Pole, while kids in the center foreground are being pulled by huskies on a sled named for Outcault's wife, Mary Jane. The Yellow Kid is still plugging for Bryan, Democratic forces presumably having staked Mickey's spiffy parka as earlier they had provided his jewels and "new piece."

In "He Was Chasing the Duck" (August 23, 1896), the Yellow Kid is called Mickey Dugan for the first time in print. Naming the Yellow Kid was a gradual process. In his earliest magazine and newspaper cartoons, Outcault had named the speakers of the dialogue captions, following the playlet formula of Woolf and many other cartoonists. By the time the Yellow Kid became a major character, he had all but abandoned below-panel captions; the name Mickey Dugan evolved in the signs and lettering within the cartoons. Outcault had listed the name Mickey Dugan on the bill of the "Fistic Carnival of the Cherry Hill Athletic Club" (February 16, 1896), a cartoon that does not depict the Yellow Kid. In "First Grand Coaching Parade of the Season in Hogan's Alley" (June 7, 1896), the name Mickey

Dugan was painted on the barrels that formed the Yellow Kid's coach. In "The Bicycle Meet in Hogan's Alley" (June 21, 1896), the Yellow Kid identified himself with manic glee in his nightshirt lettering: "I am de Dugan kid, aint I hot stuff? Well say!" The full name first appeared at the end of August, just weeks before the first performance of a skit featuring the Yellow Kid in the Weber and Fields vaudeville show where he was identified as Mickey Dugan.

Although as a *Journal* cartoonist Outcault would have been anathema to other papers and most magazines, he must have been interviewed by writers from cheap gossip sheets of the time. There were upwards of forty such gossip sheets in New York in the 1890s. Any well-known person who would hold still for five minutes, particularly anyone with lowbrow appeal, was likely to be interviewed, and in this context Outcault might have been asked to name his creation.

On September 7, 1896, Outcault wrote to the Librarian of Congress for permission to copyright "this little character" called "The Yellow Dugan Kid." His letter included a drawing and a description of the Yellow Kid: "His costume however is always yellow, his ears are large he has but two teeth and a bald head and is distinctly different from any thing else." His request was granted, and just one month before the Dugan Kid moved to the *Journal*, he became definitively and legally Outcault's own. The theatrical appearance of the Yellow Kid, the need for copyright protection for his increasingly valuable character, and opportunities for publicity were probably key reasons Outcault felt it necessary to give him a name.

"The Great Bull Fight in Hogan's Alley" (August 23, 1896) and "The Great Lawn Tennis Tournament in Hogan's Alley" (August 30, 1896) are grand Hogan's Alley extravaganzas. In what may be the first instance of a cartoonist breaking the boundaries of the cartoon panel (in this case, the entire newspaper page functions as the panel), a kid is butted by a bull and flies off one page onto the next. With these two panels, Outcault also begins to create narrative links between his Sunday cartoons, using the characters' actions. Action and consequence link the

two cartoons as the Yellow Kid's "new piece" gets torn from his nightshirt and trodden underfoot in the "Bullfight's" melee, then is pinned back on his gown for the "Lawn Tournament." This novel device continues in comic art to this day as do the two types of running gags Outcault continues to develop here: artistic self-reference and humorous manipulation of a character's costume. A poster in the "Bull Fight" announces the "Monthly Meeting of the Illustrators Club" with an admonitory, "Pay up yer dues, boys, an yer poker debts," while in the "Lawn Tournament" the Yellow Kid's nightshirt sports a second new feature, a pocket complete with pocket-watch chain.

On September 3, 1896, the increasing popularity and public recognition of Outcault's Sunday cartoon was confirmed by the debut of a Hogan's Alley pantomime skit at the famed Weber and Fields Broadway Music Hall. Outcault sketched from life a sparkling panorama of the whole cast, published on the *New York World*'s drama page the following Sunday. It showed the seven "Hogan's Alley Folk" featured in the skit, much as they must have lined up for their bows. One wonders how real the artificial ears worn by the actor who played the Yellow Kid appeared from the front-row seats.

"Li Hung Chang Visits Hogan's Alley" (September 6, 1896) marks the visit of China's viceroy and minister of foreign affairs who stopped in New York to visit the tomb of his friend Ulysses S. Grant

43. RICHARD F. OUTCAULT.
Cartoon from the
New York World
(September 6, 1896).

while travelling to the coronation of Czar Nicholas II. President Grover Cleveland hosted a reception for Li at the residence of former Secretary of the Navy William C. Whitney, and all his activites were extensively covered in the press. In October, Weber and Fields opened "The Geezer," a musical comedy about the ambassador that played to capacity houses. Although Outcault's strip was often topical and political (even here the Yellow Kid wears a tag reading, "vote at least once for Bryan"), no public figures were ever portrayed in the scathing caricatures typical of the New York press. When actual persons did appear, their features were rendered in a realistic style that duplicated the appearance of the engraved illustrations on the news pages. Li is depicted in this way, surrounded by a lively cartoon scene filled with fireworks and paper lanterns. Outcault imitates Asian scrolls, using blocks containing text in characters and his signature.

Below the block he signed appears a suggestive note, "Do not be deceived, none genuine without this signature." This suggests that Outcault may already have signed aboard the new flagship Hearst paper for a major berth in the California mogul's long-planned Sunday comic supplement, and had given some sort of notice to the *World*. Outcault's move was delayed a bit by last-minute tinkering on the *Journal's* new color press, and the *World* apparently remained willing to print weekly *Yellow Kid* cartoons by Outcault as long as it could. Outcault was aware that the *World* had legal rights to the title *Hogan's Alley* and would turn the feature over to the convenient Luks after his last page had been printed. His note appears more a friendly, inside jibe at Luks than a serious attempt to tell his readers about the coming changes. The actual event would be the talk of New York the day it happened, and no one would be in any doubt about where the genuine Yellow Kid could be found.

Craft and business fraternal organizations and lodges are guyed in "A Secret Society Initiation in Hogan's Alley" (September 13, 1896). The Ancient Order of Hibernians becomes "the Ancient Order of Sons-o-Guns" and the Odd Fellows become the "Hod Fellers," emblazoned on the Kid's sash and referring to hods of bricks carried by Irish workers employed in the building trades. Entry to the Masonic "33rd degree tent" is restricted: "if yez has de dough yer in it."

The Yellow Kid is getting very gabby, filling sizable placards with comments far beyond the capacity of his nightshirt. One placard and the topmost sign on the building feature scathing comments on publishers, remarking on their failure to pay royalties and unwillingness to publish the Yellow Kid's "new book of poems." No book of "Mickey Dugan's" poetry is known actually to have been published, and one wonders how developed such a collection might have been. One poem had appeared in the strip, held in the Kid's hand as he stands high up in a tree on the bucolic outing shown in "Hogan's Alley Children Spend a Day in the Country" (July 19, 1896). Although it is headed "My poem wot I've just wrote," Outcault credited it to Terence McSwatt in an article published in the *World* on May 5, 1898.

Children falling from upper-story windows and fire escapes were and still are an all-too-common tragedy of the summer months in New York City. Children falling from high places form a recurring motif in Outcault's Yellow Kid cartoons, first appearing prominently in "The Residents of Hogan's Alley Visit Coney Island" (May 24, 1896) and "Hogan's Alley Children Spend a Day in the Country" (July 19, 1896). In context, readers would see children falling from carnival rides and tree limbs as comic rather than tragic.

When Outcault begins to use the motif in the tenement setting of Hogan's Alley, he is at pains to indicate that what he is showing is cartoon violence in which no one is actually hurt. In most of the Alley scenes, the same boy is shown falling. In some of his first appearances, Outcault uses dialogue balloons to make it clear that the same child falls again and again, always escaping entirely unscathed. On September 6, a parrot at upper left remarks as the kid falls past, "That kid is always falling off the house. Some day he will be hurt." In the September 13 page, the tumbling boy himself moans, "I wish I could break myself of this habit."

"What They Did to the Dog-Catcher in Hogan's Alley" (September 20, 1896) is a rousing drawing that represents the peak—or the depth—of the antisocial vulgarity allegedly epidemic in the *New York World's* comic supplement. Two romantic pairings bracket the central action as the dropsy-suffering tumbler falls for Miss Molly Brogan, the girl "whose face always wears an expression of astonishment," while the Yellow Kid basks in the admiring glances of a girl at far right. All other eyes are on the trapped, dog-pinned, writhing miscreant conned by a Tammany ward heeler into the thankless job of dog catcher in an Irish slum. In New York at the time, unlicensed dogs from the tenements were gassed upon their arrival at the pound as a matter of course. There was no waiting period to enable owners to recover their pets, the assumption being that "those people" had no means of buying a license anyway.

This cartoon remains a remarkable graphic salute to the downtrodden as they take justice into their own hands. One can imagine anarchists pinning copies of this page on their tenement walls and toasting the creator of *Hogan's Alley* with red wine. The city's gentry must have been infuriated at the implications of the drawing; if such people would do that to a dog catcher, what would they do to a policeman? One wonders if Joseph Pulitzer himself, the gentle and ailing but forceful publisher of the *World,* didn't blanch at what Outcault and Brisbane had served up to the public this week. Hearst probably chuckled, but he was cautious in his own way, having his eye on his personal political fortunes in New York. It is noticeable that nothing remotely like this gorgeously brutal attack on the cold, remote bureaucracy of the city ever appeared in Outcault's Yellow Kid cartoons in the *Journal.*

A letter held by the Yellow Kid in this drawing is a direct message from Outcault to his readers: "My correspondence is gittin' so durn big dat I can't open all my mail. Wont some pretty type riter gal please donate her services till I kin answer a few of my letters?"

At the "Opening of the Hogan's Alley Athletic Club" (September 27, 1896), gambling and drinking are as central to the activities of the athletes as exercise. The flaccid, collapsed wrestlers (one of whom is pushing over the Yellow Kid's box seat at the poker table) seem to have just returned from a workout at the "horizontal bar" downstairs. A microscopic notation on the horizontal bar sign reads: "don't owe any bar bill. then you won't owe more than you kin pay." The Yellow Kid's mountains of chips attest to his poker skills. To his right, an armed poker player uses his knees to hold the kitty securely closed. The Yellow Kid's goat, which here displays remarkable ladder-ascending competence, is sitting things out while the kids risk their necks on trapezes and their purses on poker hands. A poem by Terence McSwatt, scrawled on a box seat at the poker table, proclaims that Hogan' Alley is like "de little busy bee . . . it's

44. Jacob Riis.
Safe From the Cops
(1880s-1890s).

always on de move," possibly another Outcault nudge to the readers about his coming move to the *Journal*.

An odd Luks drawing, showing a giant slum kid of lowering countenance, appears at the top of the page, looking down at the denizens of the feature Luks would take over by mid-October. It seems a last-minute substitution (notice the square cut across the ladder) for four columns or so of filler text. Possibly the scheduled text didn't make it by press time and Luks was asked for a quick drawing. The fact that Luks's addition was printed in only two colors, saving plate-making time for the pressroom, also suggests that the piece was a last-minute addition.

"The Amateur Dime Museum in Hogan's Alley" (October 4, 1896) was Outcault's graphic farewell to the *New York World*'s comic supplement. The title refers to the famed Dime Museum of showman P. T. Barnum, confirmed by the flag flying from the tent: "Barnum Ain't in It." Dimes being a little hard to come by in Hogan's Alley, the kids' "dime museum" costs only a penny for admission. The posters in the cartoon ridicule several other targets in addition to the sensational exhibits of the Dime Museum. One denounces actors while another rags the English humor magazine *Punch*, notorious among Americans for the elusive points of its cartoon gags. Outcault also targets the American comic weekly *Life,* apparently in retaliation for the moralistic denunciations with which the magazine had been scalding the *New York World*'s comic supplement for months.

Graphically, Outcault has let out a good many stops this time. The tumbling boy sails gently to earth with the aid of an umbrella, while kids in the foreground dance to barrel organ tunes produced by a derbied man busily cranking a hurdy-gurdy. The Yellow Kid waltzes merrily with Liz while Kitty Dugan and Molly Brogan look on with jaundiced eye. One gifted dog rides another bareback while a sign on its tail urges, "Yes vote for Hobarth," equating a political campaign with a dog act. Outcault's drawing, with the mounted dog's pince-nez indicating that it is male, is suggestive of a sight routine around the Alley, but one that would hardly be permitted in cartoons. A mass readership conditioned to expect only the perfectly proper in art would have been hard put even to see the sexual imagery. A slumming kid from Park Avenue perches atop the main sign, cruelly applauding the ricocheting pellet from the shooting gallery which strikes a child on the upper balcony in the eye. His mocking speech includes the phrase "bully carrom shot," telling Outcault's readers all they needed to know about his class origins.

At the upper left, on a kite held by the slumming kid, Outcault includes one last reference to his move to the *New York Journal* which would take place the following week. "Jist wait till ye see us next week. We are always busy." The editors apparently left it in since it could just as easily be read as a promotion for the *Hogan's Alley* strip by Luks, who already must have been chosen as Outcault's replacement. As it happened, this promotional message came to refer only to Luks's page since a final glitch in the preparation of the Hearst color press delayed the new *Journal* supplement for another week, until October 18. Only the *World* held Hogan's Alley carnivalia in New York on October 11.

The first of a yearlong series of Luks *Hogan's Alley* color pages in the *World*, "Training For the Football Championship Game in Hogan's Alley" (October 11, 1896), displays a new, savage and vigorous graphic competence, differing from his treatment in "Hogan's Alley Attacked by the Hoboken Pretzel Club" (May 31, 1896). However, Luks's work on the series was never to equal Outcault's; it was particularly lacking in the elaboration of background detail and rendering of familiar figures of the *Hogan's Alley* cast. Eschewing Outcault's diamond sharpness of line, Luks's first pages are rigorously composed, but their action is unfocused. Worse still, the Yellow Kid's girl Liz disappears, replaced by the nondescript girl driving the Kid's goat. This benighted animal's offspring makes a very flat joke about being "de new Kid." Mickey Dugan himself is a stiff, overprecise approximation of Outcault's creation. He will become a much more loosely rendered figure as Luks makes the feature his own, developing an approach to the characters more congenial to his active and restless pen. The poster jokes are rowdy and entertaining, and Luks retained other regular characters such as the tumbling boy, who falls with a closed umbrella rather than the open one Outcault had given him in "The Amateur Dime Museum in Hogan's Alley" (October 4th, 1896). The two battling brats in the foreground are destined to become Luks's own *Hogan's Alley* regulars, to be named Alex and George; they will pester the Yellow Kid in various ways and eventually replace him in Luks's pages.

Luks continued to draw the *Hogan's Alley* panel for the *New York World* for another year and a half, but he never substantially altered the pattern he inherited. When Outcault moved to the *New York Journal,* he joined many of his old *World* cronies in pursuit of the financial gain offered by William Randolph Hearst. But Hearst also offered something else to his artists and writers. At the *Journal,* Outcault found an exciting atmosphere in which to work and a new freedom for graphic development in the Yellow Kid—a freedom that was to give all of us the rich and lasting art of the comic strip.

45. BROWN BROTHERS.
Bicyclists in Central Park
(late nineteenth-century).

Seven

The Yellowing of Journalism:
The Journal-Examiner Bicycle Marathon
versus the Yellow Kid (1896)

The Great Yellow Kid Newspaper War is supposed to have led to the creation of the term "yellow journalism" by traditional journalists, shocked and angered by the ignoble spectacle of two major newspapers slugging it out over a vulgar comic character. In fact, the phrase was first used in response to a national bicycle marathon sponsored by Hearst's California and New York newspapers. Although it was a promotional event, planned and carried out expressly to increase newsdealer sales, it was covered as news. That led to the coining of "yellow journalism" as an expression of abhorrence for what was seen as the sensationalistic, titillating, and self-aggrandizing character of reporting in the *New York Journal* and, by extension, the *New York World*. The tepid "battle" between the two competing Yellow Kid cartoons, always linked to the term in journalistic histories, helped perpetuate its use, but the term originated with the stories published in the papers' news columns.

In October 1896, when Outcault and his Yellow Kid moved to the *New York Journal,* an advertising conflagration ignited on Manhattan walls as the paper relentlessly promoted its new cartoonist with colorful posters featuring the Yellow Kid and other comic supplement characters. Joseph Pulitzer's *New York World* responded aggressively with its own advertising, and smiling Yellow Kids by Outcault and Luks soon appeared everywhere. Outcault had prepared his readers for the change of newspapers, indicating several times in the weeks before the move that only he could draw the original Yellow Kid and that they should look for his signature if they wished to continue to enjoy the genuine article.

Despite the publicity surrounding Outcault's move from one competing paper to the other and the hyperbolic advertising that greeted the inauguration of the *New York Journal*'s new comic supplement, few New Yorkers saw these as major events. Most newspaper readers who could afford to were already buying both the *Journal* and the *World*, and the addition of the color Sunday comic section to the *Journal* meant only that readers now had two Yellow Kid cartoons to enjoy each week rather than one.

Hearst's brilliant stroke of pricing the *Journal* at one cent had impelled Pulitzer to reduce the *World*'s price as well. The circulation of the *Journal* soared as the *World*'s readers discovered that they could buy a new newspaper that offered all the same features as the *World* for one penny. Even when Pulitzer halved the price of the *World*, its circulation grew far less than anticipated; readers found that they did not have to choose one paper over the other. They were delighted to spend two pennies a day as they had all along; for their money, they were able to get two exciting papers where previously they had been able to purchase only one.

The addition of the comic supplement and Outcault's Yellow Kid had its primary impact on sales of the Sunday *New York Journal* outside metropolitan New York. In this limited but lucrative market, there was real competition between the Sunday editions of the two New York papers for the nickels of Chicagoans and Los Angelenos. Although burdened with a higher newsstand price (to defray the costs of shipping), the New York Sunday editions attracted newspaper readers of other

cities, competing successfully with local papers and the sometimes bizarre contents of their own Sunday color sections. In that presyndication era, features usually appeared in only one paper, and the *Yellow Kid* found a following in cities outside New York.

In this national market, *Journal* sales shot past the *World*'s, largely because of the greater appeal of Outcault's *Yellow Kid*. It is perhaps ironic that the most direct beneficiary of these sales was ultimately to be Outcault himself. National sales brought national recognition for his bald, nightshirted character, and he continued to realize income from merchandising Mickey Dugan's image across the country long after the feature itself had disappeared from the New York papers.

The true nature of the circulation war between the *World* and the *Journal,* which was in fact an intense rivalry for substantially the same readership, was well understood by New York newspaper and magazine writers and editors of the time. The other newspapers, such as the *Sun, Herald,* and *Times,* were older and had long-established identities and higher prices. Although most New York newspapers had been founded in the 1830s as part of the "penny press," achieving success by using almost identical tactics to those employed by Hearst and Pulitzer, they had long since adopted a more sedate approach to journalism. They appealed to established readerships that did not include the new immigrant and working-class readers who bought the *World* and later the *Journal*.

Once Hearst's new paper established itself as a contender, its competition with the *World* for the highest sales involved essentially the same few hundred thousand people in Manhattan. These were the readers who were fought for by the two papers through their advertising and by trumpeting inflated circulation figures to make the papers seem even more popular than they actually were. (Before audited figures were legally required, papers like the *World* and the *Journal* printed falsified circulation figures prominently on their front pages.) As most journalistic observers knew, the real fight between the two rivals was for street sales of the papers on any given day to individuals who were not regular readers of either. Such sales were almost always impulse purchases made by passers-by on bustling metropolitan sidewalks. Startling headlines, gripping news features in prominent topfold display, and the hoarse spiel of the newsboys captured the pennies of New York pedestrians who bought freshly printed copies of the competing newspapers, produced in as many as six different editions each day.

Among the practices that the established newspapers purported to find most reprehensible was the promotion of events sponsored by the newspaper itself, which were reported as news. Almost equally criticized was baiting readers with headlines on news that was fundamentally trivial and should have been confined to inside-page columns.

Now almost forgotten, one such *Journal* gambit roused the ire of its fellow papers—the *World* apart, of course. The California-bred Hearst, unlike the majority of his Eastern colleagues, had a genuine sense of the vast extent and varied landscape of the United States and of the excitement that traversing such distances could engender. Hearst decided to boost street sales of both his *New York Journal* and *San Francisco Examiner* by inaugurating a "*Journal-Examiner* Yellow Fellow Transcontinental Bicycle Relay" in the late summer of 1896. This two-wheeled marathon was intended to set a new speed record for the delivery of a message by mounted individual riders traveling from coast to coast.

The marathon began when a cyclist dressed all in yellow, from his cap to his shoes, left the *Examiner* building on August 25, carrying a yellow dispatch pouch. The pouch was to be handed from cyclist to cyclist in a continuous relay, repeating the transfer in small towns and big cities until the last relay rider rolled down Broadway to the *Journal's* quarters in the *New York Herald* building. The marathon lasted over two weeks, ending on September 7 when the final rider delivered the dusty pouch and its contents (letters of no great importance from San Francisco postal officials to their fellows in New York) in a ceremony outside the *Journal's* offices. All of this, reported breathlessly day after day in big *Journal* headlines, tickled readers enormously at a time when other papers were concentrating almost exclusively on news of the bitter presidential race between Bryan and McKinley. The Hearst papers' sales were spectacular during the big, yellow-hued event.

This display was seen as journalistically questionable by newsmen at other papers, particularly given the boost in street sales enjoyed by the *Journal* at the expense of its competition. The two-week cleanup riled old-line editors and writers across Manhattan. One of them, editor Ervin Wardman of the *New York Press,* garnered the plaudits of his fellows by coining the term "yellow journalism" in an editorial blast leveled at the *Journal* on September 2, 1896. It will be noted that this pejorative term, apparently appearing in print for the first time in Wardman's editorial, was given its first public use a good six weeks before the Outcault *Yellow Kid* appeared in the *Journal,* predating the Yellow Kid circulation battle between the *World* and the *Journal.*

Why did Hearst decide to dress his cyclists in yellow? In the mid-1890s, yellow was in vogue with decorators and dressmakers. It was made fashionable and even alluring in a slightly risqué way by the writing and art of Oscar Wilde and Aubrey Beardsley in the cloth-bound

London magazine, *The Yellow Book*. Among Beardsley's fictional creations was a grubby character named The Yellow Dwarf. In the United States, popular spinoffs included *King in Yellow*, Robert W. Chambers's short story collection popular with the literati. However, although the cosmopolitan Hearst was fully aware of these currents in literature, art, and fashion, they probably did not enter into his commercial calculations for the bicycle marathon. The intended audience consisted of street readers, urban residents who were unlikely to have given a damn about the nature of English literary movements or the fashionable color of the season.

The Yellow Kid was equally unlikely to have been responsible for Hearst's choice of color. Planning for so involved an event must surely have started in June or, at the latest, July 1896. At that time (and in fact, throughout its *World* run), the Outcault feature was called *Hogan's Alley*. The title varied from week to week depending on the subject of the cartoon, but the feature was never called the *Yellow Kid*. The *World's* reading public had begun to refer to it as "The Yellow Kid" early in 1896 (once the color of the nightgown had been established), but the *World's* editors continued to use *Hogan's Alley*, a copyrighted title that remained behind when Outcault moved. Hearst would have found no advantage in linking his yellow-costumed cyclists with the cartoon hero of a competing sensational paper. Although he took great personal pleasure in hiring the best journalists and artists for his newspapers and usually succeeded in hiring the people he wanted, it is unlikely that he expected to have Outcault's creation in his camp any time soon.

In the end, the only answer appears to be that Hearst simply found yellow the most striking color to use for his cyclists. It uniquely identified his riders in a way that other primary colors might not; it stood out at a distance, drawing maximum national public attention to the ochre specters; and it provided him with a neat, catchy title in "yellow fellows."

It was this use of yellow, and no other, that led an angered editor to speak of "yellow journalism" a century ago. The term was not linked initially to the competition over the Yellow Kid cartoons although such a linkage appears in nearly every history of comic art or journalism. The error arose from the mistaken assumption that when Hearst conducted his famous raid in January 1896 on the editorial and artistic staff of the *World*, he came away with Outcault along with everyone else. Outcault, who was then free-lancing for the *World,* would have been of no use to Hearst at the beginning of 1896 because the publisher did not yet have a color press. The artist remained at the *World* and continued to draw the *Hogan's Alley* feature every Sunday until October 1896. The comics war between the *Journal* and the *World*, usually thought to have been raging through all of 1896, did not begin until the fall when Outcault moved his Yellow Kid from one rival paper to the other. Hearst biographer Swanberg mistakenly suggested that the "Yellow Fellow" name was used in the bicycle rally to promote the Yellow Kid feature in the *Journal,* but the *Journal* had neither begun its comic supplement nor acquired Outcault's services at the time the marathon took place.

The *Journal-Examiner* bicycle marathon was not an entirely unique event. Pulitzer had created a similar sequence of sensational stories for the *New York World* between November 1888 and January 1890 when he sent reporter Nelly Bly off to retrace the steps of Jules Verne's fictional hero from the novel, *Around the World in Eighty Days.* She reported her progress in daily front-page updates, and it must have been much to Hearst's chagrin that he was forced to send *Examiner* reporters to interview her after her arrival in San Francisco. Like the bicycle marathon, this story was created entirely by a newspaper with the sole purpose of increasing its circulation.

However, this trip around the world had a certain literary quality because of its association with the Verne novel, with an added drama and romance as a woman reporter sped around the world. The bicycle marathon, which featured speeding messengers as heroes and was limited to the terrain of the United States, had a populist quality with very different class associations. The term "yellow journalism" was coined when Hearst created a promotional event that exploited the craze for bicycles that swept the working and middle classes of the United States at the end of the nineteenth century. It did not originate, as myth would have it, as a response to a great Yellow Kid circulation battle that had not yet begun.

47. ANONYMOUS.
Offices of the New York
Journal *on Park Row.*

Eight

In Hearst Signo Vinces:

The Yellow Kid in Perihelion and McFadden's Flats
(1896)

On Sunday, October 18, 1896, the *New York Journal*'s long-awaited Sunday comic supplement appeared. Called the *American Humorist,* its masthead resembled the Great Seal of the United States, with a ragged, grinning vulturine bird substituting for the eagle and and a harp replacing the shield; the bird held the sheet music to "Yankee Doodle" in one claw while playing the harp with the other. The newspaper's name was several times the size of the supplement's title. Both were emblazoned within classical scrollwork, emphatically announcing from newsstands and paperboys' arms that the color competitor to the *World's* supplement had arrived at last. The format was similar to the *World's* supplement, with full-color cartoons on the front cover, last page, and center spread; the other four pages were duotone, a step up from the *World* which printed these pages in black and white. The *Journal's* advance huzzahs for the new section included some quite remarkable essays in promotional prose and poesy. The assault on New Yorkers' literary sensibilities included this half-page ode, which appeared Friday, October 16.

> Sunday's the day I come to make you smile
> And all your thoughts to humorously beguile
> The Yellow Kid you'll see him caper free
> Along my colored pages hully gee!
> You'll see the antique masher in a whirl
> Caught in the sunshine of the ballet girl;
> The goldbricked reuben and the cowboy quaint,
> And the wild Choctaw, yelling off his paint,
> The latest and the greatest out always:
> I am a daisy, and I've come to stay!

While it would appear that the *World's* ex-staff didn't have much in the way of poetic talent, brashness was in plentiful supply, and brashness was what Hearst and the *Journal* had to sell. On Saturday, October 17, the day before the comic supplement debuted, one advertisement included a full-page praise song for color printing. It has been quoted in nearly every comic history.

THE YELLOW KID—TOMORROW! TOMORROW!

An expectant public is waiting for the 'American Humorist,' the New York *Journal's* Comic Weekly, 8 full pages of color that make the kaleidoscope pale with envy. Bunco-steerers may tempt your fancy with a color supplement that's but a black and tan—4 pages of weak, wishy-washy color and four pages a desolate waste of black. But the *Journal's* Colored Comic Weekly, ah there's the difference. Eight pages of iridescent polychromous effulgence that makes the rainbow look like a lead pipe. That's the sort of a Colored Comic Weekly the people want—and—THEY SHALL HAVE IT!

Nor did the uproar cease after the appearance of the first American *Humorist* on Sunday, October 18. In the following week, claims that all copies of the paper had been sold out by ten o'clock Sunday morning raged through the *Journal's* pages. This may well have been true. Other, presumably more objective sources reported that copies of the Sunday *Journal* containing the first comic supplement sold for fifty cents, as opposed to the newsstand price of a nickel. On Thursday, October 29, a new venture into poesy reached print.

> Sing ho for the luminous maid, yes, yes;
> Sing ho for the lonesome crow,
> Sing ho for the Kid with the aureate dress
> That lives in McFadden's Row.

Another boisterous claim followed on Friday: "Eight pages, every one in the varied tints of an Italian sunset!"

Certainly, the new color supplement was a hit and, while there was little doubt that Outcault's Yellow Kid was the main reason, the work of other cartoonists and writers contributed to its popularity. Chief among them was Archie Gunn, a pin-up artist whose mildly risqué drawings of showgirls had kept *Truth*'s head above water during lean times. The first *American Humorist* cover was graced by one of the lovely Gunn girls, the second featured Outcault's Yellow Kid panel for the week (October 25, 1896), and the third was a collaboration between the two artists. Clearly, they were the star cartoonists of the new comic supplement. Their collaborative cover (November 1, 1896) featured an uncredited three-stanza poem about the Yellow Kid, the Gunn girl, and Gunn's signature image, a crow in a pierrot hat. Gunn's girls always were shown in theatrical costumes, wearing elaborate hats, tights, and billowing tutus. The crow, aptly called "lonesome" in the accompanying poem, represented the girls' male admirers. The Outcault-Gunn covers are the first collaborative drawings by U.S. cartoonists to combine the continuing characters from their respective features in a single cartoon, another of the Hearst comics' many firsts.

In addition to his work for the *Journal,* Gunn also drew for other publications during the mid-1890s. Gunn, Hy Mayer, and other pin-up artists translated the appeal of New York's developing musical-comedy stage productions to pen and ink. Outcault, however, was probably locked into an exclusive contract as his last drawing for *Truth* appeared in mid-1896.

Besides Gunn and Outcault, Hearst also brought the work of writer Edward W. Townsend to the *American Humorist.* Townsend was the author of sentimental books about slum children, including *A Daughter of the Tenements* and his most popular work, *Chimmie Fadden* (both 1895). Like the Yellow Kid, Chimmie Fadden was Irish and had grown up in the tenements of the Lower East Side. In Townsend's

48. ARCHIE GUNN and RICHARD F. OUTCAULT. Advertisment for the *American Humorist* from the *New York Journal* (October 11, 1896).

stories, he is in his twenties and, although his only work experience has been as a paperboy, he is hired by a young settlement-house worker to serve as her family's driver.

The Chimmie Fadden stories were enormously popular when they were serialized in Charles A. Dana's *New York Sun*. When the stories were collected in a book, it became a best-seller. Townsend was commissioned to write letterpress narrative for Outcault's Sunday Yellow Kid pages in the same Bowery dialect he had written for Chimmie Fadden. Perhaps Hearst liked his books—a lot of readers did at the time—and it may have pleased him to hire another writer who had achieved success in a rival newspaper. Certainly, the combination of Outcault's cartoons and Townsend's writing meant there would be no mistaking the *Journal's* version of the Yellow Kid for the *World's*.

In the comic supplement, Townsend's text was overlaid with color washes bleeding from Outcault's cartoons and distributed over the entire page in oddly broken columns. Rather than being treated as single stories, this layout resembles the supplement's other pages where jokes, gag dialogue, and short anecdotes were mixed with cartoons. Perhaps this was appropriate; there was little coordination between Townsend's stories and Outcault's cartoons. Author and artist may have agreed on a common theme each week, then gone their separate ways, turning out drawing and text independently in reasonable time for publication but without further consultation. Townsend's texts are rambling and poorly structured, distracting from the drawings rather than enhancing them.

Despite these shortcomings, readers probably found Townsend's narratives a welcome addition to the comic supplement. Many used the Sunday editions of the *Journal* and the *World* for their entire week's reading and "looking" material. In that era of ten-hour or longer workdays and six-day workweeks, the comic supplement—with its accessible magazine format—was retained when the rest of the paper was discarded and read as time permitted. Books were costly and the borrowing period of lending libraries too brief to allow for the reading time that working people and their families needed. Townsend's work found a huge new readership while the author enjoyed weekly payments from the *Journal*.

Thus, Hearst had assembled a fine group of writers and artists for his *American Humorist*. Beginning with the second issue, editor Rudolph Block assigned Outcault to draw a second Yellow Kid comic for each issue. In addition to the full-page panels like the *Hogan's Alley* cartoons he had done for the *World*, Outcault also drew an extra half-page on a different topic. The contrast with the *World's* color supplement, where the editors apparently believed that Luks's inferior *Yellow Kid*

49. ANONYMOUS.
Advertisement for
The Yellow Kid
from the *New York Journal*
(October 17, 1896).

could replace the Outcault original adequately, could not have been more marked. Such shortsightedness impeded the development of newspaper comic art for the next twenty years until competition among the national syndicates raised standards for the new art.

Despite the high quality of the comic supplement's content, its production values were inferior to the *World's*. From the first issue, it was apparent that Hearst's color press, despite the work it had undergone in 1896, could not deliver a color page so sharp and crisp as the *World's*. Further, the *Journal's* paper was inferior to the high-grade newsprint used by the *World*. However, the zest and graphic spice of Outcault's pages captivated readers so completely that most paid little if any attention to what must have seemed trivial differences in nickel newspapers. In the new arena of color comics, Hearst and Outcault had effectively won not only the day but the decade and the start of the next century from old-line papers.

Outcault's weekly full-page Yellow Kid panels for the *Journal* had to be given a new series title, as *Hogan's Alley* remained the property of the *World*. The new name, *McFadden's Flats*, was apparently an invention of Townsend's, redolent of the popular *Chimmie Fadden*. Hearst and his editors also wanted to use the public's own invention, the *Yellow Kid*, which found a place in the titles for Outcault's separate series of half-page *Journal* drawings each week. These were entirely Outcault's own, unencumbered by Townsend's title and story line.

In the first *McFadden's Flats* (October 18, 1896), the Yellow Kid and his gang, dogs, and loyal smoking goat move wholesale from Hogan's Alley to their new neighborhood. With their luggage piled up near the entrance steps to the "row" of flats, the ex-Hogan's Alley bunch jeeringly dismiss their old "balmy mater" with placarded tweaks: "De Alley's on de bum, an it's got ter be a slum," and "SAY! Hogan's Alley has ben condemed by de Board of Helt—an we was gittin tired of it anyway." The Yellow Kid leads the procession, his nightshirt text assuring readers that he and the gang will be changing nothing other than their address: "Say! when we gits in our new home we're goin ter be de real ting." The tumbling boy celebrates the move with his entire repertoire of aerial acrobatics, shouting happily as he passes a startled lady, "Hullo! Mrs. Murphy, did is me foist fall out of dis place." It was certainly clear to the most disinterested reader—if the *Journal* could harbor such—that the Yellow Kid and crew were completely at home in their new residences and ready to raise Tophet at the drop of a cat.

The second *McFadden's Flats* (October 25, 1896), one of the most delightful *Yellow Kid* pages to date, shows the gang on parade to celebrate their new home. The ragged procession is headed by a marching band complete with fife, drum, horns, and a kind of piccolo. The

50. RICHARD F. OUTCAULT. Advertisement for Hogan's Alley from the *New York Journal* (October 15, 1896).

Yellow Kid, dressed as a drum major, leads the parade. One sign celebrates his fame: "Everyting dese days is Yaller Kid. Buy de Yellow Kid glove, Yellow Kid cigar, Yellowfeller Wheel, &c, &c, &c, &c, &c, &c. Say! Every goat in de ward has a yaller kid. Quit yer kiddin." The "Yellow Kid glove" is a pun while the "Yellowfeller Wheel" is a belated reference to the *Journal-Examiner's* cross-country bicycle marathon. The toys, dolls, and figurines appealed to all ages, though sales of Yellow Kid items were confined largely to the wards of Manhattan. A flourishing cigar-making industry included among its products Yellow Kid cigars.

Another sign puffs up the whole gang, at the same time suggesting that topical and political subjects will continue to be targeted by Outcault's pen.

> McFadden's Guards. Just see us coming with a tum-tum-tum; we bang and batter on a big base drum; were a little out of practice, but we aint so bum; fer we allus try to do our best. When we plays de Spangled Banner—say!; it sounds dead fine; or Viva Cuba Libre or Wacht am Rhein; wit Johnny Git Yer Gun an Auld Lang Syne; Just Tell em at yer saw me and de rest. Oh! We are McFadden's Guards—an ye ought te see us marching—were de hottest ting wot ever happened—see! We has knocked de country crazy - fer de Yellow Kids a daisy—an de ladies all is crazy as kin be—SEE!

In the upper right-hand corner of the page, Outcault copied Luks's version of the tumbling kid from his first *Hogan's Alley* (October 11, 1896), juxtaposing it with a very different image. Arms sternly folded, Outcault's tumbler quips, "Dere's a kid imitating me, He'll kill hisself. Imitators always do." Outcault here makes clear that in his brand of cartoon violence, no one is actually hurt. The Yellow Kid comments further on his nightshirt balloon: "I spose dat kid wit de dropsy will want ter fall off of de Waldorf, jist te be swell—he'll git arrested fer tryin te commit suicide if he does."

Arrestingly forthright in the near background stand the four Riccadonna Sisters, "balley dantsers" who offer courses in "couche-couche" dancing (i.e. "cootchy-cootchy" or "hootchy-cootchy" dancing, the belly dance popularized on midways). The sisters are teen-age prostitutes, dressed in showgirl costumes. Their tights and tutus serve to identify them with the stereotype of immoral actresses and to associate them with the prostitutes of concert saloons and theaters. In the late nineteenth century, efforts by reformers to close brothels increased prostitution in tenements where rents were cheap. On the Lower East Side, prostitutes were part of the life of the streets, and would advertise with pictures in the window or signs for front businesses. "Come early and avoid the rush" underscores the real nature of the Riccadonnas, while the observing woman's comment, "Look at them Riccadonna girls, dressed fer 5th Avenue," refers to the fact that young working women, many of them employed in the garment industry, frequently surprised outsiders like settlement-house workers by the care and stylishness with which they dressed. Such assertions of independence and self-worth were usually condemned by members of the upper classes.

Townsend's text for October 25 is completely unrelated to the parade panel. His thin and silly story, about a pair of kids who have tied up Mickey Dugan so he can be butted by his own goat, is completely at variance with the character Outcault had created. The Yellow Kid's slats are obviously not for kicking, and it would be a short-lived pet goat that would butt its closest buddy. Townsend and Outcault danced to separate pipers in their works about the Yellow Kid, but Outcault has dutifully provided an illustration for Townsend's dithyramb. Similar vignettes for the Townsend texts followed in succeeding weeks, but most were much more linked thematically to the main drawings.

The *Journal's* first half-page *Yellow Kid* drawing appeared on the last page of the October 25 *American Humorist*. It filled the upper half of the page while the lower featured a piece of sheet music for the piano, a regular feature in the first few weeks of the supplement. The song, "It's Forty Miles From Schnenectady to Troy," is illustrated with cartoon art by pin-up artist Hy Mayer.

Outcault's five-panel narrative, the first appearance of the Kid in sequential drawings, is called "The Yellow Kid and His New Phonograph." Quietly unassuming in its simple set of pictures portraying nothing but a nightshirted Yellow Kid, a phonograph, and a parrot, it is in fact an extraordinary graphic event.

It is nothing less than the first definitive comic strip in history.

51. Jacob Riis.
*Girls Returning from
Fresh Air Fund Vacation*
(1880s–1890s).

Nine

First Balloon Trip to the Rainbow:

Outcault's Accidental (and Unnoticed) Invention
of the Comic Strip (1896)

With "The Yellow Kid and His New Phonograph" (October 25, 1896),
Richard F. Outcault invented what was soon to be called the comic strip
in the United States and the world. To explain his invention, unnoticed
at the time and published as a secondary feature ancillary to his weekly

McFadden's Flats panel drawings, it is necessary to define the term "comic strip" in a manner that takes full account of its history and the worldwide popularity it has enjoyed.

For many, the comic strip is exactly that and nothing more: a strip of successive pictures telling a continuing story. The placement of dialogue, whether in the panels or beneath them in blocks of printed text, is irrelevant. Such a broad definition could include a variety of narrative forms in European art, encompassing such disparate works as the Bayeux Tapestry, the *Biblia Pauperum,* or Giotto's frescoes in the Arena Chapel. However, the innovations which make the modern comic strip so vastly popular an art form are precisely those that first appeared in combination in Outcault's half-page comic strip of October 25, 1896. The pattern or template for the modern comic strip established in this five-panel strip soon dominated comic art in the United States and spread around the world.

The comic strip is a composite art form, halfway between drama and illustration. It may be defined as a serially published, episodic, open-ended dramatic narrative or series of linked anecdotes featuring recurrent, named characters. The successive drawings regularly include ballooned dialogue that is crucial to telling the story. As in drama, the narrative is constructed primarily through the characters' dialogue while other sorts of text are minimal or absent. This definition includes the majority of works we know as comic strips today.

It excludes similar forms that do not continue indefinitely as narratives but rather confine a given set of characters to a single complete story, distinguished by the terms "graphic story" or "graphic novel." It also excludes oddities found on the comics pages of newspapers that are not comic strips. Sequences of drawings without words are pantomime. Stories told with drawings plus in- or below-panel blocks of narrative text, including all dialogue, are forms of illustrated prose fiction. Both forms existed before the comic strip and coexist with it today. Although the terms comic and comic strip are used to encompass virtually everything in panel narrative, the more rigorous definition above isolates the real distinctions that set the comic strip apart from anything else in narrative art.

In his large panel drawings, Outcault had already created crucial elements of the comic strip: a recognizable cast of characters in an open-ended series in which narrative texts were minimal or absent and dialogue was confined to word balloons. In "The Yellow Kid and His New Phonograph," the special ingredient—the innovation that unites all the elements necessary for a true comic strip—is balloon dialogue that *must be read* to get the point of the cartoon. In the strip, the Yellow Kid invites the reader to listen to the "Woids of Wisdom" from his phonograph:

praise for himself, the *Journal,* and its "Colored Supplement." The Yellow Kid thought he was playing the recorded voice of an authoritative speaker whose legitimacy was reinforced by modern technology. (As a former employee of Edison, Outcault was sensitive to the power of recording technology to enhance fame and influence public perception.) When the Kid discovers in the final panel that the "woids" come from a talking parrot, not a recording, his emotional response is comprehensible only to those who have read each panel in sequence.

This strip may be read on multiple levels. An illiterate reader or one without fluent English can enjoy the joke about the jack-in-the-box parrot; Outcault was certainly aware that he had many such readers. However, the full impact—the reversal of the social level of the voice's source, from influential speaker to McFadden's Flats parrot; the change in the nature of the praise from objective evaluation to the Kid's and the *Journal's* own puffery, prated back by the parrot; the commentary on recording technology itself, equated with a parrot—comes from the combination of sequential drawings and dialogue balloons. Simple as it appears, this particular and vital thing had never happened before, in this specific combination, in the entire history of graphic and narrative art. It was a whole new ball game, a graphic dawn where there had only been twilight before, an art form and an industry from a joke about a parrot.

In all similar work from the eighteenth and nineteenth centuries, from Hogarth's social panoramas to Rowlandson's Dr. Syntax illustrations to the English comic papers' *Ally Sloper,* the individual, isolated drawing always says it all. The art provides exactly what the printed caption tells us we are going to see, and nothing more of real consequence. Text found in the drawing, whether in balloons, on signs, or elsewhere, is always secondary to the visual component and could be completely omitted without affecting the graphic point of the art. In the continuous panel narratives published during the century or so preceding Outcault's revolution, usually in book form rather than as prints, the text is often crucial to comprehending scenes and characters in the panel but is invariably printed or lettered below the sequential drawings and contains virtually all the crucial dialogue. The small amount of text sometimes included in balloons usually is little more than an exclamation or profanity added to spice a character's reaction. In the wealth of humorous narrative and character-centered graphics produced prior to Outcault by such brilliant talents as Cruikshank, Rowlandson, Phiz, Doré, and Daumier, the simple format adjustments necessary to unlock the liberating potential of the comic-strip form never appear.

Outcault apparently never realized the significance of his invention. Nor did anyone else see anything out of the ordinary in the "The Yellow Kid and His New Phonograph," other than perhaps the odd gaffe

52. JACOB RIIS.
Minding the Baby
(1880s–1890s).

the *Journal* colorists committed in making the Yellow Kid entirely yellow from head to bare toe in every panel. Outcault made no attempt at the time to duplicate what he had devised. Clearly he had to continue the large panels that had established the character's popularity in the *New York World*, but even the half-page *Yellow Kid* strips with which he supplemented the big theatrical pages through his remaining months on the *Journal* were rarely fully realized comic strips. On the contrary, Outcault turned to pantomimes and captions in these half-page story cartoons, never again giving any intrinsic narrative importance to the dialogue. By the time he had established his second success, *Buster Brown*, his invention had been widely adopted, but there is no doubt that Outcault invented the form.

Visual work was important to both the *World* and the *Journal*. Newly arrived immigrant families who often knew little English were an important component of the papers' readership, and the big, funny weekly panels were a great hit with them. Funny characters who merely talked to each other would not have succeeded in such a market, and had Outcault made a serious attempt to pursue his innovation, his editors probably would have protested. Because "The Yellow Kid and His New Phonograph" operates on multiple levels, accessible to a wide spectrum of readers, it would have been extraordinarily difficult for Outcault to create such a complex work each week in addition the large theatrical panels that were the cornerstone of his success. His real passion remained invested in the full-page drawings.

"Receiving the Returns in McFadden's Row on Election Night" (November 1, 1896) was as raucously lurid as anything he had ever done. In the election of 1896, the *New York Journal* was the only important newspaper in the East to support William Jennings Bryan, nominee of both the Democratic and Populist parties, over Republican William McKinley. Although Bryan's position supporting the end of the gold standard and free coinage of silver was the most debated issue of the campaign, the intense business opposition to his candidacy was also fueled by the Democratic party's support of the income tax and direct election of U.S. senators, and its opposition to monopolies, tariffs, and the use of injunctions in labor disputes. Bryan was reviled as a madman and an anarchist, as was Hearst, but the *Journal* became one of the nation's foremost Democratic papers and attracted thousands of new readers in New York and throughout the Eastern United States.

The Kid's wild parade takes place under a sign trumpeting "Both Elected," perhaps referring to the *Journal's* success, or putting the best face on Bryan's anticipated defeat on November 3. Mark Hanna, McKinley's chief advisor and Republican fund raiser, was effectively skewered throughout the campaign by premier *Journal* cartoonist Homer Davenport, whose caricatures showed him covered with dollar signs. The wads of bills in the Yellow Kid's pocket and hands refer both to Davenport's cartoons and to the enormous funds that business poured into Republican coffers. The panel's energy is somewhat diminished by several crudely rendered background figures, a clear indication that Outcault had hired an assistant.

The drawing of the background figures returns to Outcault's earlier high standard in "The Season Opens with the Horse Show in McFadden's Row of Flats" (November 8, 1896), particularly notable in the identical, insouciant poses of the four cigarette-puffing Riccadonna Sisters. The "Horse Show" is rather subdued in comparison with the preceding election-night extravaganza and the following cartoon, "Inauguration of the Football Season in McFadden's Row" (November 15, 1896), a lively melee of rowdy tacklings, mad whirlings, and cheering spectators. Amid the scrimmaging players, the Yellow Kid wears a nightshirt transformed into a football sweater, and his "new piece" reappears only to be ripped away by a ferocious opponent. A coach parked in near left field serves as a platform for the cheer-leading Riccadonna sisters as well as a visual pun. One of its wheels is labeled "The Yellow Fellow," a reminder of the *Journal-Examiner* bicycle marathon. A sign to the right proclaims that "everything is yellow this fall—even the trees turned yellow—but de parrot is so durn green with envy dat he couldn't & he is not the only one." The big game, as described in Townsend's accompanying text, pits "the Tim McFadden Flatters" against a team "from Hogan's Alley," while back-fence rooters cheer the team's star in rousing chorus: "Yell yell yell; Kid Kid Kid yell oh! Yell oh! Yellow Kid! Hot stuff." Completing these elaborate panoramas on weekly deadlines seems to have given Outcault a bit of trouble at times. Here he has left the arm incomplete on the Arnica salesman at right, while the hurried staff colorist has left a patch of white paper under the arm of a tackled player a few inches to the vendor's left.

"A Turkey Raffle in which the Yellow Kid Exhibits Skill with the Dice" (November 22, 1896) features some of Outcault's best caricatures and funniest captions. A frog in the foreground says, "I wish I could jump like the *Journal's* circulation," while a fence inscription bites the hand that feeds the cartoonist: "Everybody is a artist in his line, dentists draw teet, EDITORS DRAW SALARIES, an gamblers draw cards." A sign at left skewers a clothing shop using a Yellow Kid figure without payment to Outcault: "De Yeller Kid dont work in no clothing store—if he did he would work where they sold good clothes." Songbirds and Mickey Dugan's goat comment on the charms and morals of the lissome Riccadonna Sisters, whose theatrical finery includes elaborately feathered hats in keeping with the week's theme. In a visual pun, the Yellow Kid is drawn as a Turk while the metal-spurred fighting rooster in front of him suggests Outcault cocking a snook at the proper citizenry with such explicit celebration of cockfighting. His nightshirt promotes a forthcoming cartoon depicting a cockfight.

"A Few Things the Versatile Yellow Kid Might Do for a Living" (November 22, 1896) shows the Yellow Kid in the garb of various professions. In a marvelous outburst of poesy, the Yellow Kid sings a ballad about the hegira from the Alley to the Flats, accompanying himself on the Irish harp. For the first time in the *Yellow Kid* half-page cartoons, typeset captions appear under each drawing. Apparently written by Outcault, they recall his earliest cartoons about children.

In "The Yellow Kid Introduces a Monk Who Enlivens the Pool Tournament in McFadden's Flats" (November 29, 1896), Mickey Dugan has acquired a monkey and is exhibiting his skills at the local pool hall. He is preparing to compete "fer de champeenship" against a cunning old stager of the pool table. The Riccadonna Sisters have enlarged their theatrical repertoire to include juggling the balls while the parrot mouths (or beaks) Outcault's now almost-weekly slam at actors. The promise in "A Turkey Raffle in which the Yellow Kid Exhibits Skill with the Dice" (November 22, 1896) is fulfilled in "The Yellow Kid Indulges in a Cockfight . . . A Waterloo" (November 29, 1896), a half-page cartoon complete with a kibitzing parrot and a knockdown, drag-out finish resulting in an ignominious loss to Terence McSwatt's bird.

In the season's first turn to winter sports, "McFadden Flatters' Skating and Tobogganing Expedition" (December 6, 1896), an expansive winter landscape is the setting for the pleasures and hazards of the season. In the far background Outcault plugs the *Journal's* Fresh Air Fund, a charitable organization that brought poor urban children to the country and also supported the paper's Junior Republic, a citizenship event for young people. The Yellow Kid's new monkey is pestering an old couple on skates while Mickey Dugan scrolls "Dead Easy" into the ice, neatly balanced on one skate. The Riccadonna Sisters, still gamely smiling, have all toppled into a heap, eliciting from a startled kid: "Oh shocking, or stocking!"

Two weeks before Christmas, Outcault delivered "A Merry Christmas in McFadden's Flats" (December 13, 1896), apparently timed to ensure that the nationally circulated copies of the *Journal* would arrive in advance of the holiday, especially in Western states. All the

McFadden's Flatters receive appropriate gifts; the Yellow Kid gets new pajamas, eyed by an eager goat who remarks, "Just what I need," while the Riccadonna Sisters at last receive their longed-for theatrical contract. A note of social concern, harking back to the classic Woolf cartoons, appears in the letter posted just behind Santa Claus: "Deer Santy Claus, Cant you change de date of Christmas to de Fort of July cause we are so cold we cant enjoy it in the winter time. Dunnigan Twins." A white-haired lady to the right of the "Santy" is more cheerful, telling a young girl, "I am pleased most to death I got a keg of beer and a lorgnette."

53. Jacob Riis.
Didn't Live Nowhere
(1880s–1890s).

The Yellow Kid also gets a camera for Christmas, a handy prop Outcault uses to link the week's full- and half-page cartoons. In "Dark Secret; or How the Yellow Kid Took a Picture" (December 13, 1896), the Yellow Kid snaps a portrait of Liz with tragic results. The gag is a good one, but the graphic work is slipshod; some of it appears to have been by a much cruder hand. The cartoonist may have been forced by the pressure of the extra weekly half-page to ink his own pencil work only partially and turn the rest over to an assistant.

Within the narrative limitations of the large panel format, Outcault is beginning in these cartoons to use devices such as the camera and secondary characters including the monkey, fighting cock, and parrot, to create continuing story lines that link both the full- and half-page cartoons. At "The Opening Night in Kelly's Bowling Alley" (December 20, 1896), the Yellow Kid's tailless monkey laments his lot to the unsympathetic parrot perched on the blackboard, only to receive the gleeful reply, "Never monkey with a parrot." Below, the Yellow Kid has met the frustrations of bowling with the ring-a-ding solution of a cannon, while two Flatters bowlers manage to get a strike by sending two balls at the pins simultaneously. Outcault gaily anthropomorphizes the bowling balls with smiles, frowns, and worried looks; one says, "Here I go for a good big bump." In the lower right corner, a svelte pin taunts a rotund ball, using "many" to mean powerful or tough: "You think yer many cause you knocked me down; it's only yer shape."

In "The Yellow Kid's Great Fight" (December 20, 1896), the Yellow Kid faces an African-American opponent in the ring. African Americans were prominent in boxing in New York at the time; an African American would take the world heavyweight championship just a few years later. This cartoon relies on the most invidious African-American caricature in the Yellow Kid oeuvre. There was usually less racism directed at African Americans in the Hearst and Pulitzer comic supplements than in the national cartoon magazines that made such a point of denouncing the newspaper supplements for bad taste and vulgarity. Outcault—who exploited such stereotypes in later strip and cartoon work for other publishers—seems to have slipped this one in despite an apparent prohibition against demeaning images of African Americans and anti-Semitic stereotypes in the *Journal* comics. The grotesquely caricatured features were a stand-by in American humor, drawing on the exaggerated "blackface" make-up of white minstrel shows. The colorist (presumably following Outcault's instructions) has not applied bright red to the boxer's lips, a common device in racist cartoons.

The eventful year of 1896 bowed out in the *Journal* with "The New Year's Fancy Dress Ball in McFadden's Flats" (December 27, 1896). The McFadden's Flatters welcome the New Year with a billboard full of resolutions, opening with that of the tumbling boy, Slippy Dempsey, who is named for the first time. Although seasonal here, resolutions would become a popular feature of Outcault's *Buster Brown* strip as its mischievous protagonist learned his lesson in each week's misadventure. Everyone at the ball is in costume, including the adults jamming "Chimmy Fadden's Box" at right.

This final cartoon of 1896 is remarkably decorous for a Yellow Kid affair, characteristic of the gradual change in the large panels that commenced shortly after Outcault's move to the *Journal*. The violence and thumb-in-yer-eye vulgarity of the *Yellow Kid* pages Outcault had produced for the *World* gradually ebbed in the *Journal*'s single-panel cartoons through the fall and winter of 1896, while finding a new home in the multipanel drawings. Sweetness and charm became the keynotes of the large weekly drawings, while the Yellow Kid raised hell in the half-pagers.

The saucy and irreverent tone may have been muted at the request of Outcault's editors, perhaps because Hearst wished to enlarge *Journal* home subscriptions when streets sales reached the highest levels they were likely to attain. The newspaper's sales had skyrocketed during the election campaign, but Hearst also lost huge amounts of money when advertisers withdrew to protest his support of Bryan. It must have been time to secure and expand the new circulation base; toning down the cartoons would make them more acceptable to women readers, who usually decided which newspapers came into family homes.

Certainly, the next step the *American Humorist* editor, Rudolph Block, was to take with the Yellow Kid and his crew—ferrying them away to visit the towns and crowns of Europe—was aimed at an untapped segment of the *New York Journal*'s audience. Hearst wanted a new, upgraded readership, and he sent Outcault and Block, bag and baggage, drawing board and writing tablet, to Blighty, Paree, and points east to help him get it.

54. ANONYMOUS.
   Her Latest Portrait,
   photograph of Queen Victoria
   (1900).

Ten

Over the Sea to Guy:
The Kid and Gang Give Europe the Royal Rinkydink
(1896–1897)

Mickey Dugan and gang might just as well have voyaged to Europe with
Vanderdecken or aboard the Walloping Window Blind as on the ocean
liner that appeared in the strip, for all the relation that the Flatters on
a continental spree bore to any sort of literary realism. The iconoclastic
Flatters let loose in Europe was an appealing notion that recalled Mark

Twain's popular humorous novel, *Innocents Abroad.* (Hearst later engaged Twain to cover the festivities surrounding Queen Victoria's Diamond Jubilee celebration in London.) Setting off the New York tenement kids against the decor and decorum of England and the continent was a scenario rife with novel comic possibilities, and the *Journal's* hopes for increased sales from the series ran high as the vessel taking Outcault and editor Rudolph Block to England lifted anchor early in the new year.

The series did indeed prove popular, and the Yellow Kid's shenanigans abroad did wonders for *Journal* sales at newsstands in New York and across the country. People who had never purchased the *Journal* began to do so, but apparently, most new readers attracted by the Yellow Kid's European adventures bought the paper only at newsstands. There was no marked increase in subscriptions by the middle-class readers the *Journal* was attempting to lure from the *World.* Despite its popularity, the McFadden's Flatters' Grand Tour ultimately was not successful in expanding the readership base of the paper in such a way as to make it a more effective competitor for the advertising dollars of department stores.

The first two weeks in January saw the publication of the last stateside *Yellow Kid* pages before the new series began. "The Studio Party in McFadden's Flats" (January 3, 1897) is memorable for being both the last *McFadden's Flats* Sunday page written by Townsend and the first in which the Outcault art and Townsend story meshed almost perfectly. For the continental series, Rudolph Block was assigned to write texts, and after the series concluded, the cartoons ran without texts. Later in 1897, Townsend collaborated one final time with Outcault, writing the first and only Yellow Kid book published until the present volume.

"The Studio Party" achieves a certain European flavor through references to George Du Maurier's Parisian novel *Trilby,* a best-seller that had titillated readers with mildly sordid tales of studio life in the Latin Quarter. *Harper's* eight-part, illustrated serialization caused a sensation in 1894. Publication in book form followed almost immediately, a play in 1895. Trilby events gained popularity among members of New York society with a taste for the bohemian. "What sums Trilby has earned for charity no one will ever compute," observed E. S. Martin in *Harper's Weekly* for May 18, 1895. "There have been Trilby tableaux, Trilby burlesques, Trilby nights, and Trilby shows of every kind from one end of the land to the other."

Du Maurier, a caricaturist who had cartooned for the British *Punch* for years before becoming a novelist, illustrated his own fiction. In Outcault's drawing, the Flatters have joined in the fun. A neighborhood girl is posed in full Trilby regalia, cigarette at the ready, in the center of the page, appearing exactly as Du Maurier had depicted Trilby in the novel. "It was the figure of a very tall and fully developed young female, clad in the gray overcoat of a French infantry soldier, continued netherwards by a short striped petticoat, beneath which were visible her bare white ankles and insteps, and slim, straight, rosy heels, clean cut and smooth as the back of a razor; her toes lost themselves in a huge pair of male list slippers." The cartoonist, however, has replaced her feet with those of the Yellow Kid.

A transitional work, this cartoon combines the saucy humor of preceding Yellow Kid episodes with a new gentility designed to attract, or at least not to repel the middle-class readership the *Journal* was now courting. Aside from the goat's devouring interest in a painting, there is no violence or destruction and the composition is relatively static. In earlier cartoons, the kids had gamboled through tenement streets, pool halls, and bowling alleys, while Outcault mocked bourgeois pretensions by having them recreate horse shows, night clubs, and balls in their own environs. In "The Studio Party," however, the setting is a painter's studio and the kids are artists; the mildly risqué humor depends on appropriate clichés. Seated next to the Trilby *poseur*, Kitty Dugan says (via her expressive bonnet), "I guess I will pose for the whole altogether," recalling the well-known passage from Du Maurier's novel in which artist's model Trilby describes posing.

> "I'm posing for Durien the sculptor, on the next floor.
> I pose to him in the altogether."
> "The altogether?" asked Little Billee.
> "Yes—*l'ensemble,* you know—head, hands, and feet—
> everything—especially feet."

This passage has been credited with introducing into English the phrase "in the altogether" as another way of saying "in the nude."

A jointed, wooden artist's model, called a lay figure, sprawls in a gaily exhausted pose before the dancing Riccadonna Sisters. It is the object of the sisters' saucy gazes, a suggestive linking reinforced by the Yellow Kid's nightshirt: "De lay figure is intoxicated by de charms of dem Riccadonna Sisters." The poster uses a *franglais* pun to conjure the stereotypical dissolute artist; against the background of a cemetery, a caption reads, "Poor d'Auber. He went down to Bourbon County Kentucky to sell water color pictures an here's where he is now." In the foreground, Outcault reprises the figures from "Fourth Ward Brownies" (*New York World,* February 17, 1895), his first newspaper cartoon featuring a nightshirted kid. In the original, the child was transformed into

55. JAMES VALENTINE.
*Westminster Abbey from
Dean's Yard*
(circa 1870s).

a Brownie; here he becomes one of Raphael's cherubs as Outcault satirizes both his own earlier work and the comic changes he apparently was being asked to make.

In a half-page, panel-story episode published the same week, "How the Yellow Kid Planted a Seed and the Result" (January 3, 1897), Outcault returns to the formal comic-strip design of "The Yellow Kid and his New Phonograph" (October 25, 1896). This delightful strip, concerning the miraculously fast growth of a potted sunflower, is revealed in the final panel to be a dream. As the first comic strip to use the device of a fantasy revealed to be a character's dream, it is the precursor to *Little Nemo in Slumberland*, the surrealistic masterpiece created by Winsor McCay in the early 1900s. Like "The Yellow Kid and his New Phonograph," the full meaning of the comic strip can only be understood by a viewer who has both followed the drawings and read the crucial comments on the Yellow Kid's nightshirt. Just above his signature in the last panel, Outcault cites the copyright he filed to protect his rights in the Yellow Kid as a name and an image, the first and only time he did so in the series. In this cartoon, Outcault also experimented with the means of separating individual panels. Although this is a sequential panel narrative, the pen and ink original was drawn without borders. The scrollwork dividing the panels was apparently created when the color plates were made, following specifications of the artist. In subsequent half-page *Yellow Kid* cartoons, Outcault experimented further with panel borders, treating them as permeable membranes that linked as well as divided sequential drawings.

"De Yaller Kid's Mother Goose Vaudeville Co. Lt'd" (January 10, 1897) is a remarkably tame cartoon about a neighborhood vaudeville show. The stage is alive with fun and games, but it is all very proper, an image that would not have been out of place in the children's magazine *St. Nicholas*. In their final appearance in the strip, the Riccadonna Sisters are transformed from showgirls into angelic dancing children. Other regular characters enact fairy tales like Little Bo Peep, Puss in Boots, and Little Boy Blue for a remarkably well-behaved Flats audience, some of whom sport monocles. The French singer Yvette Guilbert is guyed by a girl wearing long gloves, while the boy with bulging biceps imitates Sandow the strong man, lifting a pair of black balloons suspended on a stick. Unlike earlier witty, irreverent cartoons, the Yellow Kid's nightshirt comment here is as perfunctory and functional as the drawing itself. The only hints of rowdy capers are the tumbling boy dropping in through a fractured ceiling and the Kid's voracious goat ingesting a bit of proscenium wall.

All in all, it is a scene to warm the heart of Anthony Comstock, head of the New York Society for the Suppression of Vice who had more than once growled about obscene vulgarity in the Sunday comic supplements. The narrative, Block's first, is by-lined Mickey Dugan and accompanied by a vignette not drawn by Outcault. It is an unreadable hash of Outcault's Yellow Kid vernacular, foreshadowing the texts that will hang over the European drawings leadenly.

The first few episodes of *Around the World with the Yellow Kid* were decked out with double by-lines for Block, appearing both in the header and below the gabble written for the Yellow Kid. Block's credit-grabbing was ended in short order. First the by-line "Mickey Dugan" reappeared below the text, then Block's name disappeared from the header as well. Outcault remained content with his usual modest signature at the foot of the page, although the Dugan by-line may have led readers to suppose that he had written the miserable text.

Around the World with the Yellow Kid debuted on January 17, 1897. Leaving the city under full steam, the ocean liner SS *Greater New York* pulls away from the dock in a gorgeous panorama filled with Outcault's own prose. Signs and placards cover the pier of the "United States S.S. Line" as well as the ship's cabins, a trunk, two nightshirts, and a dress. Most of the commentary deals flippantly with customs, tipping, and ship's passage: "Our ships bust their records or their boilers every trip." "Gee! But we wont do a ting te Yoorup—Poor Yoorup," says the Yellow Kid, while George and Alex, the twin Yellow Kids George Luks had created in his *World* panel, sit forlornly on the pier waving a flag reading, "We ain't goin too we're left." On deck, a nervous older couple clutches two kinds of life preserver while kids sip champagne. One Flats boy lugs a fiercely burning stove, the only hint of the innocence of our travelers who cannot imagine leaving behind their only source of heat.

Much of the usual mischief is pursued, but on a lower key in keeping with the new tone of the strip. One kid swats a seasick buddy, two crapshooters engage in a brutal tussle over the dice, and kids armed with peashooters pepper dignitaries on the dock. Despite these indignities, the kids are granted ambassadorial status by the graphic presence of such wellwishers as Theodore Roosevelt, then a reform-minded police commissioner; William L. Strong, the Republican mayor of New York City; and standing on a soapbox, Chauncey M. Depew, president of the New York Central Railroad and a mellifluous orator who worked tirelessly for the Republican Party and its candidates.

Neither Outcault's comments nor Block's text raise the whys and wherefores of the Yellow Kid's trip. Since there can be no explanation for tenement kids sailing to Europe on an ocean liner, the incongruity is simply ignored. Outcault's strips had focused frequently on antics that mocked the manners of the upper classes, and regular readers would have had no trouble understanding the European trip as satirizing the Grand Tour customary among the wealthy.

The second episode is set in London, where the McFadden's Flatters are shown the sights by Prince Albert Edward, Queen Victoria's son and heir (January 24, 1897). In a crowded street scene set in front of Westminster Abbey, all the kids are on their best behavior but Terence McSwatt, who assaults a man in a sandwich board with a beanshooter. Not coincidentally, the board advertises the famed English humor magazine, *Punch,* and its cartoonists, Phil May and Harry Furniss (spelled "Furnace"). The other kids appear awed by the presence of royalty, but the queen turns out to be a regular gal. Leaning from her carriage to address the prince, she says, "Say, Al, bring 'em around to the house for dinner." The elderly couple from the ship, who have the thankless task of chaperoning the gang, have seen to it that everyone is neatly turned out; the Yellow Kid, dolled up in velvet and topper, sports a monocle as do the cat, dog, goat, and the chaperone duffer himself. Only the parrot is impertinent enough to exclaim, "Why there's the Queen hullo Vick."

It is an odd spectacle of rowdiness brought smartly to heel, where the written and spoken comments are a good deal more vulgar and provocative than anything the kids are doing. This mixture of genteel tone and tart language, foreign color and lively commentary, must have been what Hearst wanted in the new series, and it is a mixture that prevails, with a lapse here and there, for the rest of the continental junket. In a blue sign at left, Outcault indicates that the kids have assigned themselves royal "tilels" (titles), another incongruous example of the curious obeisance the gang makes to their new surroundings.

The third episode was the first to carry an individual title, "Mickey and His Friends Hobnob with Royalty" (January 31, 1897). Much rowdier than on their arrival, the McFadden's Flats kids are acting up royally, having seltzer fights, making saucers fly, doing hand stands, and playing dice with a tipsy Prince Albert Edward while a watching dog warns, "Look out, Whales, dem dice is loaded." The prince, who would take the title Edward VII upon his accession to the throne in 1901, was an outgoing and flamboyant individual who was notorious for enjoying the pleasures of the table, the bed, the track, and the casino. He delighted in full dress occasions and was famous for extravagant expenditures on his wardrobe, much to the gratitude of the "Pants makers to H.R.H. the Prince" in the preceding cartoon. Inordinately fond of high-stakes card games, he wears a sash bearing the symbols of card suits.

By contrast, Queen Victoria is treated with relative reverence. Despite the amount of champagne in evidence, the general tone is decorous enough for a Yellow Kid page. "Diss is de glass chandelier," says a sign hanging under that glittering object, "it aint to be climbed upon"—and it is left alone. Advice on etiquette is given by the Yellow Kid in a large "Notiss" signed "Mickey": "Dont stay too late and wear holes in yer welcome, ye might want to come agin." The "Notiss," one column wide and set at the top of the cartoon, seems a calculated riposte to Block's text above.

"At Balmoral Castle—A Lawn Party in the Kid's Honor" (February 7, 1897) was printed sideways in the comic supplement. This was the first time this format was used for a *Yellow Kid* cartoon. The Yellow Kid and his gang have been whisked off to bonnie Scotland at the invitation of the royal family. They are enjoying a visit to Queen Victoria's country home at Balmoral Castle which had been built by her husband, Prince Albert, prior to his death in 1861. Here, a distinctly less dignified Queen Victoria does a sword dance during the royal outing while a kid offers to play leapfrog with a tipsy Prince Albert Edward "fer de drinks." Rather obvious jokes are made about Scottish thistles, heather, the Campbells, bagpipes, and the bonnie briar. Only the Yellow Kid lacks a kilt—his comments would have been illegible against the plaid—when a load of Scots jams the entrance to the "Free Drinks" tent. Outcault makes reference to industrialist Andrew Carnegie and writer Ian Maclaren, getting in a crack at the popular humor magazine *Life*, which had an upper-class readership and frequently attacked the New York newspapers' comic supplements. Maclaren's fiction featured texts, written in what was meant to be Scottish dialect, that enjoyed brief but widespread popularity. The vogue for his writing and lectures was frequently tweaked in *Life*.

Ireland was the next destination for *Around the World with the Yellow Kid* (February 14, 1897). Although he puffs a cigarette debonairely, the Yellow Kid sports an Irish topper and clay pipe to celebrate his arrival in "de land of me 4 fadders." This page departs from the idealized, travel-poster presentation of the other episodes. It is a compendium of negative stereotypes regarding the Irish, something comparatively absent from the comic strips set in New York, where the humor was based primarily on class rather than ethnic stereotypes. The falling boy, who also tumbled from Balmoral Castle in Scotland, plummets from Blarney Castle into the midst of an all-out Irish imbroglio complete with flailing canes and flying bottles and stones. At center page, a victim of delirium tremens has a vision of a snake—an offensive image that combines reference to alcoholism with the most famous miracle of Ireland's patron, Saint Patrick. The scrappy locals are obviously about to assault various Flats kids and animals, including the Kid, whose yellow garb has caused him to be mistaken for an Orangeman or British Loyalist, but his nightshirt sets the record straight: "I'm a real Irish setter."

"High Life in Paris—The Yellow Kid (*L'Enfant Jaune*) Takes an Outing" (February 21, 1897) features a spectacular balloon ascent over the roof tops of Paris. Visual and verbal puns with a local accent abound. The tumbling boy's fall is broken by an umbrella labeled "My Paris shoot," while the frightened black cat clinging to the Yellow Kid's balloon cries out not from fear, but at the possibility of having to go to its namesake *boite* or night club, the infamous Le Chat Noir. Du Maurier's sensational novel *Trilby*, first mentioned in "The Studio Party" (January 3, 1897), gets a second ribbing in a note tied to the Yellow Kid's toe reading, "Trilby ain't so many." Trilby's foot, "the handsomest foot in all Paris," was the symbol of the model's nudity and the novel's sensuality; scarf pins, plaster models, and smoking accessories replicated it in a merchandising frenzy that included shoes and stockings plus a variety of products associated with the pedal extremities, corn cures and bunion eradicators, garters, and shoestrings. While Trilby does not appear in the Paris cartoon, Svengali (the novel's evil genius who made Trilby sing under his hypnotic spell) can be seen behind the overjoyed woman with the muff. The gang's traveling cast-iron stove reappears, hanging from the basket of the hot-air balloon and spewing the catch phrase, "I ain't so warm." (The slang expressions "ain't so warm" and "ain't so many," variations on "ain't so hot," and "ain't so much," appear frequently in *Around the World with the Yellow Kid*.)

"In the Louvre—The Yellow Kid Takes in the Masterpieces of Art" (February 28, 1897) is an ingeniously composed, full-page tableau crowded with adults and kids. Experimenting with the broad canvas available when his cartoons were printed sideways, Outcault created a classical composition in keeping with the Louvre. The Yellow Kid, poised on a pair of stilts, is placed at the center of the page. Jokes on his nightshirt and on the dress of the girl immediately below refer to the Yellow Kid's elevated status and dripping palette, but he is yards from any canvas. The real purpose of the stilts is to create the central figure of a triptych, balanced by the Venus de Milo at right and the Pierrot and painter on a ladder at left. There is a great sense of bustle and fun in the drawing without the kids getting involved in much actual damage (some dripping paint and a torn canvas) while the adult figures seem relaxed and amused. They provide sharp contrast to the adult spectators in the earlier McFadden's Flats pages. Only one museum goer appears upset; the famous actress Sarah Bernhardt is a trifle perturbed at the paint cascading from the Yellow Kid's tipsy palette.

The extremes of winning and losing at the gambling tables of Monte Carlo are depicted in "Fortune Smiles Upon the Yellow Kid" (March 7, 1897). Despair written literally on his face, a ruined player slinks from the casino, leaving behind a scrawled suicide note: "Dear Ma when you get dis I wont be in it any more I bin up aginst it an dropped me dough an now Im goin to blow a hole where my brains ought to bin Good by Chames." Other kids weep, collapse, and tug at pockets emptied by card games and roulette wheels. The big winner is the Yellow Kid, resplendent in a diamond stickpin, carrying heavy sacks of newly won gold. Liz, happy to have been his mascot at the game tables, has to help him carry off his haul. She steps past the outstretched limbs of a pair of less lucky players, passing others who are still transfixed by the penny ante stakes at the craps table. Perhaps the most satisfied casino visitor of all is the goat, shown relishing a thousand-franc note he has just ingested.

56. Anonymous.
Venezia. Ponte de Rialto
(nineteenth–twentieth centuries).

In "The Yellow Kid Shakes His Trotters in Old Madrid" (March 14, 1897), everyone dances, with or without castanets. The broad yellow banner flying at center is the flag of imperial Spain. Outcault has drawn the Kid in a pose that echoes the flag and its pole and has lettered messages on both. Like a character from Bizet's opera *Carmen,* the smiling Yellow Kid says he will use his stiletto to prevent Liz from romancing the young Spanish king, Alfonso XIII. A revolution against Spanish rule had begun in Cuba in 1895, and both the *Journal* and the *World* had given increasingly strong support to the rebels and American intervention. This cartoon mocks General Valeriano Weyler, military commander of Cuba, who had been unable to crush the rebellion. The falling boy strums a Spanish guitar, lyrically predicting the fall of Spain itself.

Outcault had begun to use a variety of devices to create narrative links between episodes in successive *McFadden's Flats* and *Yellow Kid* cartoons in 1896. Although the European cartoons are joined by overall conception, only the two Spanish cartoons are specifically related. A poster advertises Don Michealo Dugano's fight with the Wall Street Bull for Cuban relief, subject of the following week's page. (Opposition to American intervention was centered in the business and financial centers.) In smaller lettering at the bottom of this poster, Outcault comments acidly on bullfighting, and on the far side of a placard in front of the poster, he takes a slap at New York stage pirates, referring to unauthorized vaudeville adaptations of the Yellow Kid.

In "A Bullfight in Honor of the Yellow Kid" (March 21, 1897), a pistol-waving Terence McSwatt wildwests it on the back of the bull that chases a delighted Yellow Kid around the "Plasa de Toros." The bull ring is filled with excited McFadden's Flats kids running hither and thither among the picadors. Other kids watch from the grandstand, whooping it up with Spanish children and the Irish-American chaperones. However, the most remarkable figure in the bullfight cartoon is not a kid. Outcault has included a sympathetically drawn portrait of a Cuban of African descent wearing a rescued picador cap, shown facing the viewer from the side lines with an expression of amused amazement. The graphic salute to the rebels battling Spanish imperial troops, combined with the dismayed expression of Alfonso XIII, makes the bullfight cartoon a metaphor for the Cuban conflict.

"Mickey and His Friends Climb the Alps" (March 28, 1897) finds the Yellow Kid and his crew clambering over a Swiss mountainside. Although Rudolph Block's by-line disappears from the texts beginning with this page, the general tone and idiosyncratic nature of the writing do not change. One must assume that the same author, whether Block or a ghost writer, wrote these witless dialect pieces, although the reason for abandoning the by-line remains a mystery.

On their Alpine ascent, the members of the McFadden's Flats party are roped together, scrambling to reach the summit already attained by the Yellow Kid's nimble goat. One member of a craps-playing duo uses the safety rope to garrote the other, a dispute doubtless caused by the loaded dice rolling seven once too often. A toboggan full of misguided youths plummets towards the Flatters' lead climbers while rum-laden Saint Bernards await the disaster. The seal of the state of New York includes the motto "Excelsior." Outcault has included the small figure of a handsomely dressed New Yorker in a top hat and fur coat, depicted as a stake-restrained fanatic who marches forever forward under a banner with this motto, a reference to the classic Longfellow dirge. On a statue of William Tell, Outcault includes a pair of puns on the name of the legendary Swiss hero.

A romantic and hospitable Bavarian ambiance surrounds the gang in "The Yellow Kid Invades Germany" (April 4, 1897), set in a town where the steins are as big as the kids and the barrels as tall as the houses. It is hard to imagine how the raucous, rioting kids of the *Hogan's Alley* and early *McFadden's Flats* cartoons could be reduced to a more demure and proper group than that portrayed here. A doggerel ode to the Rhine country fills a placard as meerschaum smoke fills the air. The idyllic, *gemutlich* atmosphere is disrupted only by the disgruntled parrot who finds the sausage-stuffed scene "de most wurst place I ever wuz at," and his buddy, the cat, who is less than charmed by the oom pah pah band, mewing, "I hope I wont get dat ole katzenyammer." (Rudolph Dirks's comic strip *The Katzenjammer Kids* would become a popular feature in the Hearst papers just a few years later.) Although spelled "Marsielles," the ironic inclusion of the French national anthem in the concert program and the "invasion" of the cartoon's title refer to the history of French and German military conflicts, from Napoleon to the Franco-Prussian War of 1870–71. The slang negatives, "I don't think!" and "nit," are common throughout the Yellow Kid; nit, apparently derived from the German word *nicht,* became "nix" in the 1920s and 1930s when it was frequently used in comic strips, notably by Bud Fisher in *Mutt and Jeff.*

From the Baroque weather vane at the top of the page to the Yellow Kid's toast with "dis luvly beer," the German panel takes a festive, tourist's view of Europe. In striking contrast is "The Yellow Kid Afloat on the Grand Canal" (April 18, 1897), where Outcault's tone turns decidedly sour. Although Liz bestows a look of affection upon her beloved Yellow Kid, speaking volumes about the effect of Venice on her, the other children remain inactive and confined to their gondola. Despite its dependence on stereotypes, offensive ethnic epithets are rare in the Yellow Kid. The appearance of one here, together with the invidious caricatures of the occupants of the second gondola, suggest that Outcault reacted unfortunately to Italy.

In "The Yellow Kid's Soliloquy" (May 2, 1897), the dignity and quiet drama of the Yellow Kid contemplating the Sphinx suggests Outcault's dependence on the atmospheric engravings that illustrated turn-of-the-century travel literature. The drawing provides a moving contrast to the kid-packed pages that precede and follow it: an oasis of reflection where the fancy, temporarily surfeited with slapstick and foreign ceremony, can pause with the Yellow Kid, silent on a dune, lost for a moment in an image as vast and redolent with mystery as any ocean. The soliloquy is a silly jingle provided by the unsigned scribe of the series.

Difficulties with color printing are evident in the early cartoons of *Around the World With the Yellow Kid.* A weakly printed shade of red is one index of the problem. It shows up in the Paris scene on the skirt of a muffed Frenchwoman (February 21); at the bottom of Sarah Bernhardt's skirt in the Louvre (February 28); and in Liz's gingham dress at Monte Carlo (March 7). The printing improves briefly, with a stronger red visible in Liz's dress as she dances with the Spanish King (March 14) and on a Viva Cuba Libre sign at the bullfight (March 21), but it fades again in the Alp-climbing page (March 28) where a tobogganist's red word balloon lettered, "Look out down dere we aint got no break," and the cover of the Guide Book from "The Snow Trust Publishing Co." are almost illegible. Continuing problems can be seen in the name on a Venetian gondola, "The Spaghetti" (April 18), and in

57. ROBERTSON AND BEATO.
Mosque with dome and minarets,
crumbling walls, and four Arabs
in foreground
(late nineteenth century).

Outcault's signature by the Sphinx (May 2). Although best seen in this red, all the colors were subdued in the 1896 and early 1897 color pages. Apparently the *Journal's* printers had not mastered Hearst's color press when the comic supplement began. After the middle of 1897, however, the problem seems wholly corrected and the printing becomes much brighter and sharper. "The Yellow Kid in Cairo" (May 9, 1897) marks Outcault's riotous return to the uproar of earlier *Yellow Kid* pages. Kids fly in all directions from the back of a glowering, cigarette-smoking camel as dust clouds billow from the streets of the old city. Poor Vincent Farrell, mounted on a donkey behind Terence McSwatt, finds his hair providing lunch for a second camel. The upended feet of a pistol-packing craps player are tattooed with a seven and an eleven. With the scrawled words "strawberry" and "vanilla," Outcault compares the bands of brickwork characteristic of Islamic architecture with multiflavored ice cream bricks.

This cartoon is signed "R. F. Outcault, Park Row," indicating that the artist had returned to New York. As in "The Yellow Kid's Soliloquy," Outcault may again be working from engravings or photographs. He also could have derived the drawing from the pseudo-Islamic architecture and camel rides among the exoticizing mix of amusements at Coney Island. Notes and puns are filled with references to New York. The donkey's harness identifies him as Manhattan Bey's private mount. Fatimas, one of the earliest brands of cigarette, are referred to in a pun on a cabaret sign: "We has got Fatimas and Fat Emmas to burn. . . " Vaudeville is the real subject of a sign on a camel reading, "Dis is a camel not no ole hump back horse." Unlike the real camels available at Coney Island, stage camels in Manhattan theaters were horses padded with artificial humps. Someone, perhaps a mischief-maker in the color layout department, has included a note in blue letters at the bottom of the page: "We have our imitators too." Irrelevant to the art and text of the page, it seems unlikely that Outcault would so crudely have equated his friend George Luks, artist of the competing *Hogan's Alley,* with the posterior of a horse.

Apparently the reader is to assume that the kids have returned to Italy, on their way back to France or England to catch their return steamship, and have stopped off at Vesuvius just in time to catch "An Eruption in Honor of the Yellow Kid" (May 16, 1897). Outcault manages to insert some scatological humor with a punning sign to the lower left of the crater reading "to the Lavatory." Combined with the parrot's assertion that it was all the result of "Slippey fallin in," it must have elicited a lot of startled male grins that Sunday. Slippy Dempsey himself delightedly hopes to be blown to a height he has never tumbled from before.

Heat jokes proliferate on signs and in bits of business appearing around the crater, while a well-prepared Yellow Kid flees down the slope under an asbestos umbrella. Overall, the action in this penultimate cartoon is perfunctory and unimaginative, with most characters simply falling or running to escape the eruption. Perhaps this is a sign of the artist's flagging inspiration as he approaches the end of the extended series.

"The Yellow Kid Returns" (May 30, 1897) is a climactic recapitulation of the departure scene, with political bigwigs from Washington and New York City gathered on the dock to welcome the Yellow Kid and gang back to the United States. President William McKinley stands to the right, framed by the American flag, while William L. Strong, the Republican mayor of New York City, stands opposite him on the other side of the gangplank, sporting a Yellow Kid ribbon. The Yellow Kid's return is headline news in the evening extra lying on the dock at the mayor's feet. Elegantly dressed women strew roses in the path of the returning hero, who wears a victor's laurel wreath. As the goat makes a meal of the Kid's wreath, another kid leans from a porthole to warn, "Hey! Mickey, de goat is stealin your laurels." Below this dialogue balloon is one of Outcault's own gentle jibes at George Luks and his competing cartoon in the *World:* "P. S. He is not de only one." The Kid's nightshirt proclaims, "An now me an Liz is going to be married an live happy ever after. See," as his radiant betrothed follows him down the gangplank. A sign above the gangplank announces the Yellow Kid's intention of becoming "a candidate for the furst mayor of Greater New York" (in 1898, Manhattan, Brooklyn, Staten Island, Queens, and the Bronx would be consolidated into a single city). All this graphic hoopla did not herald any real changes in the subjects or story line of the strip. No marriage took place, nor did the Kid run for mayor. It was back to business as usual around McFadden's Flats, although that business was to be delayed most unduly.

After the second appearance of *McFadden's Flats* in the *Journal* on October 25, 1896, each Sunday comic supplement had included two appearances of the Yellow Kid. In addition to the large *McFadden's Flats* panel, the supplements had included either a cover featuring the Yellow Kid or a second cartoon in the form of a half-page comic strip. For the most part, these were dispensed with during the tour sequence. Only four second features appeared interspersed with *Around the World with the Yellow Kid*; all were half-page comic strips. Whether on his own initiative or at his editor's suggestion, Outcault apparently drew three of them before leaving for Europe, while the fourth was drawn after his return to New York.

"The Yellow Kid Goes Hunting Becomes a Dead Game Sport" (the missing "and" was apparently overlooked by Outcault or his letterer) appeared in the same Sunday *Journal* that featured the full-page drawing of the arrival of the Yellow Kid and his entourage in London (January 24, 1897). It may be merely coincidental that Outcault takes a shot at the English humor magazine, *Punch*, in the London panel and includes a jesting put down of his first magazine, the comic weekly *Truth*, in the half-page strip. The strip's jibe is the wittier of the two: "Dont shoot im Mickey just tell im a joke from 'Truth.'"

In fact the Yellow Kid appeared three times in this edition of the comic supplement. The third cartoon was not by Outcault but by Carl Anderson, the artist who created the popular and long-running pantomime comic strip, *Henry*, in the 1930s. "The Billposter and the Kid, a Tale of Revenge" is, appropriately, a pantomime kid strip as well as a subtle comment on the vast number of posters pasted on city walls to advertise the *Journal's* Yellow Kid.

"The Yellow Kid Studies Music and Tries It on the Dog—and Others" (February 7, 1897) is an impressive piece of graphic fantasy. As the Yellow Kid plays a trumpet, wriggling and writhing notes leap from his sheet music while his pets suffer expressively and faint in a heap. The repetition of "flats" on the Yellow Kid's nightshirt is a punning reference to his failings as a muscian and the title, *McFadden's Flats*. One of the musical notes speaks in a word balloon: "I am a full note although I swore off on New Year's." This is both a marvelously surreal touch and an anticipation of the whimsical asides that will be part of the charm of many future comic strips and cartoons, from Ted Dorgan's sports panels to the editorial cartoons of Pat Oliphant. The saliva pouring from the trumpet in the last panel is a vulgar note in an otherwise delightful fantasy cartoon, a punch line reinforcing the rowdy image readers had come to expect.

The "Yellow Kid's New Phonograph Clock" (February 14, 1897) is a beautifully drawn comic strip that is experimental in structure but not in story telling. Most of the narrative is contained in the title; the panel continuity shows that the clock features a harsh, phonographic voice that overdoes its job, but nothing beyond the title need be read to grasp the point of the cartoon. The innovative elements of the cartoon are the figures that break the panel borders and the animated, framed portrait of Liz. Outcault had first broken panel borders in the *World* cartoon "The Great Bull Fight in Hogan's Alley" (August 23, 1896), in which the entire newspaper page functioned as a panel. Here, the gestures and reactions of the Kid and his pets gain added emphasis when they break the tectonic structure created by the double outlines of the panels.

The cartoon also features the first use of an animated framed picture in newspaper comic features. Moving pictures in the form of the kinetoscope, in which the viewer peered through a peephole, had first received public exposure in 1893 at the World's Columbian Exposition in Chicago. By mid-1896, projected films were appearing in vaudeville theaters and other venues throughout the country. In Outcault's strip, a framed photograph is transformed into a moving picture as Liz is jolted backward by the shock of the sounding alarm clock. Former Edison employee Outcault has subtly combined two new mass media—sound recording and motion pictures—in a third, the comic strip.

Perhaps Outcault intended to continue drawing half-page cartoons while abroad, but he did not do so. The next and, as it turned out, the last apparently was drawn and published after his return. "The Yellow Kid Makes a Century Record" (May 23, 1897) was printed just one week before the final episode of the tour sequence. Although its chief charm consists in the pyramid of pets in the first panel, recalling the fairy tale of the Musicians of Bremen, it is also linked to the other half-page *Yellow Kid* strips in which new technology provides the springboard for the jokes. This cartoon is a small tour de force of perspective, unified by the opposing orthagonals of telegraph lines and railroad tracks compressed within the tall, narrow panels.

The half-page *Yellow Kid* cartoons are not so spectacular as the complex and intricate panels of the *McFadden's Flats* and *Around the World with the Yellow Kid* series, but they are frequently small masterpieces of design. They were marginal to the large panels and, as is often the case with margins, they proved to be the locus of Outcault's most innovative work, most strikingly in "The Yellow Kid and His New Phonograph" (October 25, 1896). After the tour, the half-page cartoons took center stage, and the Yellow Kid was never to be quite the same.

Eleven

Foolscap in Newsprint:

How the Kid's Weekday Nightshirt Notes Shook Up the Journal's Pundit Page (1896–1897)

Beginning on Thursday, November 9, 1896, and continuing until Friday, May 7, 1897, Richard F. Outcault became a regular contributor to the editorial page of the daily *New York Journal,* writing and drawing a series of columns that were purportedly entries from a diary kept by the Yellow Kid himself. Each bore the title *A Leaflet from the Yellow Kid's Diary,* and included one or two simple drawings of Yellow Kid capers with remarks apposite to the diary entries emblazoned on his shirt front. These brief essays, written in the same dense slang that crowded the signs and placards of the Sunday pages, carried Outcault's by-line only a few times. However, all the drawings were signed with either the initials R. F. O. or the same full signature, R. F. Outcault, as the Sunday cartoons.

Until *Around the World with the Yellow Kid* began its five-month run in the Sunday comic supplement on January 17, 1897, there were no by-lines of any sort on these diaries. It cannot be determined with absolute certainty whether Townsend, Block, or Outcault wrote any or all of them. However, both Townsend and Block were apparently only too eager to take prominent by-lines for their indifferent prose when it was published with the Sunday Yellow Kid pages in the *Journal's* comic supplement. It seems reasonable to assume that they would have been equally if not more insistent on receiving credit for prose published on the editorial page, where it appeared next to Hearst's own signed editorials. Outcault, however, probably would have seen his own writing as an embellishment to his art, requiring no credit beyond the already signed drawings. The leaflet texts were usually wittier and wiser than the work by Townsend or Block, and almost certainly were written by Outcault himself.

In the comic supplement, Hearst presented Outcault's popular work in the most elaborate and impressive manner possible. *McFadden's Flats* cartoons or collaborations that included the Yellow Kid, such as those with Archie Gunn, were featured frequently on the supplement's cover. The publisher also commissioned writers to create original stories to accompany the cartoons, extending the appeal of the feature to an even wider audience. He chose the well-known humor writer Townsend for the *McFadden's Flats* stories and editor and journalist Block for *Around the World With the Yellow Kid* although unfortunately, neither meshed well with Outcault. The daily vignettes, however, were not of the same importance as the color panels in the new Sunday comic supplement. They were simply comic filler for an already crowded editorial page. Surrounded by drama reviews, letters, signed editorials, and other features, the image of the Yellow Kid served primarily to enliven pages of typeset columns. If Outcault could supply a sprightly bit of text with his drawings, so much the better.

The Yellow Kid's Diary had three antecedents in Outcault's newspaper work, brief features written and illustrated by the artist. The first appeared three weeks prior to "At the Circus in Hogan's Alley" (May 5, 1895), the first Sunday color cartoon to include a nightshirted kid. It was "Mickey at a Recital" (*New York World*, Sunday, April 14, 1895), by-lined "Mickey der Kid," a report of a visit to a music hall by a poor child older than the Yellow Kid and rather like Townsend's character, Chimmie Fadden. Second, under his own by-line, Outcault wrote the theatrical notice to accompany his drawing of the cast of the Weber and Fields skit based on *Hogan's Alley* (*New York World*, Sunday, September 6, 1896). Although it was not composed in the Bowery dialect of the cartoons and Diary, it was the first *Yellow Kid* cartoon published with a relatively extensive text and is the first and apparently only description of the strip's characters. Finally, the first Yellow Kid cartoon to appear on a weekday was "The Yellow Kid at the Horse Show!" (Saturday, November 14, 1896). Outcault used the same format as in the Weber and Fields sketch for a series of drawings spanning the width of the newspaper page with columns of text below. The cartoon was topical, forming part of the *Journal*'s coverage of an equestrian event at Madison Square Garden. The next week, the Diary began to appear on the *Journal*'s weekday editorial page.

There was no fixed schedule for the publication of *Diary* entries in the *New York Journal*. All appeared on weekdays and most were topical, commenting on current cultural or seasonal activities. The initial entries set the pattern the feature was to follow until the tour entries began. In the first "Leaflet from the Yellow Kid's Diary" (Thursday, November 19, 1896), the Kid gives his account of hobnobbing with Mrs. George J. Gould, wife of the financier and railroad magnate who was the son of Jay Gould, and other Gotham socialites at the "oprer." In the second *Diary* (Monday, November 23, 1896), the Yellow Kid goes to a "Printston feetball" game without his faithful Liz, meets another girl, and gets into a fight by rooting for Yale.

A recurrent motif is the incongruous presence of the Yellow Kid at events held by New York's social and cultural elite. Among such entries are those in which he attends a livestock breeders' show (Tuesday, November 24), chides Spanish General Valeriano Weyler on the suppression of the Cuban rebellion (Monday, November 30), has "T" with the Whitneys and Astors (Wednesday, December 2), and attends a bazaar at the Waldorf (Friday, December 18).

Seasonal activities provide another motif. Appearing in fall 1896 and winter 1897, holidays and wintry weather are featured in the entries for Thanksgiving, in which the Yellow Kid overindulges in turkey (Friday, November 27) and "Crismus," where he describes the travails of shopping for gifts (Friday, December 25). The leaflet in which the Yellow Kid tells how he "helpt de noo yare in" (Friday, January 1) includes an invidious description of an African-American child. Using racial epithets, this *Diary* foreshadows the treatment of African-American characters Outcault will draw for Sunday comics after the Yellow Kid strip ended. The boy seems to be the direct antecedent of the lead character in a series about *The New Bully*, a feature Outcault would draw for the *World* in 1898.

During the period when the *Diary* was appearing on the editorial page, Outcault created two other cartoons in the format of "The Yellow Kid at the Horse Show!" (Saturday, November 14, 1896). The first, "How the Yellow Kid Saw the 'Wheels Go Round' at Madison

Square Garden" (Wednesday, December 9), is a topical sports cartoon reporting on a bicycle race at Madison Square Garden, the magnificent building designed by Stanford White that opened in 1890. The Italianate fantasy incorporated an exhibition hall, theater, and the Garden Roof where White himself fell victim to the revolver of a rival for the affections of showgirl Evelyn Nesbit. The Garden was the site of many exhibitions and events, including bicycle shows, flower shows, and the annual horse show attended by New York society. Following the 1895 Yellow Fellow bicycle marathon, the *Journal* sponsored a bicycle carnival and rented the Garden for an awards ceremony, where prizes were distributed by actress Anna Held.

"The Yellow Kid Takes in the Aquarium" (Saturday, December 12), also a sequence of drawings spanning the page with text below, is unlike the topical *Diary* entries. Its subject is a public amusement, comparable to Outcault's Sunday panels such as those featuring Coney Island (*New York World*, May 24, 1896) or a dime museum (*New York World*, October 4, 1896). The New York Aquarium that the Kid visited was located at Battery Park inside the immense sandstone walls of historic Fort Clinton, which had been built during the War of 1812 to repel an expected British invasion. Roofed over and renamed Castle Clinton, between 1855 and 1890 it served as the port of entry for almost eight million European immigrants until it was replaced by Ellis Island. As the New York Aquarium, it was an accessible amenity enjoyed by generations until closed in 1939.

After the entry for New Year's Day, the *Diary* disappeared from the editorial page for three weeks, commencing again on January 20, 1897, with the first of a series of lively reports from Europe. The opening entry in the European series, credited to Rudolph Block was the first *Diary* to be published under a by-line. Outcault and his party were already overseas, and someone on the editorial staff probably decided that Block, who was writing the Sunday page texts, also must be author of the "Leaflet from the Yellow Kid's Diary" series. Outcault had not placed his own by-line on previous *Diary* entries, and probably saw no reason to begin doing so on those sent from Europe. The erroneous Block credit continued to appear until February 6, when Outcault must have learned of and stopped it, imposing his own by-line or "Mickey Dugan" for the rest of the series. (A *Journal* employee seems to have slipped up and included Block's by-line one last time on the *Diary* for March 13.)

In the first of the European *Diaries* (Wednesday, January 20, 1897), date-lined London, the Yellow Kid calls on Queen Victoria, who ends their discussion of contemporary political issues to race off to a

60. X. Photo.

Musee du Louvre.

La galerie d'Apollon
(nineteenth–twentieth
centuries).

"bargen" sale with Liz, leaving Mickey to chat with former Prime Minister William Gladstone. In the second London *Diary* (Saturday, January 30), the Yellow Kid pesters the Queen into trotting a cotillion with him at a society ball, then goes off with Prime Minister Robert Salisbury in search of some action at cards with the flamboyant Prince Albert Edward. The final English *Diary* (Saturday, February 6) in which the Yellow Kid is presented at Court, is actually a comment on the infamous Bradley Martin ball, which was to be held at New York's Waldorf on February 10. Mrs. Martin's invitations asked guests to imitate Louis XV's Court of Versailles, unleashing a storm of condemnation from press, clergy, and politicians, aimed at the heartless extravagance of the rich. Dressed as Mary Stuart, Mrs. Martin sat on a throne on a dais as each guest was announced by name and historical character; the lavish event, rumored to have cost more than a quarter of a million dollars, featured a two-hour cotillion.

After the three *Diaries* from London, there were nine more detailing the Yellow Kid and party's adventures in seven different countries: Scotland (Saturday, February 13, 1897); France (Saturday, February 20, and Sunday, February 28); Monte Carlo (Saturday, March 6); Spain (Saturday, March 13); Germany (Monday, April 5, and Monday, April 12); Russia (Monday, April 19); and finally Greece, where the series ended with a report from a battle front of the Greco-Turkish war (Friday, May 7). Oddly, there were none from Ireland, Italy or Egypt, despite their prominence in the Sunday cartoons. In the absence of any written record, it is impossible to know whether Outcault and Block were to supply a predetermined number of Sunday and daily pieces over the course of their trip and fell short, or whether they provided work over and above what was expected.

No note was taken of discrepancies between the Sunday cartoons and the *Diaries*. They were printed apparently as received, and on those Sundays when no Yellow Kid appeared, no explanation was given. The comic supplement was still a new medium; readers had not yet come to expect a particular feature every week, and editors had not yet come to understand that powerful reader loyalties could be created by regular comic features. The *Yellow Kid* was the first feature to demonstrate that newspaper circulation could be increased by the regular appearance of a comic strip starring a popular character. Although the long trip abroad must have cost a great deal and disappointed the publisher when it resulted in no sustained increase in home-delivery subscriptions, in the long run the popularity of *Around the World with the*

Yellow Kid helped establish the importance of regular features in the Sunday comics.

Diaries from the cities and countries featured in the Sunday comic supplement's pages both recapitulate the full-page cartoons and describe additional adventures. In Paris, the Yellow Kid goes to the Louvre, but also takes in a show at the Moulin Rouge, drinks absinthe in a cafe, and visits Napoleon's tomb, "a pretty comfortable place." In the Monte Carlo *Diary*, the Kid learns that you don't break the bank with dynamite; all you need is luck.

Some secondary characters from the Sunday pages also appear in the *Diaries*. In Paris, Liz confuses the Louvre department store in Paris with the museum, and Terence McSwatt gets his hair cut with a guillotine. Mr. Kelly, the kids' chaperone, admires Terence's stylish cut, but the Yellow Kid advises him against getting a shave at the same place. The female chaperone, Mrs. Houlihan, makes the Kid go to bed early in Germany, and even the Riccadonna Sisters are mentioned in passing.

In addition to the story lines, the Yellow Kid comments on stateside news and issues. In Berlin, he and the Kaiser deplore the lack of a local equivalent of the Raines Hotel Law of 1896, which forbade the Sunday sale of liquor by the drink in New York City, except in hotels. On other occasions, the Yellow Kid engages royalty in discussions of the boxers Jim Corbett and John L. Sullivan. He teaches Alfonso XIII of Spain how to box like Sullivan, and hears Bismarck lament Corbett's defeat in the famous 1891 match between the two famous pugilists.

61. ANONYMOUS.
Nuremberg. Nassauer Hause (circa 1870s).

The most striking *Diary* entry on domestic issues is that set in Monte Carlo. The Yellow Kid notes that William McKinley has just been sworn in as president, and suggests that he and Mark Hanna will soon have plenty of other things to swear about. The entry also includes an attack on the Ellsworth caricature bill, then under consideration in the New York State Legislature. The boss of the New York Republican Party, Thomas C. Platt, had orchestrated resounding Republican victories in 1894, electing Levi Morton governor and William Strong mayor of New York City. Angered at cartoonists' insulting lampoons, Platt instructed Senator Timothy E. Ellsworth to introduce a bill in the state legislature to prohibit cartoons directed at public figures.

In the *Diary*, the Yellow Kid wishes he could lobby in Albany against the bill, speculating on the motives of its sponsors: "If I looked like some uv dem guys wots pushin dat bill I might kick about havin me picture put in de papers." The bill was defeated in large part because of withering attacks by the state's cartoonists. Rudolph Dirks, artist of the *Katzenjammer Kids,* created one of the most delightful cartoons on the proposed legislation: "First the Anti-Cartoon Bill. Then, Perhaps This!" (*New York Journal,* February 20, 1898). It shows a beleaguered cartoonist who has been treed by characters from the Sunday comic supplement, including the Yellow Kid.

Unlike its predecessors, the last *Diary* entry deals with a single important story, the Greco-Turkish war (Friday, May 7, 1897). Both the *World* and the *Journal* sent their star correspondents to Greece to cover the conflict; the *Journal's* team including the novelist and war correspondent Richard Harding Davis (who soon would be sent to Cuba with artist Frederic Remington). The New York reporters were on the front lines in the war's decisive engagement in Thessaly just before this *Diary* appeared. Outnumbered by the Turkish forces, the Greek army was overwhelmed and Greece was forced to accept an armistice on May 20.

This *Diary* may have been requested by the *Journal's* editors. Although it is written as a report from the front, Outcault was not among the correspondents who witnessed the engagement. In the entry, the Yellow Kid is recruited by Prince Constantine, commander of the Greek forces. As the fighting begins, his nightshirt puns: "Gee how dese Turkish bullets fly pasha." When the tide of battle turns, the Yellow Kid is captured and recruited by the victorious Turkish army.

In addition to Davis, the New York correspondents in Greece included Stephen Crane, author of *The Red Badge of Courage* and reporter for the *Journal,* and the *World's* dashing Harry Scovel, recently released from a Cuban jail. For them, the brief Greco-Turkish War was a dress rehearsal for the action they would see in Cuba the next year. For Outcault, the *Diary* and its final, fanciful military report proved to be a rehearsal for a weekday feature he would draw in 1898: a feature with a military theme, created for another newspaper, that was destined to make comic history.

Twelve

The Outward Swing of the Trapeze:
The Kid Who Didn't Come Back (1897–1898)

62. ANONYMOUS.
Newsboys and street peddler
(nineteenth–twentieth
centuries).

In the four months after the last panel of *Around the World with the Yellow Kid* was published on May 30, 1897, Outcault's popular creation disappeared completely from the newspaper. May, June, July, and August passed without a single Yellow Kid cartoon. Although George Luks's rival Yellow Kid continued to appear in the *New York World* during most of this period, it too went into limbo for most of August and September. The Yellow Kid's popularity with the public continued unabated as new toys, magazines, foodstuffs, and whatnot appeared and sold well. When Outcault's *Yellow Kid* returned in the last week of September 1897, it was reduced to a half-page and the drawing and composition were greatly simplified. Less than six months later, it disappeared from newspapers forever.

There is no published explanation for the four-month disappearance of Outcault's Yellow Kid or the *American Humorist'* s failure to reinstate the full-page weekly layout. Based on the disappearance of Block's by-line from both *Around the World with the Yellow Kid* and "The Yellow Kid's Diary," it may be that Outcault and Block had had a falling out during their trip abroad. Perhaps Hearst was disappointed with the failure of the costly trip to bring increased subscriptions and dropped Outcault's feature for a time. Possibly the cartoonist himself took a leave from the demanding production of his intricate weekly cartoons, or perhaps both he and Luks who were, after all, friends of long standing, withheld their work to receive compensation more commensurate with the popularity of the Yellow Kid. The coincidence of the gaps in both series is notable, as is the fact that Luks's feature reappeared in the *World* the very next week after Outcault's Yellow Kid returned to the Journal on September 26, 1897.

In any case, neither the *Journal* nor the *World* announced or remarked on either the disappearance or return of the readers' favorite comic feature. Presumably the Kids sold more papers when they were in than not; it may well have been the purpose of the *Journal* and the *World* to test whether they needed to keep their Yellow Kids on hand. It is possible that as a successful cartoonist, Luks simply took an extended vacation from the newspaper and New York City at the end of the summer.

It may be that the *World-Journal* circulation war eased after the summer of 1897. Growing public concern with the revolution in Cuba, and the leading role taken by the Hearst and the Pulitzer papers in pressuring Congress and President McKinley to take direct action for the relief of the Cuban rebels, made it possible to sell as many copies of the papers as they could print to concerned New Yorkers who sought more information on the events that seemed clearly to be leading to war. Weekly full-color pages for the Yellow Kid cartoons of the two papers were a thing of the past. Both papers brought the Yellow Kids back as half-page productions, on a somewhat irregular basis. The readers liked and wanted their Yellow Kids and the *Journal* and the *World* were willing to give them what they wanted, but in a less expensive format, now that the war bucks were rolling in.

The *Journal's* Mickey Dugan returned in "The Yellow Kid Stakes a Claim at Klondyke" (September 28, 1897). Although it is a half-page cartoon and the figures are fewer and larger in scale than those of the panoramic panels, it is one of the best drawings ever produced by Outcault. Its subject is the Alaskan Gold Rush, which had begun in earnest in the summer of 1897. In a short accompanying text, Outcault suggests that the Yellow Kid had dropped out of the readers' view to prospect for gold in the North, while at the same time giving notice that his Yellow Kid would be returning, having him say "I aint gaw'n t' stay heer mutch longer." A multilevel verbal and visual pun fest, the composition carries the viewer's eye from the Yellow Kid's nightshirt announcing his conversion to "free gold," a reference to the free silver issue of the recent Bryan campaign, to the golden pawnshop balls the Kid has excavated, to the placard stating that his jackpot was opened "wit one spade." At upper left, the tumbling kid says "I hope I'll fall in a good claim," while familiar faces from the old McFadden's Flats gang arrive eagerly behind the Yellow Kid. The coat of arms on the spade by "de gote's claim" that one Outcault devised for his and Townsend's *Yellow Kid in McFadden's Flats,* published in March 1897.

Unlike the humor magazines, each issue of which was designated a number within an annual volume, the *American Humorist* color supplements for the *Journal* were numbered sequentially like contemporary comic books. The cover of Number 50 celebrated the "Journal Comic Supplement's First Year" (October 3, 1897). (The supplement was not printed for two successive weeks in the summer of 1897.) This cover drawing was a collaborative effort by several of the *Journal's* regular cartoonists, featuring their most popular characters and comic types. In a musical analogy, contemporary comic artists call this kind of collaborative drawing a jam. Featured most prominently on this cover are African-American children drawn by Edward Kemble, the illustrator of Mark Twain's *Huckleberry Finn,* recently hired by the *Journal.* The rather perfunctory Yellow Kid who stands near the center of this mélange in an almost angelic pose may or may not be a product of Outcault's pen; the other, livelier characters in the ensemble appear to be from the hands of the artists whose characters are represented.

Whether or not Outcault participated in the drawing, the page is historically important in the development of the comic strip. It demonstrates that William Randolph Hearst and Rudolph Block had learned some important lessons from the success of the Yellow Kid. They had realized that recognizable comic characters were an effective means of selling newspapers week after week. A regular, loyal readership would buy the Sunday paper to obtain the comic section.

The following week, the authentic Kid returned in an active, detailed, half-page "The Yellow Kid Inspects the Streets of New York" (October 10, 1897). The cartoon brings most of the old McFadden's Flats gang together at a construction site on Fifth Avenue, which is being torn up to lay utility lines. The humor deals with an issue of the day involving "one dollar gas." The difficulty of getting across town while the avenue is torn up is guyed by the Yellow Kid's nightshirt, comparing it to "de time when Napoleon crost de Alps only de Alps wuz'nt in it wit Fift Avenue." In its July 9, 1896 issue, *Life* had made a similar comment, not-

63. JACOB RIIS.
The First Patriotic Election in the Beach Street Industrial School (late nineteenth century).

ing that the utility and transportation companies "seldom tear up any street to such an extent that an able-bodied man who has devoted a few summers to mountain climbing cannot make his way through it." Below Outcault's signature is the note "from photograph." Before the perfection of the half-tone process, in which photographs are screened for reproduction, all the illustrations in newspapers were based on drawings that could be engraved on the printing plates. Many illustrations were drawn from photographs taken specifically for that purpose. Outcault must have used a *Journal* photograph as a reference for this topical cartoon.

The streets of New York are again the topic in "The Yellow Kid Treats the Crowd to a Horseless Carriage Ride" (October 17, 1897). The cartoon shows horses rearing in fright at the gang's automobile, while hapless pedestrians are crushed by its wheels and strewn in its wake. This drawing is full of movement and fun, but the subject was already hackneyed. Constraints of the half-page format may be partially responsible for the lack of imagination, but Outcault had accomplished fine work within the same restrictions numerous times. There are a number of individually fine drawings in the piece including the animals flying at the ends of their tethers and the startled horses that flank the scene, but they do not cohere as well as in Outcault's earlier work. The cartoon includes very little text, another indication of Outcault's lack of time for proper work. The fire in the awning is unexplained, no sparks fly from the vehicle, and the racing firemen in the background, responding to so small a fire, seem a bit farfetched. On balance, this is the poorest of Outcault's big production pieces.

In contrast, the next three half-pages are among Outcault's best work. "The Yellow Kid Takes a Hand at Golf" (October 24, 1897) combines the energy of the panoramic "Golf—the Great Society Sport as Played in Hogan's Alley" (January 5, 1896) with the tectonic structure and lively, panel-bursting design of "The Yellow Kid's New Phonograph Clock" (February 14, 1897). "The Yellow Kid Loses Some of His Yellow" (October 31, 1897) is a charmingly simple comic strip, focused on the facial reactions of the Yellow Kid and Liz. The last of this trio of knockouts, "The Crowd Gets Up an Election Bonfire and the Yellow Kid Plays Nero" (November 7, 1897), is as visually arresting as anything Outcault ever drew. It also introduces *Ryan's Arcade* as the new name of the series.

The name *McFadden's Flats* appeared only in the *Journal* and in the title of Outcault's and Townsend's collaborative book based on the Sunday panels, *The Yellow Kid in McFadden's Flats.* Outcault probably could have continued to use it, but presumably it was Townsend's invention; it may have been viewed as too closely associated with the writer and his popular book, *Chimmie Fadden,* once Townsend was no longer providing stories for the cartoons. Outcault's first cartoon featuring a child in a nightshirt, "Feudal Pride in Hogan's Alley" (*Truth,* June 2, 1894) had included street signs reading "Hogan's Alley" and "Ryan's Arcade," surely inspiring the new name.

"The Crowd Gets Up an Election Bonfire and the Yellow Kid Plays Nero" (November 7, 1897) is a topical cartoon about the 1897 New York mayoral election. Outcault had referred to it in "The Yellow Kid Returns" (May 30, 1897), the last cartoon in *Around the World with the Yellow Kid,* where a sign announced the Yellow Kid's intention to become "a candidate for the furst mayor of Greater New York." Consolidation of the areas surrounding New York harbor into a single city had been promoted by the mercantile and financial elite of the region so that central planning and development of its infrastructure, including roads, railroads, and shipping facilities, could enable the city to compete effectively in national and world markets. It was approved in a referendum in 1894.

In that same year Tammany was booted from City Hall, and Republican-fusion candidate William L. Strong became mayor. The astute U.S. Senator Thomas C. Platt, called the "easy boss" because of his persuasive style, controlled New York's Republican party and won the approval of the state legislature for consolidation and a new city charter in 1897. Richard Croker, the boss of Tammany Hall, was an Irish immigrant and street fighter who had risen from the Fourth Avenue Tunnel Gang to a position of great personal wealth and power. He spent much of Mayor Strong's term in Europe, enjoying the pleasures of the race track with such companions as Prince Albert Edward, then returned to oversee the 1897 mayoral nomination and election of the little-known chief judge of the city court, Robert A. Van Wyck. During the electoral campaigns that year, the candidate for district attorney and other Tammany men were given to shouting in their speeches, "To Hell With Reform!"

Outcault lampoons both bosses in the title of the volume resting at the base of the Yellow Kid's soapbox: "Me by T. Platt with sketch of I by R. Croker." The bonfire-lit drawing shows the gang gathered around a crackler set ablaze in a trash barrel on a dark Manhattan street that election night. During election day, there had been plenty for the Tammany men to do as they rounded up their repeat voters (in one of his first elections, Croker was proud to have voted seventeen times), intimidated those who might not support their candidates, and made sure that only the right ballots were counted: "De goat et all de ballots in de sixt ward but it didnt make no difference in de returns you bet." Although kids had no role in elections, they celebrated them by lighting bonfires like this one. The Yellow Kid plays Nero, sawing away at his fiddle while the fires burn, and a kid next to him toasts George Luks's twin Yellow Kids over the fire.

Luks's Alex and George were to appear repeatedly in this final half-page series of Outcault's *Yellow Kid*. They were entirely Luks's creations, and he had made them the central characters of his cartoons, ultimately dropping the Yellow Kid entirely. On October 24, 1897, the last weekly *Hogan's Alley* episode appeared in the *World*. One more *Yellow Kid* panel appeared in the *World* on December 5, 1897, but until he left to begin a career in painting in 1898, Luks's main work for the *World* consisted of an original comic, *Mose, the Great Trained Chicken*.

Outcault's surprising and nearly continuous inclusion of the dwarf team in his *Journal* pages between November 7, 1897, and January 16, 1898, seems to have been a tribute to a fellow cartoonist's original and memorable but discontinued characters. Outcault lampooned their small size—Luks made them half the size of the Yellow Kid—by hanging them like puppets on a string in several cartoons. In addition to being toasted, they were garroted, dumped in a trash can, and showered with bricks. In a tone of good-natured rivalry, Outcault lettered their shirts with deprecating comments such as "We are getting roasted; aint you glad?" and "Alex gives me a pain; I am getting tired of George." Perhaps Outcault disliked seeing a good comic image slip into limbo, preferring to keep it on stage a while longer.

"How the Goat Got 'Kilt Entirely'" (November 14, 1897) mocks Van Wyck's victory in the 1897 mayoral election. "Don't hurt him Bill he is a Tammany man," reads the Yellow Kid's nightshirt as his long-suffering goat does himself in with a maddened leap at an impervious cigar store Indian, in a visual reference to Tammany Hall, which took its name from a legendary Native American leader of the Lenni-Lenape nation. In its early years, members dressed in paint and feathers to celebrate holidays and march in parades. Under Boss Tweed, the organization adopted the tiger as its symbol; on election night, according to the *New York World*, men and women from New York's notorious Tenderloin district marched through the streets with toy tigers under their arms. However, images associated with Native Americans continued to be used by Tammany, and the boss's title in the organization was "sachem." The accordioned goat with his broken horns is a rather sad sight, but the Yellow Kid can't help chortling at his own tumble and the goat's misfortune even while voicing condolences on his shirt.

"Thanksgiving Day in Ryan's Alley" (November 21, 1897) finds the Ryan's Arcade bunch gathered at the goat's graveside. "Billy," a note on his grave says, "we hope dat you will have a better pair of horns where you have went at." The Yellow Kid's ever-ready pocket is crammed with cranberry sauce. In these late cartoons, the space limitations of the half-page format tend towards a limited repertoire of compositions, most showing kids lined up behind a fence or in informal processions. The Yellow Kid wears skates to facilitate his access to the turkey while the cat has been mittened to hamper his. The unfortunate fates of Slippy Dempsey, the tumbling boy, and baseball player Swipsey Phelan are detailed on the fence poster while the turkey is about to meet his end on a chopping block of Union Pacific stock.

"Grand Opera in Ryan's Arcade" (November 28, 1897) is a Yellow Kid episode redolent of high culture. While the Yellow Kid portrays Mephistopeles with obvious zest, most of the kids sitting on the fence face the other way, suggesting limited interest in *Faust*. Liz and another kid are putting their all into the roles of Faust and Marguerite, joined by a delightedly shrieking parrot whose aria is "Oh I dont know." On a sign at right, Outcault's summary of the plot describes Marguerite's arrest and imprisonment in the Tombs, New York City's infamous prison. She calls for Abe Hummel, a lawyer whose clients included famous actors and producers as well as the city's most notorious criminal gangs, a fixture at theater openings and parties who profited from pursuing and defending both showgirls and playboys in breach-of-promise suits. The sign explains that after the opera, the audience will repair to the Waldorf, which had become the sumptuous Waldorf-Astoria that fall, or dine with the sporting crowd at Shanley's lobster palace on Longacre Square at the foot of the Great White Way, or perhaps join the Bradley Martins' party, on whose opera box the Yellow Kid stands.

As noted above, the *American Humorist* included four pages printed in full color and four in duotone (black plus one color). "A Christmas Festival in Ryan's Arcade" (December 5, 1897) marked the first time since its first appearance in the *World* on May 5, 1895, that the Yellow Kid was printed in a comic supplement in less than full color. A full-page advertisement for the Chickering Piano Company has ousted the *Yellow Kid* half-page from its normal position in the weekly section; the Christmas *Ryan's Arcade* panel is printed in black plus an anemic orange. The *Humorist*'s editor must have known that the *Yellow Kid* would not be part of the *Journal* much longer. Three of the next six Yellow Kids are duotone, not as the result of last-minute displacement by advertising, but by the editor's choice.

The Christmas cartoon is nothing too special. The leaping Noah's Ark animals are charming, but the extreme surprise and dismay of the gang members at seeing the Yellow Kid dressed as "Santy Claws" seems pointless. The gifts listed or tagged in the drawing are mostly for public figures like Anthony Comstock or Mayor-elect Van Wyck. Cuba gets her independence, while face powder goes to Spanish General Valeriano Weyler, recalled from Cuba under diplomatic pressure from the United States, and exploding Cuban cigars go to his successor, General Ramón Blanco y Erenas.

"The Ryan's Arcade Gang Go Sleighing" (December 12, 1897) features an unusual two-panel format. The cartoon makes great fun of a wintry sleigh-ride spill that submerges Alex and George in the snow. Outcault has drawn the twins to larger scale, making them look very much like a pair of Palmer Cox's brownies rather than the doll-like figures of the later Yellow Kid cartoons. A disaster for everyone else, the upended sleigh leaves the Yellow Kid, his pets, and a cool raven unperturbed.

Two weeks later, Outcault winds up 1897 with a strangely dispirited depiction of a New Year's morning-after. "Scene in Ryan's Arcade on the Morning of New Year's Day" (December 26, 1897) appears on the same page as an early episode of Rudolph Dirks's *The Katzenjammer Kids*. The coupling is ironic. As the Yellow Kid was fading from the comic supplement, the *American Humorist*'s pages gained the first of many comic strips featuring recurring characters like the Katzenjammers. These characters would star in enduring features in Sunday funnies that had been opened to them by the popularity of the Yellow Kid.

Outcault's New Year's Day cartoon, which notes that 1898 will "initiate Greater New York," is grim enough to have been drawn by George Cruikshank at the peak of his powers as a graphic crusader against the harsh realities of urban, working-class life in the 1860s. The few puns in the text are flat. Even the drawing is tired and slipshod, with the Yellow Kid sadly misproportioned. The cat's dismal German comment, "Oh Katzenjammer," might be seen as a trace of the verve of previous Yellow Kid pages if it were possible to assume that Outcault knew the half-page would appear above the new Dirks comic, but given the cavalier placement of these last few Yellow Kid drawings, it is unlikely he would have known the layout in advance.

In the *Journal's* first Sunday section of 1898, Outcault's Yellow Kid drawing is less than a quarter-page in size and the Yellow Kid is colored green, an absurdity demonstrating the carelessness with which the departing Kid was treated in the comic supplement he once dominated. "Signs of Snow" (January 2, 1898) is simple, competent, and quietly charming, but is the work of an artist doing the minimum on the last few drawings for which he is obligated contractually. Although hardly as intensely detailed as the Yellow Kids of earlier days, "The Yellow Kid's R-

R-R-Revenge" (January 9, 1898) returns to the two-panel format with much of the graphic zest of Outcault in peak form. The gag would have been virtually incommunicable in monochrome, and the color-splashed concept of the second panel almost seems designed to assure Outcault of at least one more full-color half-page in the *Journal*. If so, it clearly worked.

The following week's "The Yellow Kid Gives a Show in Ryan's Arcade" (January 16, 1898) returns to the format of a single large panel. With its heavy, crosshatched shadows and leering death's-head, it has the look of a copperplate engraving. Possibly drawn as a Halloween cartoon in 1897 and shelved to be used as filler on a duotone page, this penultimate Yellow Kid shows him as a stage magician. Liz has been lifted with a fifty-thousand-pound weight fastened to her ankles, and the Kid's top-per relieves itself of an endless heap of gold bricks onto the ill-fated George and Alex. The horrified audience flees the stage, running and falling out of the panel. The cartoon includes an appalling depiction of an African-American boy in an image both offensive and disturbing. The Yellow Kid pulls a chicken from his coat and causes doves to fly from his mouth as he quakes in fright, while loaded dice, concealed aces, straight razors, and eggs fall from his clothes. His posture and open-mouthed expresson make him the mirror image of the skeletal apparition behind him.

64. Anonymous.
The Yellow Kids.
Saranac Lake (N.Y.)
Carnival.

Outcault's last Kid cartoon in the *Journal*'s comic supplement is "The Yellow Kid Experiments with the Wonderful Hair Tonic" (January 23, 1898). The Kid leaves the supplement in style. His nightgown is exchanged for a fur coat, and a top hat perches at a jaunty angle on his bald head.

Outcault now found himself a cartoonist without a character. He entered a period of experimentation, and in 1898 could be found working for both the *Journal* and the *World* as he sought a new direction for his work. He began to use more African-American characters, and drew a series of Sunday color panels featuring them for the *World*.

While doing this series, he slipped a final Yellow Kid panel into the *World*'s comic supplement, "The Casey Corner Kids' Dime Museum" (May 1, 1898). In both format and style, it is similar to the final *Ryan's Arcade* series in the *Journal*, and may have been drawn months before but left unpublished when the series was cancelled. The Yellow Kid is portrayed in a green nightshirt, with white eyebrows and a beard, as though to disguise his identity. The cartoon mocks the questionable exhibits of the dime museums that proliferated in Barnum's wake and were popular on the Bowery in the 1880s and 1890s. The lead-weighted figure of "Billy de Boy Bridge Jumper" satirizes Steve Brodie, who parlayed a faked jump from the Brooklyn Bridge in 1886 into careers as a dime-museum exhibit, actor, and owner of a Bowery saloon popular with the sporting crowd. The Yellow Kid's antiquated nightshirt (copper-yellow gone green with age?) reads ambiguously, "Gosh, I've growed old in makin dis collection."

The Yellow Kid had made the fame and fortune of two newspapers at the peak of the 1890s. Its weekly graphic whirlwind ensured the success of the *World*'s and the *Journal*'s comic supplements, the first Sunday funnies and the birthplace of the comic strip. The Yellow Kid was the first great newspaper comic character in history and lucrative predecessor to Maggie and Jiggs, Popeye, Blondie, The Gumps, Dick Tracy, Flash Gordon, Buck Rogers, and Charlie Brown and Snoopy. After Outcault's last Sunday panel, a few more appeared, drawn by other hands, and he returned to the drawing table once more to create a short-lived but extraordinary daily Yellow Kid comic strip. The Yellow Kid was also resurrected a few times in Outcault's later *Buster Brown* strip.

Apart from these few exceptions, the Yellow Kid disappeared completely from U.S. newsprint, never recreated, reprinted, or featured in books or magazines. The press runs were over and lead plates melted down. For the most part, the originals were thrown away immediately or tacked to newsroom walls for a few weeks, then thrown away. Gone and, except in the memories of cartoonists and students of comic art, forgotten. It was forgotten largely due to the newspaper-nourished war with Spain which not only made Teddy Roosevelt president but also contributed directly to the astonishingly abrupt polishing off of the golden goose called the Yellow Kid.

Thirteen

Yellow Death For the Yellow Kid:

How the Fortunes of War Finished Mickey Dugan

(1898)

Inspired by the revolution of 1776 in the United States and that of 1789 in France, most of Spain's American colonies had gained their independence in the period between 1810 and 1830. Only Cuba, "the ever-faithful isle," and Puerto Rico remained, the last colonies of an American empire that had once encompassed most of the Western hemisphere. Cuba had been the focus of diplomatic conflicts between Spain and the United States for decades. An unsuccessful Cuban revolution between

1868 and 1878, called the Ten Years' War, had led to calls for war in the United States. A second revolution began in 1895, when expansionists in political and academic circles were becoming increasingly influential in the United States; their calls for overseas military intervention and colonial possessions were beginning to find a receptive public, especially in the Republican party.

In the streets of New York, the *World* and the *Journal* encouraged military intervention in Cuba almost from the moment the revolution began. With lurid headlines, the papers competed to report Spanish atrocities of all sorts. Their stories were picked up by newspapers across the country, and expansionist politicians of both parties began to pressure first the administration of Democrat Grover Cleveland, then (after the 1896 election) that of Republican William McKinley.

In January 1898, the last Yellow Kid cartoon by Outcault appeared in the *New York Journal*'s comic supplement. In April 1898, the United States went to war with Spain, much to the delight of the *New York Journal* and the *New York World*. Historians have long associated the Yellow Kid cartoons with the editorial stances of these papers, particularly with their frequent and unrestrained calls for war with Spain. Ironically, the Yellow Kid had faded and disappeared months before the war began. Even more ironically, public support for the war, fostered by the very newspapers that featured the Yellow Kid, probably played a key role in the character's demise.

By the beginning of 1897, Spain was perceived as a personal menace by millions of Americans, particularly in New York. Demonstrations demanding intervention became more frequent on Manhattan streets. Spanish General Valeriano Weyler, who led the imperial troops against the Cuban uprising, was mocked in effigy, once being wrapped in the Spanish flag and set afire in front of the Pulitzer building. There is no doubt that the stories of atrocities were exaggerated and that incidents were invented by the New York press to inflame public opinion and increase their own sales. The *World* and the *Journal* delightedly exposed each others' misrepresentations. At the same time, the Spanish tactic of reconcentration, in which the civilian population was moved forcibly into fortified and garrisoned cities and towns while Spanish troops systematically reduced the countryside, provided more than enough genuine horrors for sensational newspaper stories.

In New York, newspaper readers were treated to both daily indictments of Spanish cruelty and the thrill of a circulation battle. Readers relished the circus excitement as adventurous reporters from the two battling newspapers, plus their colleagues at the *Herald,* competed to outdo each other in daring coverage of the fighting. As usual when war frenzy is stirred, ostentatious patriotism and attacks on perceived enemies became central to public discourse. At such times, the most unexpected symbols may be chosen as objects of passion. One target was the most prominent color on the most readily identifiable symbol of Cuban oppression, the Spanish flag. That color was yellow.

It may have been a surge of antiyellow feeling in 1897 that led the *World* to begin cautiously phasing out George Luks's *Hogan's Alley* in April, cutting its size from a full to a half-page. Although Luks continued to draw other comic features, his Yellow Kids were eased off the comic supplement altogether in October.

The reduction in size took place while Outcault's *Around the World with the Yellow Kid* was running in the *Journal*. In contrast to the treatment of Luks's drawings, Outcault's work included seven spectacular, full-page drawings printed sideways on the supplement's pages. "The Yellow Kid Shakes His Trotters in Old Madrid" (March 14, 1897) included a sizable image of the Spanish flag itself, only a few weeks before the space allotted to Luks was cut in half.

Outcault's Yellow Kid vanished from the *Journal* comic supplement completely for four months after "The Yellow Kid Returns" (May 30, 1897). Perhaps this was convenient from the viewpoint of a paper promoting intervention in Cuba, but probably hearing its share of objections to the weekly appearance of a yellow-garbed character. However, it is unlikely that the Yellow Kid cartoons went on hiatus as a direct result of impassioned protest by a yellow-hating crowd. The *Journal* would not have abandoned the readership that wanted the Yellow Kid to the *World*'s competing feature, regardless of anti-yellow feelings. The Yellow Kid returned to fairly regular appearances in the *Journal* in October 1897, suggesting that its disappearance was not caused by popular pressure.

News items about patriotic revulsion towards the color yellow just before the Spanish-American War are rare. Newspapers engaged in building their circulations by stirring up war fever would not have been interested in reporting the more embarrassing excesses caused by their stories. Sophisticated citizens would have been contemptuous of open editorial support for such excesses, while open condemnation would have alienated the sizable number of readers who supported the groups demanding intervention. It was easier to ignore the public expressions of jingoism.

However, in at least one case, the powerful and apparently spontaneous reaction to the color yellow

66. Elite Studios.

I'm the Yellow Kid.

by a prominent women's club was reported in the society pages of a metropolitan daily. On May 18, 1897, the article appeared in the *Denver Times* under the headline, "Yellow Blotted Out," with the subheads, "Woman's Club Will Tolerate Nothing of Spanish Hue" and "Badge of National Colors."

> The Woman's Club yesterday overstepped the bonds of parliamentary restriction and patriotically trampled under foot the obnoxious colors of Spain.
>
> The cause of the unprecedented procedure was an innocent little badge which three months ago the club voted upon as the emblem of the local biennial board members to wear during the coming convention of women's clubs. The style and color were sanctioned by the club according to parliamentary rules. Unfortunately, in the combination of colors was the yellow of Spain.
>
> Since American sentiment has become so strong against Spain yellow has become an eye-sore to the people. The Woman's Club caught the spirit of the hour . . . and yesterday, when the yellow of their chosen badge stared the members in the face there was an outburst of indignation spontaneous and overwhelming.
>
> "Strike out that color," exclaimed Mrs. Platt, as soon as she saw the badge. "As Americans we cannot allow it to enter into our decorations in any form."
>
> Mrs. J. B. Grant was acting as presiding officer. She realized that according to parliamentary law if a change were to be made it would have to be done at the second and not later than the third meeting after that at which it was made a rule.
>
> "Let us override the rules" came from all sides of the house. Sentiment won, and without a single dissenting vote, it was decided to throw out the yellow and supplant it with the red, white, and blue.

Although women's suffrage was not achieved until 1920, women's organizations were increasingly influential in the United States in the late nineteenth century, especially in the cities. Some had specific political goals like the National American Woman Suffrage Association, dating from 1869 (with even older roots in the early abolitionist movement) and based in New York City, and the Woman's Christian Temperance Union, begun in 1874. The most broadly based organization was the General Federation of Women's Clubs, formed in 1890. It unified many already existing local groups into a single national organization. For the most part, the constituent clubs of the Federation were literary clubs in which professional women and the wives of upper- or middle-class husbands met to discuss not only literature, but social and political topics. The first treasurer of the Federation was Phoebe Apperson Hearst.

On August 17, 1897, the *New York Journal* published an article about a young woman, Evangelina Cosio y Cisneros, who was being held in a Cuban jail. The "Cuban Girl Martyr," as the headline described her, had been imprisoned after an attempt to free her father, a member of a prominent family who had been an active revolutionary in the Ten Years' War, and was being held on the Isle of Pines. Cosio had been held for ten months in the Casa de Recojidas, Havana's notorious women's prison, when the *Journal* began a campaign to win her release.

The newspaper organized a petition drive aimed at the women of the United States. Fifteen thousand signatures were collected and forwarded to Queen Regent Maria Christina of Spain. Women's clubs organized mass meetings across the country. On October 6, the story came to a thrilling climax when the *Journal* arranged to have an agent in Cuba free Cosio by bribing the guards to look the other way while she was led across a ladder stretched from an adjoining building. Spirited to the United States, she was feted at a huge rally in Madison Square Garden and received by President McKinley at a reception in Washington, D.C.'s Convention Hall. *Journal* publisher William Randolph Hearst, who had enlisted the women of the United States in his campaign to free the "Cuban Joan of Arc," arranged a cross-country speaking tour for her that included many women's club audiences.

In such a charged atmosphere, the Yellow Kid cartoons in the *World* and the *Journal* must have presented a highly visible target to the anti-Spanish wowsers roused by those selfsame journals. The papers had been tagged already with the "yellow press" label by their marginally more restrained Park Row rivals. The character's fame would have prevented any easy solution such as shifting to a red, white or blue night-shirt. Further, too many products bearing the Yellow Kid's image were available, and these were beyond the control of the newspapers. The pirated products, advertising signs, and stage productions were beyond the control even of Outcault, who held copyright to the character.

The final episode of George Luks's *Hogan's Alley* appeared in the *World's* comic supplement in the fall of 1897. War was just around the corner and public support for military intervention was reaching its apogee. Luks had firsthand experience of the rebellion, having been an artist-reporter in Cuba for the *Philadelphia Evening Bulletin* prior to working for the *World*. In December 1895, he had accompanied correspondent Maurice O'Leary to Havana, and had sent back lively sketches of the insurgents in action against Spanish troops. Before going to Cuba, Luks had worked at the *Philadelphia Press* and had become friends with the artists who would form the nucleus of the Ash Can

School. Their depictions of urban life would alter the course of painting in the United States in the early twentieth century. Luks shared a New York studio with one of these artists, William Glackens, and it was at Glackens's suggestion that Luks began painting in 1898, and soon thereafter abandoned cartooning.

The *Journal* resumed publishing the Yellow Kid in October, although the cartoons were considerably reduced in size. The editors must have felt that the charm and humor of Outcault's work would sustain it as a popular *Journal* feature despite the clamor for war. The feature was finally cancelled in early 1898, when it was clear that war was imminent. It may have seemed that circulation could be threatened by the yellow-garbed character. It was an ignominious finish for the hugely popular and widely loved comic feature, coming a bare handful of years after its hero's first, unheralded appearance in a cartoon magazine, then in the new medium of the newspaper comic supplement.

Despite cancellation of the *Yellow Kid*, Hearst still admired Outcault and his work. In a kick upstairs for the artist, the young publisher made him editor of another innovative feature, a daily page of cartoons and humorous pieces for the *Evening Journal*. Outcault continued on full salary in this post into the early months of 1898. He was to achieve nothing less than introduce the world's first daily comic strip featuring, against all odds, the Yellow Kid.

67. BROWN BROTHERS.
U.S. Army camp
during the Spanish-
American War.
(1898)

Fourteen

Easter Weekday for the Kid:

His Return and Last Bow (1897–1898)

In the 1890s, the major newspapers were morning papers. They were
intended for home subscription and their content was designed to attract
the women readers who made many of the decisions on domestic con-
sumption. Morning newspapers carried most of the department store
advertising and published large Sunday editions filled with special features, attracting advertisers of many sorts.

Many morning newspapers also published an evening paper,
often with the same name as the morning paper but a markedly different content. Focused on sports, gambling, and crime news, the evening

68. RICHARD F. OUTCAULT.
The Huckleberry Volunteers
(*New York Evening Journal*,
Friday, April 8, 1898).

papers appeared only six days a week, Monday through Saturday, and were intended for daylong street sales to urban office and factory workers. Evening papers, called "hawkers" because their multiple editions were hawked in the streets by newsboys, were rarely sold by subscription. Many of their readers were commuters who bought them to read on the way home at night; they often left them on the train or bus, considering them too lowbrow to bring home.

In 1896, Hearst added his own evening paper, naming it the *New York Evening Journal* to distinguish it from his flagship paper, the *New York Journal*. Although both were owned and published by Hearst, each had its own editorial staff and included features not found in the other. Soon after launching the evening paper, the maverick publisher decided to use it to experiment with a daily comic page. Although this new feature occupied only a single page and was printed entirely in black and white, it followed the *American Humorist* in layout and content and included cartoons by such Sunday supplement regulars as Rudolph Dirks, James Swinnerton, Ed Kemble, and R. F. Outcault. The daily comic page featured single- and multipanel cartoons, columns of jokes, and short humorous pieces by *Journal* staffers and free-lancers. Outcault was invited to serve as editor of the page early in 1898, when his Sunday **Yellow Kid** feature was fading from the *American Humorist*.

In addition to his role as editor, Outcault contributed many original cartoons to the page, publishing a dozen or more each week. Although he continued to draw cartoons set in tenement neighborhoods, the Yellow Kid never appeared in them. Some of his contributions featured animals and were very much like his earliest cartoon work, while

69. RICHARD F. OUTCAULT.
The Huckleberry Volunteers
(*New York Evening Journal*,
Monday, April 11, 1898).

others were populated by stereotyped African Americans. Since no
recurring characters were included, nothing resembling a comic strip
appeared on the daily page until Outcault brought a character he had
developed in the *New York World* to his *Journal* page and—again acci-
dentally—made comic history.

Two Outcault cartoons, featuring stereotyped African-American
children, had been published in the *American Humorist* during the four-
month disappearance of the Yellow Kid. Like the Yellow Kid cartoons,
they were set in a fictional ethnic neighborhood, an African-American
community in the South called Rushville. Featuring characters based on
theatrical caricatures of African Americans, with a cameo appearance in
blackface by the Yellow Kid, they were drawn apparently long before
their publication in color on June 27 and July 11, 1897.

These cartoons were probably the predecessors of the new series
Outcault drew for the *New York World* when he was editor of the
Evening Journal's comic page. In this color half-page feature, set in an
urban tenement neighborhood called Casey's Corner, the major character is an African-American boy portrayed with the same racial stereotypes as the children in the *Journal* cartoons of the previous year.

The first cartoon of the series, "Here's the New Bully. He Has a
Future" (February 13, 1898), established the attributes of the character,
who is always shown wearing a large lucky horseshoe on a chain around
his neck and accompanied by a fierce bulldog straining at its leash. The
first *World* Bully episode was followed by another half-page, "The New
Bully's First Victory—Whips the Policeman in One Round" (February
20, 1898), after which the *World* moved the new feature into a full-page

70. RICHARD F. OUTCAULT.
    The Huckleberry Volunteers
    (*New York Evening Journal,*
    Wednesday, April 13, 1898.)

71. RICHARD F. OUTCAULT.
    The Huckleberry Volunteers
    (*New York Evening Journal,*
    Thursday, April 14,1898.)

layout on February 27. It was the first time in many months that a New York newspaper's comic supplement had devoted a full page to one of Outcault's cartoons.

The early months of 1898 found Outcault working at a furious pace, editing the *New York Evening Journal's* comic page, producing a sheet of drawings for it every week, and producing a new Sunday color panel. The end of Luks's competing Yellow Kid apparently left Outcault free to work for both papers without objections from either publisher. It was during this period of extraordinary productivity that Outcault somehow found the time end energy to use his position as both editor of and cartoonist for the *Evening Journal's* comic page as the opportunity to create a new form of graphic narrative. Outcault's remarkable innovation was published in the *Evening Journal* during the second week of April 1898, on the eve of the United States' entry into the Spanish-American war. Indeed, the imminence of war was the spark for Outcault's novel notion.

During the weeks prior to his experiment in the *Journal,* Outcault's Sunday color panel for the *World* had featured a series of related cartoons showing the New Bully whipping the Casey Corner gang into military readiness as forcibly enlisted members of the Huckleberry Volunteers, a group allegedly eager and ready to fight for the Cuban rebels against the Spanish troops. These cartoons satirized the real civilian volunteer groups then preparing for the coming conflict. At the beginning of April, in the last days before an almost certain declaration of war, Outcault apparently conceived the idea of hurling his ragtag bunch into actual action. The concept required a continuous narrative carrying the volunteers from their stateside training to the field of battle in Cuba.

Outcault had already experimented with linking his Sunday cartoons. He had used various props such as a camera and a pet monkey to create unities between the large *McFadden's Flats* panels and the half-page *Yellow Kid* strips in the *American Humorist*. As he knew only too well, the narrative in a Sunday panel, if there was to be any, stretched out over many weeks. He had had extensive experience with such a sequence when he created the *Around the World with the Yellow Kid* series, which had extended over five months, lasting longer than his own trip to Europe. Such an attenuated narrative was almost certain to be outpaced by actual events, but Outcault had another option for he was in the unique position of being both cartoonist and editor for a daily comic page. He could draw and publish the narrative panels on a daily basis until the sequence was complete.

Apparently, Hearst had no objection to the artist's plan to bring a character and theme from his Sunday World pages to the Evening Journal humor page so long as no World-owned titles such as "New Bully" or "Casey's Corner" were used. Outcault went to work creating twelve successive 5-by-7½-inch panels crammed with action, telling a serial story about the Bully and his militant Huckleberry Volunteers. The first cartoon appeared Friday, April 8, 1898.

For the daily panels, Outcault not only borrowed characters from his Sunday *World* series, but drew them with the same care and intricacy. They were filled with the detail and action found in his large Sunday color panels. Each cartoon was accompanied by verses by *Journal* staff writer Paul West, printed in column blocks below the drawings. West's text added little to the series and it is unlikely that Outcault would have entered into another collaboration on his own, given his previous experiences with Townsend and Block. Since Outcault was his own editor, the assignment probably came from Hearst himself. West's verses were, however, no worse than others that appeared in the *Journal* in support of Cuban independence.

Being his own editor also gave Outcault the right to place the cartoons where he wanted them, and he chose to feature them prominently at the top of the comic page. Above each cartoon appeared the series title, *The Huckleberry Volunteers*. Although this phrase had appeared in a Sunday *World* cartoon, Outcault had used it only in the internal text of the panel, so probably felt free to use it for his *Journal* series. Although the leader of the Volunteers was the same grotesquely caricatured African-American character he had developed in the *World*, he never used the name Bully, which had appeared in the titles of cartoons done for the *Journal's* competitor.

Outcault launched the series on a Friday, with the opening cartoon showing the excited volunteers parading down a city street. In

"They Are Fired by Patriotism, and Start Off to Exterminate Spain or Anything Else" (April 8, 1898), Outcault returned to the format of the Yellow Kid cartoons, filling the panel with lettered banners and a four-sided placard. Dressed as a drum major and wearing his lucky horseshoe, the New Bully leads his raw recruits. The drummer boy swats a nosy policeman, raising stars that combine with throbbing pain lines to form a small U.S. flag. Opposite, the real Stars and Stripes flies over the boys who have armed themselves with agricultural implements, including pitchforks, a rake, and axes—the weapons of an adult mob rather than the toys of children playing at war.

On the following Monday, the series continued with "Their First Night in Bivouac is Here Depicted" (April 11, 1898). The volunteers have moved their training to the countryside and a sign on the largest of their canvas quarters proclaims, "Our war spirit is in tents." A complacent cow munches on a clump of "Huckleberry Ambushes" behind which are "The Sen-Trees." Despite the puns, the cartoon is muted and sad, an unusual mood piece comparable to "The Yellow Kid's Soliloquy" (May 2, 1897) from *Around the World with the Yellow Kid*. One kid writes a letter home, "Dear Mother, I am awful home sick." A weeping child leans on a tent, comforted by another who says, "Cheer up Jimmy, we'll have fun at the battle." The army atmosphere is completed by a group of neighborhood girls who have become camp followers, standing under a sign announcing, "We are the jolly little 'Vivandières.'" A somnolent moon wearing a Civil War soldier's cap overlooks the campfire-lit scene, while a spontaneous "Huckleberry Quartette" sings "Just Before the Battle Mother."

Skipping Tuesday, the next cartoon appeared Wednesday, April 13, the first of an unbroken run of nine sequential daily comic-strip panels that continued through April 22. The series presented *Evening Journal* readers with a graphic phenomenon then completely new to newspaper or magazine pages: a continuous pictorial narrative featuring the same imaginary characters day after day for more than a week, each episode forming a self-explanatory segment, with all the cartoons relying entirely on text and dialogue contained within the panel margins. Outcault had already created the first definitive comic strips ever published. His only real concern in drawing this series of cartoons about the impending war was to publish as many episodes starring his slum kids as soldiers before the actual fighting commenced, but with them he again made comic history. Outcault drew the first daily, narrative, sequentially linked comic strip in history.

The series began on Wednesday with "They Have Their First Battle, and It Proves a Bullrun" (April 13, 1898). Still in the countryside, the Volunteers are attacked by bees swarming from three hives. A farm

boy with a cowlick laughs at the urban kids' plight: "Gee, dose bees has got sharp little bayonets." The New Bully is sure that nothing less than a mine has exploded in his rear, while a camp follower wails, "I've got a bee in my bonnet."

The kids are still down on the farm in "Goaded by Defeat, They Attack Fort Hennery and are Triumphant" (Thursday, April 14, 1898). The Wednesday and Thursday panels are also linked by their titles, the former referring to the famous Civil War battle and the latter to the British bombardment of Fort McHenry in the War of 1812. The fort is literally a hennery, and Outcault unleashes a barrage of fowl puns. One rooster calls for "a case of Old Crow" while another, beak to nose with a Volunteer, announces, "I haven't any white feather." The Huckleberry Quartette sings a chorus of something called "Far, Far Away in Ole Madrid, On the Banks of the Wabash."

Their training complete, the volunteers are back in the city in "They Man Their War Balloons, and Are Off for Cuba" (Friday, April 15, 1898). The Huckleberry Quartette sings "Up in a balloon, boys," as they load their military supplies and provisions, including a horse-drawn cab full of cannon balls labeled "high balls," a punning reference to the balloon-basket cannon from which they will be fired. A sign behind the horse reads "Remember the Mane," a visual and verbal pun, while the boxed supplies include such vital items as poker chips and cards with which the volunteers "kin beat 'em." In an apparent reference to the debate in Congress that followed McKinley's transmittal of his war message on April 11, 1898, a scrawled slogan at left reads "We Will Be on a De Fence." The puns may refer to the fact that the president's call for military intervention did not include immediate recognition of Cuban

72. RICHARD F. OUTCAULT.
The Huckleberry Volunteers
(*New York Evening Journal*,
Friday, April 15, 1898).

73. RICHARD F. OUTCAULT.
The Huckleberry Volunteers
(*New York Evening Journal*,
Saturday, April 16, 1898).

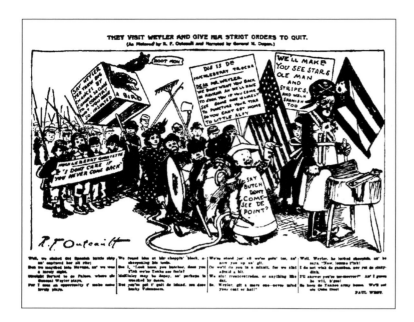

74. RICHARD F. OUTCAULT.
The Huckleberry Volunteers
(*New York Evening Journal*,
Monday, April 18, 1898).

75. RICHARD F. OUTCAULT.
The Huckleberry Volunteers
(*New York Evening Journal*,
Tuesday, April 19, 1898).

independence from Spain. The inevitability of congressional action is recognized in a banner reading, "Now dat war has really came, we are going to see its a finish fite." The New Bully stands proudly before his troops in epaulets and campaign cap, telescope at the ready, as the volunteers fly the flag, sound a bugle, and wallop a drum. Appearing amid these references to real events, Outcault's readers must have wondered at the meaning of the cryptic and anticipatory message on the balloon at right: "If we cant lick Spain we'll hunt for the Yellow Kid."

Outcault revealed his grand surprise in "Old Acquaintance Meets Them in Cuba and Assumes Charge" (Saturday, April 16, 1898), in which the Huckleberry Volunteers discover that the commander in chief awaiting them in Cuba is none other than the Yellow Kid. Cool and smiling in the midst of a ferocious battle, he carries a folding Spanish fan and wears a sword and sash, his nightshirt chortling, "Gee dat will puncture dere tire all right." The troops appear to have taken possession of a fort overlooking Havana's harbor, and are manning an immense assault cannon that blasts a ball towards the Spanish fleet. Return fire is knocking the stars out of the Volunteers' flag while a shell has punched a hole in the Yellow Kid's folded paper hat. Kids tumble and fly about, their somersaults and exaggerated expressions resembling those of children playing soldier. A letter on an empty box of "sinkers" or doughnuts reads, "Deer Mother tings is warm." General M. Dugan, as he is identified below the title, will lead his troops to a resounding victory.

No Spanish official was so vilified in the New York press as Captain-General Valeriano Weyler, who had been posted to Cuba in February 1896 to command military forces fighting the rebellion. He was promptly dubbed "Butcher Weyler" by the *Journal*, and was soon charged with a variety of atrocities against civilians and prisoners of war, "the most cruel and bloodthirsty general in the world." Diplomatic pressure from the McKinley administration forced his return to Spain at the end of 1897, but by then he was too convenient and recognizable a target to be abandoned by cartoonists. In "They Visit Weyler and Give Him Strict Orders To Quit" (Monday, April 18, 1898), the Yellow Kid and his Volunteers, suffused with confidence, have cornered an annoyed General Weyler, depicted as both a pirate and a butcher standing before a chopping block. The Yellow Kid carries a fire hose, ready to give the General the soaking promised in a placard, while the Quartette sings an appropriate ballad, perhaps to the tune of "Take Me Out to the Ball Game."

In "Terrible Consternation in the Spanish Camp" (Tuesday, April 19, 1898), the Yellow Kid impersonates Brigadier General Fitzhugh Lee, the United States Consul General in Havana. Appointed by Grover Cleveland, the colorful Confederate veteran openly advocated Cuban independence. The Yellow Kid's suitcase refers to his propensity for white dress suits as well as his tireless efforts on behalf of anyone in Cuba who could claim U.S. citizenship, culminating in his supervision of the civilian evacuation just before the war. Lee and his staff left Cuba on April 10 aboard the steamship *Fern*, which also carried the last New York journalists to depart before the war began. His intense, walrus-mustached face is aptly caricatured by Outcault in the Yellow Kid's mask.

"They Make a Cavalry Charge on the Enemy" (Wednesday, April 20, 1898) is Outcault's satirical homage to the illustrations of the war's most famous artist, Frederic Remington, who had accompanied the dashing novelist Richard Harding Davis to Cuba in 1897 to cover the rebellion for the *Journal*. The control exercised by Spanish authorities over U.S. journalists meant that most of his drawings were based on reports received from rebel sources or other journalists. Remington, who

76. RICHARD F. OUTCAULT.
The Huckleberry Volunteers
(*New York Evening Journal*,
Wednesday, April 20, 1898).

was heartily in favor of war with Cuba, illustrated a book by Evangelina Cosio y Cisneros on her imprisonment and escape. At the time this cartoon was drawn, Remington was aboard the battleship *Iowa* waiting to go to Cuba as a free-lance artist-correspondent. Outcault captures the spirit of Remington's equestrian drawings while gently mocking them by placing a tag reading "By Frederick Remington" on the jointed wooden leg of a carousel horse.

The joint resolution of Congress that issued an ultimatum to Spain was passed on April 19, and signed by President

77. RICHARD F. OUTCAULT.
The Huckleberry Volunteers
(*New York Evening Journal*,
Thursday, April 21, 1898).

78. RICHARD F. OUTCAULT.
The Huckleberry Volunteers
(*New York Evening Journal*,
Friday, April 22, 1898).

McKinley on April 20, 1898. The *Evening Journal*'s huge headline read, "Now To Avenge the Maine." In "They Deliver An 'Ultimato' to Alfy, and Await His Answer" (Thursday, April 21, 1898), the Yellow Kid and his gang stand face to face with the juvenile heir to the Spanish throne, Alfonso XIII, who cries on a drumhead. Juvenilized representatives of the major European nations watch safely from behind a fence, representing their refusal to come to Spain's aid at this crucial hour. Below them, a mocking poster reminds Spain that the European imperial powers forced Greece to accept a disadvantageous armistice in the Greco-Turkish War. Another poster comments on the national preoccupation with the World Series. The Yellow Kid points to the "ultimato" laid at the Spanish king's feet, which reads, "Git out or git yer cans," a variation on the more familiar Irish-American challenge, "Git out or get yer bricks."

On April 22, President McKinley blockaded Cuba. In "They Begin to Think That War Has Its Pleasures, After All" (Friday, April 22, 1898), the Huckleberry Volunteers celebrate victory in their own brief but splendid little war. The Kids gather for a celebration outside the Hotel Cuba Libre, where the drinks are literally on the house and Cuban girls rush to embrace their liberators. "No wonder Cuba ought to be free," the tickled Yellow Kid comments. West's verses suggest that the Volunteers are simply pausing to enjoy the delights of fair Cuba, but there is no suggestion of this in Outcault's panel. It was drawn as the triumphant end of the series, predicting a glorious victory for the United States in the war that was about to begin.

It can never be known exactly what the *Evening Journal*'s readers made of this sudden burst of cartoon narrative at a time when no one knew what a comic strip was or could be. For most, it was probably little more than a wonderfully frequent series of Yellow Kid cartoons, coinciding with the general excitement over the impending war. As pub-

lisher, Hearst probably saw *The Huckleberry Volunteers* as a rousing cartoon series supporting his newspaper's editorial stance. Outcault's atti-
tude was more ambivalent. Despite the puns and antics, several panels
capture the grim and deadly side of war.

As the cartoonist who had scored the greatest popular success
of his day, Outcault found a continuing demand for his work. Although
the Yellow Kid was no longer a viable cartoon property, the artist was
able to work as editor of the *Evening Journal*'s comic page and was free
to develop his comic art in the *World*'s Sunday supplement. In 1899, he
began to create cartoons for other papers entering the color comic-sec-
tion competition, notably the *New York Herald.* There he entered the
new century, drawing Sunday features such as *Pore Li'l Mose,* which did
not catch on, and *Buster Brown,* which became every bit as successful
as the Yellow Kid and was ultimately far more financially rewarding.
Buster Brown's popularity led Hearst once again to hire Outcault away
from a rival paper, keeping him on royal salary until his retirement in the
early 1920s.

In his Sunday *World* series, Outcault included a last Yellow Kid
color panel, the "Casey Corner Kids' Dime Museum" (May 1, 1898).
Four days later the artist provided his hero with a final saucy—and
jingoistic—bow on his *Evening Journal* comics page. In a single-column
box cut from May 4, the Kid does a solo turn, his nightshirt gleefully
echoing the news of Spanish collapse on every front, "Say we can
all have kassels in Spain soon." Then he was gone, with the war that
finished him.

79. RICHARD F. OUTCAULT.
Yellow Kid cartoon from the
New York Evening Journal
(May 4, 1898).

80. ANONYMOUS.
Photograph of child
with Yellow Kid doll
(Late nineteenth–early
twentieth centuries).

Fifteen

The Yellow Kid as Curio:
Images and Hustles (1898–1910)

Separated from the gaudy populace of his alleys and flats or framed out
of his multipanel gag routines, the Yellow Kid could be as lifeless as
Berke Breathed's Bill the Cat. No matter. Long after the end of features
in the warring New York papers that had made him the first universally
recognizable comic character, the Yellow Kid's image remained valuable
to his creator for advertising and occasional comic-strip use. Outcault
pressed the Kid into repeated afterlife appearances in a wide variety of
commercial contexts, and sometimes revived him for *Buster Brown*
comic strips, books, and other products. These myriad turns in alien

contexts must sometimes have baffled viewers, particularly those in their tender years during the new century's first two decades. The odd intruder into the familiar world of *Buster Brown* must have perplexed those who were unfamiliar with his once-famous nightshirt, winning smile, and head innocent of so much as a single hair.

The use of the Yellow Kid's image to sell a wide variety of products had begun when the strip was at the height of its popularity. The Yellow Kid was licensed for a great variety of merchandise and was perhaps equally frequently pirated, leading Outcault to seek copyright protection in September 1896. Sometimes Outcault himself provided the art or designs for the merchandise. When he did so, the art was often up to the standards of his newspaper work, as was apparently the case with a series of colorful gum cards released by the Adams Company in 1897.

Perhaps his best work outside the comic supplements was a series of cover paintings for *The Yellow Kid,* an odd, five-cent, monthly humor and cartoon periodical. Outcault's cover paintings appeared on the first six issues; their back covers featured drawings of the Yellow Kid endorsing the *New York Journal's* comic supplement. Eleven Outcault paintings of the Yellow Kid, apparently intended for *The Yellow Kid,* are in the collection of the Bird Library, Syracuse University. This group of paintings includes the cover of the first issue, but the remaining ten never appeared. The first issue was dated March 20, 1897, and the magazine continued to be published through January 1898, changing its title to *The Yellow Book* with Volume 1, Number 9. It was not a collection of *Yellow Kid* cartoons; in fact, apart from the eye-catching covers, there was no Outcault work to be found in the miscellaneous assortment of bad jokes and worse cartoons.

The only publication that was closely related to the Sunday comic supplement Yellow Kid was a paperback book, *The Yellow Kid in McFadden's Flats.* Credited to "E. W. Townsend author of 'Chimmie Fadden' and R. F. Outcault creator of 'The Yellow Kid,'" the book was printed on stiff paper stock, contained 192 profusely illustrated black and white pages, and retailed for fifty cents. To the extent that a "comic book" (as the term is used today) can consist of reprinted newspaper comic strips in paperback, without reference to format, this 5$^{1}/_{4}$-by-7$^{1}/_{2}$-inch volume would appear to be the first ever published. It incorporated

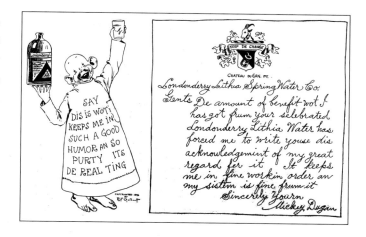

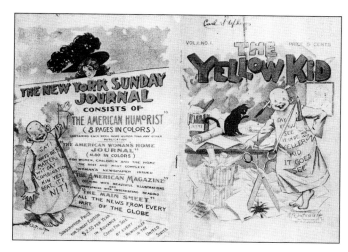

81. Richard F. Outcault? Advertisement from the *New York Journal* (December 13, 1896).

82. Richard F. Outcault. Cover from *The Yellow Kid* magazine (Vol. 1, No. 1, March 20, 1897).

"This is the story of my sweet young life."

83. RICHARD F. OUTCAULT.
Illustration from *The Yellow
Kid in McFadden's Flats*
(New York: G. W.
Dillingham, Co., 1897).

84. Richard F. Outcault.
frontispiece to *The Yellow
Kid in McFadden's Flats*,
New York: G. W.
Dillingham Co., 1897).

some definitive comic-strip half-pages drawn by Outcault for the *American Humorist* as well as reprints or redrawings of Yellow Kid Sunday panels. The book's cover and frontispiece are the only new work Outcault created for the book. Issued in March 1897 as book number 24 in Dillingham's American Authors Library (a series that added new titles monthly and could be subscribed to at four dollars per year), the covers of all six known copies claim that they are in the "thirtieth thousand" of the print run. This appears to be publisher's hype, although it may refer to the cumulative sales of all titles in the Dillingham series.

The book's indicia includes a note on the source of the drawings: "Many of the illustrations in this book were originally published in the *New York Journal*. They are reproduced here by permission of W. R. Hearst, editor and proprietor of the *Journal*, to whom acknowledgment therefore is hereby made. E. W. T. R. F. O." Although Townsend himself apparently wrote the book, which includes a foreword and stories to accompany the twelve Outcault cartoons in the volume, he claimed no copyright and the copyright notice which does appear seems to refer only to the artist's copyright on his character: "Yellow Kid, copyrighted 1896, by R. F. Outcault." The weakly linked anecdotal text purports to be "the autobiography of Master Mickey Dugan, better known as the Yellow Kid." The "autobiographical" text is written in straightforward prose rather than the Bowery dialect of Townsend's stories for the Yellow Kid panels in the comic supplement and his own *Chimmie Fadden*. Explaining this, Townsend wrote, "The reader may be surprised to find in the manuscript a general absence of those evidences of a free and independent system of grammar and spelling which mark the Kid's own, and unaided, literary productions." Indeed, it has been put into proper English by "the Kid's Boswell . . . an erudite young person of the name of McSwatt."

In the *Journal*, Outcault probably had to accept the assignment by his editors of Townsend to write dialect texts to go with his cartoons, but he may have been unhappy with the results. In this project, where he would have had greater creative control, he may have asked that Townsend write in standard English. Eleven chapters are listed in the table of contents, based on Yellow Kid panel narratives first printed in the *Humorist,* but the titles are simplified into flat and obvious phrases such as "Football, Parrot, and Monkey" or "A Curious Camera Tale."

Unfortunately, Townsend's prose is no improvement on his meandering narratives in the *Humorist*. The panels from the *Humorist* appear much as they did originally. Unfortunately, most were redrawn, faithfully if somewhat crudely, by a hand other than Outcault's (probably because the original art had already been destroyed). Engraving plates from the printed episodes would have necessitated eliminating the color, too costly a process for a one-shot title in a series. The reprinted half-page episodes include, in the order in which they appear in the book, "The Yellow Kid Wrestles With the Tobacco Habit" (December 27, 1896); "The Season Opens With the Horse Show in McFadden's Row of Flats" (November 8, 1896) and "A Few Things the Versatile Yellow Kid Might Do For a Living" (November 22, 1896); "The Yellow Kid Indulges in a Cockfight—A Waterloo" (November 29, 1896); "A Three-Cornered Fight in McFadden's Flats" (December 6, 1896); "The Yellow Kid Goes Hunting Becomes a Dead Game Sport" (January 24, 1897); "The Opening Night in Kelly's Bowling Alley" and "The Yellow Kid's Great Fight" (December 20, 1896); "Dark Secret: or How the Yellow Kid Took a Picture" (December 13, 1896); "How the Yellow Kid Planted a Seed and the Results" (January 3, 1897); "The Studio Party in McFadden's Flats" (January 3, 1897); "The Yellow Kid Introduces a Monk, Who Enlivens the Pool Tournament in McFadden's Flats" (November 29, 1896); and "The Yellow Kid's New Phonograph Clock" (February 14, 1897). The original of the last episode, appearing in the comic supplement close to publication of the book, did not need to be redrawn. *The Yellow Kid in McFadden's Flats* is a rarity, but also a disappointment.

The popular Mickey Dugan must have seemed a natural character to adapt for a vaudeville stage populated by countless comedians performing Irish acts. Even before Outcault moved from the *World* to the *Journal,* the Yellow Kid and gang had appeared at the Weber and Fields Music Hall, with the actors dressed in costumes designed from Outcault's own drawings. This was the beginning of a long series of stage acts and musicals based on both Outcault's cartoons and later, the *Hogan's Alley* series developed by George Luks after Outcault's departure.

Songs about the Yellow Kid, Hogan's Alley, and McFadden's Flats were written and published, some taken from the vaudeville productions and others apparently produced simply to capitalize on the Kid's and the comic strip's popularity. Among the first pieces of sheet music to carry the Yellow Kid's image may be "The Dugan Kid who Lives in Hogan's Alley," with lyrics by William H. Friday and music by Homer Tourjee, published by the Homer Tourjee Music Company of New York. This jaunty Yellow Kid song, which appeared when the character was a hot *New York World* property, features an uncredited drawing of the Yellow Kid holding

85. RICHARD F. OUTCAULT. Illustration from *The Yellow Kid in McFadden's Flats* (New York: G. W. Dillingham, Co., 1897).

86. Sheet music with drawings after RICHARD F. OUTCAULT and GEORGE B. LUKS (Williamsport, Pennsylvania: Fisk, Achenbach & Co.).

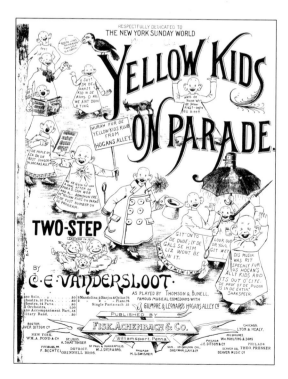

OUT OUR WAY—By WILLIAMS

SOME A YOU KIDS
IS WOIKIN YERSELFS
INTO A GOOD SWIFT
KICK IN DE BRITCHIS!
TROWIN STUFF AT
MY DOIBY!

OPERA
HOUSE
GALLERY ENTRANCE

TONIGHT
THE
YELLOW
KID

MOMENTS WE'D LIKE TO LIVE OVER — TEN CENTS,
A BAG OF PEANUTS, FIRST IN LINE AND ONLY AN HOUR TO WAIT.

87. J.R. Williams.
Out Our Way,
(November 18, 1925).

a cigar and gesturing in a manner that would have been quite familiar to readers of the Sunday page. Although the drawing is very different from those in *Hogan's Alley,* it could be by Outcault. It is nearly identical to a signed image that appeared on a poster for the *World's* comic supplement the week of August 16, 1896.

After Outcault took his character to the *Journal,* this song was reprinted as a feature in the comic supplement, appearing on the front and back of a half-page in the *American Humorist* for November 8, 1896. The music and lyrics were almost identical to those of the earlier sheet music, but the song was retitled, "The Yellow Kid, the Latest and the Greatest." While the Outcault sketches circling the music are lively and spirited, colorfully spilling over onto the lyrics, the song is contrived and commercial. One line, "You'll find his picture in the *World,*" was, of course, amended for the *Journal* reprint.

A bevy of Kids spill across the cover of "Yellow Kids on Parade," a two-step credited to C. E. Vandersloot. The chorus of this piece runs, unhappily, "For we're de yellow kids jest out on parade, and we are out o' site, Oh! all de purty gals are mashed on us and we're all rite, For we're all rite see!" Although the awkward and misproportioned Yellow Kids on the cover derive from Outcault's work, they cannot be from his hand; the song was published by permission of the *World* and must date from the period when the paper was printing Luks's *Hogan's Alley* in late 1896 or 1897. It was performed in a vaudeville show starring "Ireland's Comic Kings," Gilmore and Leonard, as Hogan and Brogan in a production of "Hogan's Alley." Based on Luks's *World* feature, it came complete with child actors playing Alex and George. At least a dozen pieces of Yellow Kid sheet music were published in the closing years of the nineteenth century, and vaudeville productions of *Hogan's Alley* continued to be performed into the early years of the twentieth century.

In addition to his vaudeville appearances, the Yellow Kid became a popular character in cartoons by other artists. His image appeared in a variety of cartoons attacking Pulitzer and Hearst for their newspapers' coverage of the events leading to the Spanish-American War. These sorts of cartoons continued to appear after cancellation of the *World* and *Journal* strips in 1897 and 1898.

Also appearing after the end of strip was a delightful Yellow Kid pastiche by cartoonist Rudolph Dirks, who created the *Katzenjammer Kids* comic strip for the *New York Journal.* Dirks drew what is essentially a full-page *Katzenjammer Kids* panel, published on the cover of the *American Humorist,* and bearing a title very much like those that had appeared on Outcault's strip: "Yellow Kid? Ach, No! It's Only the Katzenjammer Kid—(And His 'Brudder.')" (March 28, 1898).

This was Dirks's second drawing featuring the Kid's image; the first was "First the Anti-Cartoon Bill. Then Perhaps This!" (February 20, 1898). The *Humorist* cover celebrates a union of Irish and German immigrants in its comic features, with the Irish residents on the left bannering, "Germany Go Bragh!" while opposite German residents of the cartoon neighborhood have posted the sign, "Hoch Erin!" Mama and Papa Katzenjammer watch the festivities from the windows at right, one of the few appearances of the Katzenjammer Kids' dad; the good Mrs. Katzenjammer had already become the major adult character in the feature by this time. Despite the apparent point of this merrymaking cover, there would be no important Irish continuity character in the comic section until Fred Opper's Happy Hooligan appeared two years later in 1900.

Most New York readers would have known that Outcault was drawing Sunday cartoons for the *World*. Whatever brought about the publication of this oddly timed drawing, the comic device of Fritz made-up as the Yellow Kid and Hans dolled up as Liz is amusing, as are Dirks's two drawings of the Kid in a little narrative to either side of the *Humorist* logo. On the left, the mortified Yellow Kid has been stripped of his night-shirt and is cowering in a barrel while a tickled Fritz ignores the Kid's threat, "Oh, I'll kill dat Katzenjammer Kid." On the right, Hans pursues and pelts the Yellow Kid, dressed in another shirt on which he cries, "Dey're after me." This is the sort of in-house kidding that would have been drawn by Dirks to elicit a graphic riposte by Outcault rather than something Dirks would have whipped up when Outcault could not respond, suggesting that the cartoon was printed two to three months after it was drawn.

After experimenting with several characters that achieved only moderate success, in 1902 Outcault created the *Buster Brown* comic strip. He continued to draw this hugely popular feature for the rest of his career. The occasional appearances of the Yellow Kid in *Buster Brown* Sunday pages between 1907 and 1910 seem to have been intended to maintain the character and ensure that he remained a recognizable figure for use in advertising. Outcault's studio produced images of the Yellow Kid that were circulated throughout the country; these consisted of both customized advertising layouts and illustrations in the form of printer's blocks that could be converted into advertisements for local businesses by adding lines of type. The Yellow Kid was drawn by Outcault or by studio artists in a wide variety of poses and sizes to sell everything from gardening supplies to kitchen utensils and stoves to sporting goods.

88. RICHARD F. OUTCAULT studio.
Advertisement for the
Magill Hardware Company
(undated).

89. RICHARD F. OUTCAULT studio.
Advertisement from the
San Francisco Examiner
(June 26, 1910).

By 1907, when Outcault had the Yellow Kid and his new boy hero meet in the *Buster Brown* page for July 7, the brilliant work of Fred Opper in his own *Happy Hooligan* had already established the comic-strip structure created by Outcault in 1896 as the nationally preferred format for color supplement art. *Happy Hooligan,* which debuted in 1900, was the first sustained Sunday comic strip. With its success, the public came to relish recurring characters in multipanel, dialogue-balloon narratives every week. It would be some time before another Outcault innovation—six-day-a-week black and white comic strips, either single- or multipaneled—would become a standard feature in the nation's newspapers.

Buster Brown first appeared in the Sunday pages of the *New York Herald,* but by 1907, Outcault and his popular new character had moved to the color comics section of the *New York American* (as Hearst had renamed his morning paper just after the turn of the century). Outcault's Buster Brown was the scrappy, trick-playing, twelve-year-old scion of a well-to-do family residing in Manhattan's Murray Hill. His new child hero was surrounded by maids and manservants, and dressed to the nines in the best little-boy finery of the time. Always shadowed by his bulldog Tige, whose frequent Cheshire cat grins and winks to the reader made him as popular as Buster, the boy's only regular kid companion was his steady girl, Mary Jane. Outcault's crowded street scenes, which had been ideal for the grand scale of the old *World* and *Journal* full-page panels, were replaced in the panel narrative by one or two characters at a time.

In early Sunday comic strips, each weekly page carried its own title which would usually, but not necessarily, mention the lead characters. The Sunday pages were considered comparable to short stories, with such titles as "Hooray! Happy Hooligan's Luck Has Turned!" or "Fritz Gets a Camera! Hans Gets Jealous! Der Cap Gets Excited!" The weekly titles also served as a convenient means of registering copyright (titles alone were sent to Washington). Later, when syndication became common, the strips were assigned the running titles we are familiar with today, and copies of the art were filed for copyright each week.

In the case of Outcault's *Buster Brown* comic strips for the *New York American*, the copyright titles must have looked rather odd to the Library of Congress staff. The *Herald* retained ownership of the name Buster Brown, while the artist kept the right to continue drawing the character. Thus, Outcault's weekly titles would read, for example, "Mary Jane and Tige Run a Gay Race with," the last word replaced with a cut of Buster's bust. The art, of course, did not accompany the title to the copyright office and the lacunae remained unexplained.

There were four Yellow Kid visits to *Buster Brown* where the character served as an active participant in the strip's narrative and a foil for jokes involving Buster Brown, his bulldog Tige, and girl friend Mary Jane. These were "The Yellow Kid, He Meets Tige and Mary Jane and" (July 7, 1907); "Strange Things Do Happen To" (November 3, 1907); "So This Then Is the Yellow Kid's Cousin" (March 27, 1910); and "When Shall We Four Meet Again?" (April 3, 1910). The Yellow Kid also looked in on the strip a couple of times from the title panels at the top of the Sunday page, in spot gags that bore no relationship to the comic strip below.

"The Yellow Kid, He Meets Tige and Mary Jane and" (July 7, 1907) is virtually a scenic tour of the Kid's old neighborhoods. First Buster, Tige, and Mary Jane find themselves in Hogan's Alley, where an odd blank space on the brick wall suggests that a poster has been excised by the editor. The three meet Mickey Dugan in McFadden's Flats, where the Kid proceeds to use balloon dialogue extensively in the now standard comic-strip manner, his nightshirt comment limited to "Hully Gee." "There's another fellow," he says to the reader while pointing to Buster, "who is being imitated like I was." (The *Tribune*, like the *World* of old, had of course defiantly continued Outcault's character in a Sunday page by another, vastly inferior hand.) The Kid introduces the Murray Hill bunch to Liz, who gives Buster a smooch much to Mary Jane's dismay and Tige's delight. The strip includes a last look at Slippy Dempsey, introduced as he tumbles off a far roof, and the Yellow Kid's old buddy the parrot, who says, "Hello Tige," from the shoulder of a "Mrs. Moiphy," who was not prominent in the old feature. Finally, resurrected for what turns out to be Buster's dream, the Kid's long-perished goat enters the scene, kicks Tige, and knocks Buster out of bed for a finish that recalls Winsor McCay's *Little Nemo in Slumberland*. In the last panel, Buster pens a snidely moralistic "resolution" of the sort that had been closing the strip for years, with no hint of further visits by the Yellow Kid.

A few months later, however, Mickey and his deceased goat turn up again in "Strange Things Do Happen To" (November 3, 1907). When Buster Brown meets the Yellow Kid, he says, "I must be dreaming again." Buster is accompanied by a bear cub he bought for twenty dollars, and the strip quickly devolves into a farrago of panic-stricken maids, pursuing bears, jockey-ridden goats, and collapsing ladies. At the end, Buster is left asleep in the aftermath of chaos, his weekly resolution dutifully inscribed.

It was to be over two years before Outcault would again sense a need to refresh the public's memory of the Yellow Kid. In "So This Then Is the Yellow Kid's Cousin" (March 27, 1910), Mickey Dugan drops in at the Brown residence with a young cousin in tow. In this and the next, last *Buster Brown* appearance, the Yellow Kid's nightshirt is a bit more eloquent than in the first two Sunday pages, where it was limited to

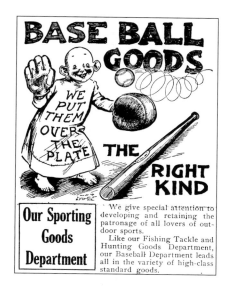

90. RICHARD F. OUTCAULT studio. Advertisement from the *San Francisco Examiner* (April 17, 1910).

91. RICHARD F. OUTCAULT studio. Advertisement from the *San Francisco Examiner* (March 20, 1910).

The Fly Was a Bee!

Just One Thing After Another

92. RICHARD F. OUTCAULT.
Detail from *Buster Brown*
(October 10, 1915).

93. RICHARD F. OUTCAULT.
Detail from *Buster Brown*
(December 13, 1914).

saying, "Hully Gee!" Here it reads, "I'm good because it pays," while in the final strip it merrily pipes, "Cheer Up!" In all four of the Sunday pages, the nightshirt text stays the same throughout the panels—a far cry from the expressive linen of the fin de siècle drawings. The joke in the "Cousin" is as flat as the busted drum that wraps up the game. Only the double entries on the resolution board, with philosophizing by Buster Brown and the Yellow Kid, provoke a real smile.

The final appearance occurred under the oddly cryptic episode title, "When Shall We Four Meet Again?" (April 3, 1910). This is the best and liveliest of the four *Buster Brown* strips featuring the Yellow Kid. The gimmick of Buster and the Kid swapping duds provides substantially more fun than the previous teamings, though the treacly resolution in the final panel undercuts the humor. This time around, Outcault has given the Yellow Kid's cousin a name—Spooks. (Floyd Gottfredson bestowed the same name more memorably on a comic gorilla featured in the *Mickey Mouse* Sunday adventures of the 1930s.) Perhaps Outcault anticipated future encounters between Buster, Tige, the Kid, and his newly named character. As it turned out, the title was singularly appropriate for the Yellow Kid's final appearance in a comic strip drawn by his creator.

With regard to Outcault's own ideas about the Yellow Kid, we are left with only the most minimal evidence. After Outcault returned to the *New York World,* he and Edward Townsend were apparently invited to contribute brief articles to the Sunday *World's* magazine supplement on how they came to create their most famous characters. Outcault's con-

134

tribution seems to have been written at an earlier date, perhaps at the request of another newspaper or magazine. Although the article was published on May 1, 1898, there is no hint in Outcault's reminiscence that the Yellow Kid had not appeared in any newspaper for months; indeed it concludes with a promise to keep drawing the Kid as long as the public wants him.

The artist's history of the Yellow Kid is brief and imprecise. He says he first drew the Yellow Kid in 1892, but does not mention *Truth* or indicate that the first cartoons featuring the character appeared in a cartoon magazine rather than a newspaper. Oddly, the Yellow Kid's name is spelled "Micky Dugan" throughout the article, a spelling that never appeared in the Sunday panels. Outcault's contribution included a frieze of Yellow Kids under the title, "The Bud and Blossom of the Yellow Kid—His First and Latest Appearance." Its outline of the development of the character closely follows the artist's discussion in the text, indicating that the drawing was designed specifically to accompany the article.

In a brief interview with La Touche Hancock, a writer for *The Bookman*, published in 1902 as part of an article on American cartoonists, Outcault discussed his working methods and characters. Outcault contributed two illustrations to the article: one of Buster Brown and the Yellow Kid, the other showing Outcault at the drawing board with the Yellow Kid and Poor Li'l Mose looking over his shoulder. The absence of Buster Brown in the latter drawing may indicate that it was executed before he created the character. The interview includes Outcault's only statement on the kind of personality he attempted to create for the Yellow Kid.

> The Yellow Kid was not an individual but a type. When I used to go about the slums on newspaper assignments I would encounter him often, wandering out of doorways or sitting down on dirty doorsteps. I always loved the Kid. He had a sweet character and a sunny disposition, and was generous to a fault. Malice, envy or selfishness were not traits of his, and he never lost his temper.

Despite the Yellow Kid's importance in the development of comic strips, few characters were patterned after him. Although characters from specific ethnic groups have been the subject of comic strips (for example, the Irish couple Maggie and Jiggs in George McManus's *Bringing Up Father*), the lives of the poor have not. Nor has the Kid's physical appearance served as a model. It has been suggested that the Asian comic character Connie, featured in Milton Caniff's *Terry and the Pirates*, resembles the Yellow Kid. Caniff has stated that he did not use Outcault's creation as a model, although he acknowledged that it could

94. RICHARD F. OUTCAULT.
Self-portrait from
"The Evolution of the Comic
Picture and the Comic Artist"
(*San Francisco Call*
November 12, 1905).

95. RICHARD F. OUTCAULT.
Self-portrait.
(*The Bookman* 1902–03).

ME WORRY?

96. ANONYMOUS.
Postcard showing bust of a boy
(early twentieth century).

97. RICHARD F. OUTCAULT.
"Outcault's Two Most
Successful Creations,"
cartoon from *The Bookman*
(1902–03).

have exercised an unconscious influence. Nor does there appear to be any connection with the anonymously created, grinning face of the boy who became associated with the slogan "Me Worry?" in the early years of this century. This figure, which appeared in a variety of popular media including post cards, calendars, signs, match books, and countless other products, was later the inspiration for *Mad Magazine*'s famed Alfred E. Neuman.

This book has touched briefly on certain connotations the color yellow had in the 1890s, primarily for those concerned with avant-garde developments in British and American art and literature. The decade itself was known to this group as the Yellow Nineties, an appellation reflecting the fame—or notoriety—of the influential publication, *The Yellow Book*, a literary quarterly clothbound in yellow that celebrated the outré writings and art of such figures as Oscar Wilde and Aubrey Beardsley. The term also has been related to such works as James McNeill Whistler's *Nocturne in Yellow,* Beardsley's *The Yellow Dwarf,* and Robert W. Chambers's stories collected in the volume, *The King in Yellow.*

Clearly, this poetic association of yellow with a cultural movement had little to do with the Yellow Kid or yellow journalism, although the movement's more scandalous aspects were reported with mixed condemnation and delight in the American press. One party might have felt that there was indeed a relationship, however, and—in collusion with a poet of the period named McSwatt—might have used his nightshirt to proclaim:

Yeller Book—nit! Why, hully gee,
Th' Yeller Nineties wuz named fer *me!*

"BUSTER BROWN."   "THE YELLOW KID."
Outcault's two most successful creations.

THE YELLOW KID DIARIES

NEW YORK JOURNAL, MONDAY, NOVEMBER 14, 1896.

THE YELLOW KID AT THE HORSE SHOW!

"I didn't do a t'ing to dat Hoss Show! 'James,' I sez to me man. 'James,' sez I, 'pack up me duds an' we'll take in de Hoss Show.'

"James wuz fresh from me country place up d' river, where he'd been sojournin' a mont' on account of a gold watch, an' he wasn't stuck on goin' to de Hoss Show, 'cause he t'ought he'd run across d' guy wot de watch belonged to.

"Wen I showed up me face in d' Garden d' goils had a fit. 'Ain't he d' little dear!' dey said. 'Ain't he cunnin'!' So I puts on me sassiety face an' sez: 'Goils, treat me gentle, 'cause me healt' is delik-it, an' don't get jealous, fer I loves ye all!'

"An wuzn't dey peaches an' cream! Mommer! Dere eyes wuz like a fist full o' search lights, an' I sez to meself: 'Mickey,' sez I, 'ye've struck it rich!' An' while I wuz wonderin' if I'd trot around wid a goil in a green blazer, wot wuz wantin' t' kiss me, or saddle up to a pearl wot had elegant colone all over her clo'se, a feller comes runnin' up an' sez, 'Mrs. Gould's compleminks,' sezzee, 'an' will ye come up to see 'er?'

"'Did I went? Well I guess! De goils looked as if dey wuz goin' t' cry, an' dey sez, 'Do not leave us, sweet child.' But I'm purty good on d' jolly meself. 'Goils,' I sez, 'Mrs. Gould is me fourt' cousin on me grandfahder's side, an' de ties of blood is strong.'

"'Did ye see me settin' in d' box wit' Mrs. Gould talkin' sassiety wid' er? Ye couldn't miss me. An' say, d' goil wid de colone smell all over 'er wuzn't in it fer a minnit wid me new fourt' cousin.

"'Edy,' I sez to 'er, ye're dressed out o' sight! I'd leave home fer dem clo'se."

"'You darlin' little kid.' she sez, kinder sweet.

"'Are ye stuck on yer fourt' cousin, Edy?' I asked. She didn't answer not'in', but I could see she wuz. So I sez, sez I:

"'I'm kinder stuck on meself.' Den she said I wuz too cute t' live! But dem goils wouldn't leave me alone. De foist t'ing I knew dey all carne trottin' over to our box and said dey wanted t' be interdooced to d' chahrming child in der yeller gahment— dat wuz me. A lady wid a joolery store on 'er hands come along, an' me fourt' cousin said it wuz Mrs. Belmont. She said she'd like t' kiss me, 'cause I wuz such a little dear; but I sez nit, 'cause all de odder goils 'd want it, and dere's only one goil in de woild fer me w'en it comes to a kissin' show-down.

"'Will ye come t' dinner wid us?' sez Mrs. Belmont.

"'Oh, he can't,' sez me fourt' cousin, 'cause he's goin' t' dinner wid me!'

(But I ain't dat's w'ere me fourt' cousin fooled herself.)

"'Den a guy wid a wall paper weskit comes along and dey sez he wuz Koi'nel Jay. 'Well,' sez I, 'cause I wuz tryin' t' be nice, 'you ain't de only one!' After dat a dood wid hoss pants on 'im comes trottin' up and I pins on me button wot sez, 'Does yer face hurt?' De goils t'ought I wuz too cunnin'. D' dood as't me how old I wuz.

"'I mean have ye got a hoss in d' show?' he sez.

"'Sure,' sez I, 'an' dere he is,' for me man wuz jest trottin' 'im into d' circus.

"'Is he a hackney?' me fourt' cousin sez.

"'No, Edy,' I sez, 'it's a trolley wictim.'

"'Poor t'ing! Wuz he run over by de trol-ley?'

"'No, Edy, dear. He wuz run out! De trolley druv 'im out o' bizness!'

"'De poor plug did 'is level best t' jump a fence like der odder nags, but 't got sort o' stuck on top, an' dey had t' get a derrick t' take 'im down. An' dere de judges sez dat seein' de perfawmince wuz kinder unusual dey'd give 'im a green ribbon. W'ich, bein' as it's me own color, tickled me right in de ribs.

"'As de goil wid de colone all over her clo'se wot's mashed on me is givin' me de wink I t'ink— well, say, I guess I wont write no more to-day.

NEW YORK JOURNAL, WEDNESDAY, DECEMBER 9, 1896.

HOW THE YELLOW KID SAW THE "WHEELS GO ROUND" AT MADISON SQUARE GARDEN YESTERDAY.

"Ah dere, Liz! Did'je see me at the bisikl show? We say hawses aint in it wid biskits is dey? I wuz so stuck on d' sho dat me hed's been trubbled wid bawl-bearings ever sints I cum home. Wen I t'ink dat I got t' rite me rekkulecktshuns uv de bisikl sho in yoo dere dey I feel week 'cause I haf rekkulecktshuns t' burn.

"I took one spiel 'round d' garden an say, Liz, hope t' die if I cudn't beet 'em all in a wawk. D' way I went kyutin' 'round dat garden made 'em all dizzy dat little boy is a preetch dey all sed an dat's troo. Dat feller Hale wuz leadin' d' band an say Liz dere aint no insecks on Hale he's a kaurker de way he shode 'em his heals wut luvly. I tink I'd rather be a champeen bisiklist dan a kop but I gess I'd rather be a bisikl kop say dey must be happy. o Liz I wud giv ten years uv me yung an imersent life t' be a bisikl kop.

"Wel as I wuz sayin' befaur I spoke dat feller Hale is a wunder. He wuz baurn on a bisikl Igess he rides so nat-cheral. Den dere wuz Peet Golden dey cant looz 'im 'cause 'e holds on like paurus plastir. Peet has got sand. He rides like if it wuz hard wok an I cud pass 'im hands down, say Liz I'm a luvly bisiklist I'm so graceful but I only cum one in a bocks an dey can't dooplikate me.

"Den kame Maijer Taylor wot's a negrow he's on dark but he's hot staff all de same. He's ridin' fer keeps but he aint gawn t' win witch is jest as wel 'cause if he wuz t' get d' prize a wite man's life wudn't be saif in Tomson street ware he lives. D' Maijer has sim-perthy an I hope sincerly he don't win.

"'D' fort' mug in d' persuasion is Wilson. D' trubble wid Wilson is dat he can't ride fast enuff he dus his best an I won't roast him. Only he'd make a fine messinjer boy he'd alwuz charj time. But dere are odders.

"'Dere wuz a dutchman in d' rase but he quit 'cause his feet wuz tired; wot he needs is a steem bisikl wot don't need no pushin'.

Say wouldn't it be fun if a feller wuz t' cum in d' rase wid a bisikl run by steem 'r lektrissity he wudn't do a ting t' dat gang, o mommer!

"'Den dere wuz a mug wot wuz ridin' round doin' stunts all d' time widout tutchin' d' handel bars. He wuz jest showin' off. Dat aint rite, 'cause me teetcher sez dat hoosover shos off is ded shoor t' get d' rinky-dink. Ye never seen me sho off did je Liz, I aint dat breed.

"'Well say on d' level wot's d' good o' ridin a bisikl ennyway dey make ye wurk so hard an dey can't beet de Empire Stait xpress at dat can dey? I tuk my bisikl to d' sho wid d' noomattick tire blone up out o' site, but dey wudn't let me in wid it, so I had t' leeve it me kab. But I only ride a bisikl 'cause it's de t'ing. W'en it's de t'ing t' do a t'ing I does it, but it's near dat fun gaw's t' de oprer.

"'Dere wuz lot's o' goils at d' show wid bloomers on, but all I got t' say on dat subjeck is dere Liz if I ever ketch you wid bloomers on it's awl over between us an... brake yer face. I ware bloomers but it's different 'cause w'en I gets me groth I'll never ware bloomers no never 'cause— well I won't say nothin' but it Liz me bleeds w'en I t'ink dat sum day you'll be warein' bloomers!

"'Dere wuz lot's o' spaurts at d' biskl sho an dey made me drink wid 'em till me hed felt like a bawl-bearin's as I... geired way up to a milyyon but all ... me hart is broke over dem bloomers...

As the document was damaged, the concluding sentences of this entry are missing.

NEW YORK JOURNAL, SATURDAY, DECEMBER 12, 1896.

THE YELLOW KID TAKES IN THE AQUARIUM.

"Friday—say, ye'd orter see de aquaryum it's full o'fishes. dere all alive an in d' swim only dey lay low on Fridays 'cause dey no w'en dere well awf Friday is de day w'en d' fishes gets d' rinky-dink. Dem fishes is grate swimmers only dey aint grate on d' flote.

"Dere wuz wun fish dat wuz gazin' at me troo d' glass like if he noo me hullo old spaurt, I sez, how's yer unkel, but I gess he didn't here me 'cause he didn't even wink say aint it funny d' way dem fishes dont blink. Dey'd make good kops.

"Dey had a fish dere wot dey called d' pike wot I'd orter no 'cause Liz tole me I wuz d' freshest dukk wot ever kame down d' pike but we wuz strangers all d' same witch shos dat Liz don't no evryt'ing. D' pike giv me d' isy stare like he wuz sayin' ware wuz you razed. He wuz fresh.

"Dere wuz wun tank wot wuz full o' skates. but it wuzn't a marker t' sum o' de ole tanks outside de aquaryum wot wuz lookin' fer skates which is a good joke wot I'll try t' sell t' de Joinal. Dey had cat-fishes dere an' dog-fishes an' t sed to d' mug wot's runnin' d' sho say mister ain't'che got any gote-fishes kum awf he sed. All d' same my gote woodn't do a t'ing t' dem glas tanks if he got a skware chants.

"O Liz ye'd orter seen d' see-liuns dey wuz grate w'en I t'ought uv all dem seel-skin saks lyin' around loos it made me mout' wauter. I had me i on wus dere Liz but I coodn't woik it d' kops wuz too fly. Wun o' de kops sez t' me say sunny, did'je see liuns but i gave bim de frozen fase an sez me gran'fadder wot fit wid Nappoleyun wuz ded stukk on dat gag.

Say Liz I'm orful glad I aint a fish jest t'ink dere in d' wauter all d' time no ware t' go but home. But I guess d' fishes is glad dey aint little kids wot gets klubbed if dey don't koam dere hare 'cause fishes aint get no hare dere bald like me.

Dey aint got leggs an dey can't ride bisikls witch aint no grate lauss, but dere orfully funny an dey don't say a woid.

Say Liz lookin' fer d' wales but d mug sed dey hadn't cum yet an if dem wales nose w'en dere wel awf dey'll kepe away f'um de aquaryum awl d' same I'd like t' see a wale dat feller Joner must 's had a grate graft sittin' in d' wale's bred-baskit an ridin' around widdout payin' fair. Dey had a shark dere but I ges he wuz only a kid 'cause he cudn't swaller a feller like d' shark in d' Golden Kross or d' Mistree uv d' Spannish Maee wot I wuz readin'. Say dat shark must a' been a kaurker, he swollered dat feller Captin Velasqueeze quikker'n greezed litenin' dat's a grate staury.

MICKEY AT A RECITAL.

Gee wiz! fellers, you'se jist ought-o-wos wit me las' night, fur me an' Kitty was too er-er— well it was at der Carnigie beer garden—Naw! I ain't got dat straight, I mean Music Hall; but if wot we heard were a sample of der noise dey makes up dere, dey got it named wrong, fer it sounds more like der Carnegie rollin' mill ter me.

Dis is how it were— dey was a note man gimme two tickets wot was good fer two seats down in front, so I says ter Kitty, er ye wit me? an she says yep!

So we gets er sack o' peanuts an' goes in early, an', gee! but dat's er lovely joint, dat is— dat's right—Aw say! velveteen seats an' carpet some hard fightin'—first dey 'ud close in, den break away, now he'd strike out wit his left hand, den wit his right. His left hand would chase his right hand all de way up, den jump over it an' chase it back. Hully gee! fellers, yer ought er saw de way dat cove could make a under cut. If some one had jist give him er beer mallet he'd a got der best er dat instrument before he did. I s'pose dey must er bin some prize ring rules, er somethink like dat, er he'd a jumped on der keys wit his feet and stomped out der whole band Wagoner operas at once. Well he stuck ter straight fightin' an' der audience commenced ter raisin' out o' der seats an sighin' ter

"TREE TER ONE ÒN DER WAITER."

on der floor— out o' sight. Dere was der funniest lookin' people comed in wot I ever seen. Everybody had on spectacles, some of 'em two pairs; all of 'em had long hair, an' dem people give der biggest sighs I ever see. But we was in it fer fair; I knowed dat de way every one looked at us.

But dey couldn't touch us, see? we jist went on eatin' peanuts— a-waitin' fer der show to git a gait on ter itself. Well, der curtain went up an out comes er mug dressed like er waiter wot ain't got on any apron, an' bows an' sits down ter a beat der bank, an say! it was excitin'. I seen Kitty was on der side of der pyanner, but I was wit der winner. All on er suddent, jist as he give er final swipe der lid went shut wit er bang, and der round was finished. By dat time me sportin' blood was up an I jumps on der seat an' hollers out tree ter one on der waiter, and Kitty leaves loose of er reg'lar Elizabeth street yell.

In a half minute er mug comes along and says say! youse jist cheese dat er git out; and everybody looked like dey t'ought we was a chuckle-head idiot.

"SINGIN' WOT WAS SINGIN'."

tree-cornered pyanner wit der lid open. Say! I'm givin' it ter yer straight, dat guy couldn't play fer sour apples—sure.

First his fingers jist done a dog trot all up an' down der ivories, den after doin' a few little plinkety plunkety plinks, he forgot hisself an' commenced ter play er nice little tune, wot sounded kind er nice as fur as it went. But, say! as soon as he found 'at he was playin' er tune, it seemed ter make him mad, an wit one swipe he hit dat pyanner like it were in self-defense—den dere follered

I was goin' ter take no slack like dat, so I says come on Kitty, dis show ain't no good no how, der pyanner ain't in it. Well, I wasn't goin' ter see Kitty left on der music business, so we jist took er cable car an went downtown an' took in er show on der Bowery, where we heard singin' wot was singin'. Aw, say! dem songs makes me cry. A bloke came out an' sung er touchin' little song called "When Mudder Comes Home from der Island," and Kitty an' me bote cried— sure we did.

MICKEY DER KID

A LEAFLET FROM THE YELLOW KID'S DIARY.

"Maybe dere's fun in de oprer, but say, it ain't a marker to de London. Did you see me at de oprer last night? Did I deadhead me way?Oh, no, I paid five hundred plunks fer me box.

"Liz sez if I don't let dem sassiety wimmen alone it's allup wid me an' her, an seein' as Liz comes only one in a case I guess I'll give de sassiety wimmen de dinky-dink. 'Cause I hadn't shown me face in de Oprer House w'en de ushers comes tumblin' over demselves wid invites frum all de boxes. 'Wud Master Mickey Dugan have de kindness t' waltz inter Box 24,' An' wud Master Mickey Dugan be so good as ter grace Box 18 wid his presents,' 'An wud Master Dugan kindly come here 'r go dere'— say, dey wuz crazy fer me.

"I seen me friend Mrs. Gould in one uv her boxes, but I went dere nit, 'cause I ain't lookin' fer trouble between me an' Liz. But some o' dem doods wot jus sittin' around Mrs. Astor comes fer me an drags me into a box. Den I seen de oprer, an' on me word I wuzn't stuck on it a little bit.

"De wimmen down stairs had dere hats off, as if dey wuz afraid de doods in de boxes wuz goin' t' t'row paper balls on dere heads. But de doods wuzn't out fer fun, 'cause dey wuz all dressed up.

"I had a bokay fer me friend Melba, an' when she comes out— say, I'm glad Liz wuzn't dere. I t'rew her a kiss an I seen by de expreshun uv her expreshun dat she wuz dyin' t' have me come down an' join in de song wid 'er, only I didn't know de wurds. Liz t'inks she kin sing, but— well, say, I ain't a-goin' t' make trouble.

"Den dere wuz me friend De Resky an' his brother Ed. Say, dey could give de Ate Ward Coterie Quartet cards an' spades an beat 'em hands down. W'en dey came out dey acted like dey wuz good friends, but before dey wuz t'rough dey got t' givin' each odder de dinky-dink. Johnny got de best of it, an' Eddy took a back seat an' shut up; but jest as Johnny wuz takin' t'ings easy, like he wuz a winner, Eddy comes trottin' out an begins t' yell 'im down all over agen. Say, I wuz jest goin' t' yell 'Go it, Eddy,' w'en me dood friend puts his hand over me face an' sez he wuz on t' me an' dat I better shut up.

"I'm goin' t' de oprer agen, I don't t'ink. I kin have more fun at de London fer half de price, an it didn't cost me a cent at dat!"

A LEAFLET FROM THE YELLOW KID'S DIARY.

"Sundy—Dere ain't nothin' wrote in me diry yesterday, 'cause I went t' de feetball game, and dere wont be much wrote to-day, 'cause I got a orful taste in me mout', an' dere's lot o' t'ings I can't tell 'cause I don't know, an' if I ever did get rid o' me killin' thirst I sign de pledge. Say, aint it orful w'en de flowin' bowl give ye de rinky-dink?

"An say, it's all up wid me an' Liz 'cause I didn't take her to d' feetball game, an she seen de luvver's-not ring wot de Printston goil wot got stuck on me— well, say, w'en I t'ink uv dat Printston goil I gess it must be a dreem, cause it wuz out o' sight, but she got stuck on me all rite, all rite.

" 'You swete, elegint little darling, aintche lovely?' she sed, an she tikkled me under de chin. "Oh, I don't know, Maud,' I sez, 'dere ain't no cobwebs on you, too.' De dood wot wuz wid her sed I cud sit on his lap, 'cause dere wuz no seats vaykint— I aint ded sure uv dat woid, but how can I wid de orful taste in me mout'? 'O, no,' sez I, 'I'll stan' by yer lady frend,' an' den she laffed like dat beautiful mewsic in Tony Pastor's, an sed I cud skweeze between 'em.

"Say, de feetball game wuzn't in it wid de Printston goil. 'D'ye luv me, Maud' I sez, an she laffed an sed I wuz too sweet an if I'd— well I guess I won't rite dat in me diry, 'cause ye can't tell wot Liz'll do if she gets her jellus up, but say, she gave me a luvver's-not ring wot I swore cross me hart an hope t' die I'd alwuz keep.

"W'en I asked her wot dem fellers wuz playin' feetball fer she laffed an sed de dood wot wuz wid 'er used t' be a quarterback wunst in '92, but say, he looks all rite, all rite, now. De feetball players looked as if dey'd jest got out o' bed an hadn't kombed dere hair. Say, wudn't de Southerland sisters make corkin' feetball players?

"It wuz funny de way de crowd yelled like dey wuz seein' a show, an w'en one o' de fellers wid de bangs wuz trun' down he got so scared he ran away an' de whole kaboodle chased 'im. If I'd been in de game I'd a chased 'im, too, an smashed 'im fer runnin' away. But de goils an de doods wuz sore on de scrappers, as dey all yelled w'en dey seen dat bloke wid de bangs wuz runnin' away. 'Rah fer Printston!' yells Maud. 'All rite Maud,' sez I, 'wot you do I do,' an I yells 'Rah fer Printston!' t' beat de band. W'en I gets tired o' yellin' I sez t' Maud: 'Now tell me dere wot wuz I yellin' fer, an she gave me de laff so I got sore an' quit.

"Den I went to de Tendelloin an' some mug I never seen befaw bauled me off an' yelled, 'Rah fer Printston!' an den anudder mug wot wuz luvvers wunst but strangers now to me bauled me off an' I yelled, 'Rah fer Yail!' an after dat a lot o' t'ings happind. W'en de clock struck twelve dere wuz a little kid wid a yeller dress wot wuz spielin' wid a soobret in Hammerstine's an' tellin' her dat he wud be troo till deth, an dat wuz me. W'en de clock struck two der wuz a little yeller kid stan'in' on a table in a restrunt yellin', 'Rah fer Printston!' an' a bum comes along an puts 'im out, an dat wuz me.

"W'en de clock struck t'ree dere wuz a little kid wid his dress lookin' like a flag dat was t'roo de war askin' a cop wot was d' quickist way to McFadden's flats. Dat wuz me, too.

"Say, dis sportin' life is tuf, an I gess I'll giv Liz de luvver's-not ring, 'cause Printston gals is too rich fer me blud, but I wish I cud shake dat orful taste in me mout'."

A Leaflet from the Yellow Kid's Diary.

"Mundy— Say don'tche go to der katl show 'cause it's a frawst an' dey ain't got nothin' but cows an shepe wot ye can see any day ye like fer nothin' over in Hobukken, my goat cud give 'em cards an' spades an' beat 'em all along de line.

I went to de katl show an' I ast a feller ware de lions wuz an de elefunts, an' he sez say, d'ye take me fer a farmer, dere wuzn't no fun dere at all. I seen two dandy roosters in a kage, but I cudn't get 'em t' skrap, I done me best, but say, dey gave me de isy glair like dey wuz sayin' little boy ye make us tired.

"Dere wuz an ole lady wid a farmer, an' she sez wot a cunnin' little luv; say, Jonny, if I give ye a penny, wot'll ye do wid it. I ain't a Jonny, I sez, but if ye give me a penny I'll get a siggeret; say I know ware ye can by 'em fer a cent, 'an ye don't have t' get a box.

"De lady sed I wuz a little lofer, but I sez kepe d' change, dat's all I did. To-day dere diry I joined a Sundy skool yesterday so's I kin come in fer a krismis present. I want a bisikle.

FROM THE YELLOW KID'S DIARY.

"Tuesday— It wuz rainin', an' de goat had a tin can in his bread-baskit wot didn't agree wid him, so I spent de day quit. I knowed it wuz goin' t' rain as soon as I got out o' bed, 'cause I did-n't have me reg'lar appytite. All I et fer breckfest wuz a cup o' koffy an a stake an pertaters, besides some donuts an two fried eggs an' some kandy wot Liz gave me, an' I guess me liver aint workin'. Say dat's a good riddle, why is me liver like Mr. Maloney 'cause it ain't workin' an I guess I'll give it t' de Journal, only Mr. Maloney can't work 'cause he's waitin' fer trial.

"I tried me new tiperiter, an' say! it's a peach. All ye got t' do is t' press a dinky button an' it comes out like a printin' press, only different, 'cause a print-in' press knows how t' spell an my tiperiter don't, which is strait goods. I tried t' rite a luv letter t' Liz wot her muther wouldn't get hold of, an de tiperiter t'run me down. I pushed d' buttons t' say dat I wuz goin' t' give dem luvly sassiety wimmen d' shake an be troo t' Liz, an de masheen wrut:

Oliz$ il(nevar dO (t agGen?

"Say, Liz wud a t'ought I wuz a bookeeper ef I'd a sent dat, so I gave de masheen t' d' goat to ete fer desert w'en e got feelin' better, an' den I tuk a strole up Fift' ave. Dere wuz a lot o' luvly sassiety wimmen in car-ridges wot wanted me t' get in wid dem an take a ride, but no, luvly critchers, I sez, I don't go back on Liz no more, 'cause me leg is sore yet where she run d' hat pin on account uv der Hoss show. One o' dem swell tailers came out an sez, let me make you a swell coat, sezzee, but say, w'en I gives up me little yaller dress it'll be a cold day on de fifty-nint' o' Decembur.

"W'en I got tired o' strollin' I tuk a car an', say, who should I meet but me old frend de Eyetalian prints wot's de nephu uv der king. Hello Mickey, he sez, Hello prints, how are dey runnin' I sez. I'm keepin' steady all along de line, sezzee, Will ye dine wid me to-night? No, sez I, havin' a date wid Liz, besides I aint goin to push spagetty into me face till I gets me growth. I'm too delikit to do dem stunts. Say, de prints is all rite, all rite, he ain't a dood, an' I'm goin' to send him an invite t' de ball.

"Dat reminds me dat I got t' dress fer de ball. So I wont rite in you no more dear diry, I'm goin to be flore mannagir to-night so wake me erly muther dear, fer to-night I walz at de Cherry Socials wid Liz.

A LEAFLET FROM THE YELLOW KID'S DIARY.

"Toisday— Did I eat toiky t'day, say I didn't do nuthin' else, an I got away wid enough kranbry sauss t' float a ship. I gess dey put nokkout drops in dat sauss, 'cause I feel queer in me bred-baskit.

Liz an' me is on de outs, but say, it wuzn't my fault, I didn't do nuthin'. I went to d' Warldawf an' Liz sez take me along, but I sez nit, jentil creetcher, dem sassi-ety goils wud be sore if dey seen your luvly fase an' sassiety goils is jest like odder goils w'en dey gets dere jealous up, so I goes by me lonesum.

De foist t'ought I had w'en I struk de hash room inside Warldawf wuz, jee wot a graft it'd be fer Terry McGorrigle's old man, wot's up de State fer cullectin' joolery. Dere wuz dimuns t' roast, say dey gave me sore eyes.

Dem goils wot I met at de patryarks' bawl wuz dere an' dey wuz makin' faces at me fer t' cum an eat wid 'em, but 'nay, nay Pauleen' I sez, 'dis is Tanksgivin's an I'll be too bizzy t' tawk w'ile I eat.' 'Will ye have oysters,' sez one o' dem doods wid a swaller-tail. 'No, t'anks, I'll have toiky,' I sez. 'Wot'll ye have afterwuds?' 'sum more toiky,' sez I.

Well, say, dat toiky wuz a boid fer fare, an' o, I cud die eatin' dat Warldawf kranbry sauss. Foist I et de w'ite meet, den et d' black meet. I put de bones in me pokkit fer d' goat—say, I gess I'll give de goat a tin kan wot had kranbry sauss inside it fer his Tanksgivin'.

Dere diry, I swallered dat toiky till I t'ought I'd bust an' me clo'es don't fit me rite t'night, but jee, w'en de dood in d' swallertail showed me d' bill, I t'ought I'd faint. 'Is dat all?' I sez, t' chuk a bluff. 'We,' sez de dood. 'Who? sez I, 'me an' you?' 'Come on,' sez he, so I sez 'all rite old spaurt, jest put me friend Astor's name on dat morgidge an' I'll settle wid him w'en I see him, witch'll be t'morrer w'en we goes drivin' t'gether. Ennyway,' I sez t' de dood, givin' him de isy glair, 'I'm t'inkin' o' takin' bored an lodgin' at de Warldawf,' an say, he didn't say a woid.

One o' dem luvly goils ast me t' brake a wishbone an' she sed dat my wish wud cum troo; den we busted de bone an' she got de rinky-dink. 'You lucky little boy,' she sed, 'wot did you wish?' 'I wisht I wuz a bisikl cop,' I sez, an' den de odder goils laffed. Say, ain't goils queer? I guess dey must all have bridge tikkits in dere heds.

P.S.— "De dorg sho is out o' site, but I wisht it wuzn't in Bruklin say ain't Bruklin a funny place all along de line? De Bruklin goils is peaches an dey all fell in luv wid me wen dey seen me in de dorg sho but it ain't dere fault is it Liz?"

Good nite, dere diry, I ain't feelin' wel at all, I gess I kaut kold.

MICKEY HOGAN

A LEAFLET FROM THE YELLOW KID'S DIARY.

Sunday— The sitchuation in Cuber is like dis—if Wiler sends me anudder box of box o' dem lalla perfecktoes he kin have de use o' me yot w'en 'e wants t' chase back t' Spane an' say I'll tell ye wot, if dey try t' give me de rinky dink I'll rite a tellygram t' me old side partner, Yoolaylee say you didn't know me an' Yooly wuz frends did je?

But 'che'd orter seen d' faces o' de doods w'en I hit de avenyoo wid one o' dem perfecktoes in me face. Me old collij chum Berry Wall cums up an sez Mickey

dat's grate graft ye're smokin', does dey cum holesail or retale. Nuy, Berry I sez dey's speshul fer me an' de Prints o' Wails don't che see me kote uv arms an I showed 'im ge gote wot Wiler put on de siggars.

Wel say I'm glad me frend de prints is gettin' de glad hand f'um dere Consy wot I wuz wunts stukk on meself, but she kan't play in my yard no maur 'cause me unkel sez de Brittish is downtroddin' de Irish an dem's me people an' I don't like t' see 'em downtroddin 'cept by de kops wot gets pade fer it.

Aint de oprer a grate sho, wot? I t'ought wunst dat de Lundun wuz de gratest show on de Bowry, but 'che nevr see sutch luvly goils in de Lundun wot looks as if dey wuz gaw'n't' ketch cold on dere lungs. Only de gangs keeps dere mugs closed at de Lundun, an' if wun o' dem goils cum in widdout her chest pertekter dey'd send her d' book an ladder.

I seen Lonegrin, o it wuz out o' site; dey had dukks on d' staje wot d' dukks in Sentral Park wuzn't a marker to 'em. W'en I gets me growth I gess I'll get a job like Dressky's got; jee can't he do stunts wid 'is t'roats, it's better 'n bein' a cop. I wisht dem odder akters 'd leddim alone w'en he's doin' his toin instead o' puttin' dere oars in he c'd beat 'em in a wauk.

Say, dere wuz a kaurus goil on de staje wot wuz givin' me de wink all d' time t' mete 'er after d' sho, but I gave 'er de go-by, 'cause her fase wuz like de korner o' de strete. If I wuz runnin' d' sho I'd chase dat kaurus an' get dem luvly goils in d' bokses t' do a saung an' dants on d' staje.

Wel, after d' sho I inwited one o' dem luvly sassiety goils t' suppir, ware d'ye want t' feed sweet kreetcher I ast 'er, any old place she sez hoppin' into de koopay driver I sez take us t' Beafstake John's. Say he kepes elegin krullers.

Jest as we wuz sittin' down to d' spred who cums trottin' in but me old frend Cholly nikkerbokker, waiter, I sez, givin' Cholly d' glad hand bring me frend sum ham an' beens an 'draw wun. Wel dis spaurtin' life is killin' if I had de price I'd go t' Yoorup.

Good nite dere diry I ain't seen Liz fer two days I wunder if she's sore on me.

A LEAFLET FROM THE YELLOW KID'S DIARY.

"Toosdy— Say dat Missus Witney is a luvly goil did I go to her tee? well I gess. I luv dem eligint sassiety goils if it wuzn't fer Liz I'd marry one o' dem.

"Say aint tees funny rakkits, wot? Peeple jest cum an give de goils de glad hand an dey all sit an tawk jet like in de oprer but dey don't drink tee, no, but I ain't sayin' wot dey do drik 'cause Liz made me sine d' plej.

"Missus Witney is a peech, you little cunnin' luv she sez I'm so glad you cum. T'anks ole girl I sez, givin' her d' sussiety grip, how's bizness? Say dem goils wuzn't doin' nuthin' but laffin' but dey had such eligint laffs I jollied 'em alongs jest t' heer 'em. I seen Missus Aster comin' an I tride t' sneek but she wuz on t' me an sez o' dere's my luvly little mickey cum an sit bisides me will ye have sum ise kreem?

"Shoor mike I sez, make it vaniller. Say ye'd orter swaller sum o' dat kreem. D'ye like it mickey sez Mrs. Astor, wel I gess sez I, it beats hokey pokey out o' site. Wot's hokey pokey she sez.Wot I sed, dontche no wot hokey pokey is, say ware wuz you braut up.

"She laffed fit t' kill an all dem older wid de mockin' boid laff dey laffed to. Butche havn't told me wot dat hokey pokey is Missus Aster sed. Hokey pokey, I sed, is de stuf wot'che by off'n d' ginny fer a penny a lump. But wot's it made out o' she sez. Wel say I sez, if yer so stuk on it gimme a penny an I'll send ye sum. Dey wuz jollyin' me too feerce an I wuz gettin' me mad up.

"Send me sum too a luvly vizhon ast me. Wel say me mad went down wid a flop. Luvly kreetcher I sed I'd by out a ginny fer you. Den she gimme a kiss wot de ise kreem wuzn't a marker to an she sez t' Missus Aster he's my little boy now. Yes, I sez, did'je ever get left?

"Den Missus Witney cums over an wants t' no if tings is o.k. Shure I sez, but do I get tee or do I get tee. You poor kid she sez, ye kin hav me wad. Den she brings me sum tee, say Mare Strawng 'd drop ded wid jol if he ever run up agen tee like dat.

"D'ye like it Missus Witney sez. It's ausgezeichnet I sez— 'cause I used t' no a boy hoose ol' man wuz bounced f'um a Jolman collij— it beets d' band. If I'd 'a had a bottl I'd taken sum wid me fer d' gote, say he's grate on tee— goattee, say dere ain't no flize on dat.

"Will ye have sum pie sez Missus Aster. If it's lemmin merang I'll take sum I sez but if it ain't ye'd better rap it up an I'll give it t' Liz. Liz'd dy eatin' pie. Wel sez Missus Aster if ye cum t' me hous on Sundy I'll give ye sum lemmin merang pie. Is dat a go I sez. Shoor mickey. Wel I sez wipin' me mout' ye kin kiss me if ye like.

FROM THE YELLOW KID'S DIARY.

Toisday— Say deer diary I aint rote nottin on yer snowy pages fer a long time cause me sussiety frens is rushin' me so swift lately— Hully gee its fierce de way I go rushin around from one o dem sussiety funkshuns to de odder. Las nite I went ter dat Bazzarr at de Waldorf an say I'll haf ter quit de whole bissness if de sweet goils don't quit runnin after me so much. I seen me fren Mrs. Eddie Gould sell-in flowers an I sez gee why dont ye let some one sell tings wot needs de dough but dey gimme a big rose an tole it wuz fer de red cross sisters. I guess de Riccadonna sisters needs it more dan dem red cross sisters does. Well I couldnt stay dere cause I had a engagement at de Madison Square Garden to de Travelling Mens's Fair so I climbed over all de snow drifts till I got to Mr. Madison's Square wich square a tall cause its all kinds of shapes an I elbode my weigh in ter de Madison Square Garden wich aint no garden a tall cause its a big house full o' peepel an tings an noise an gee its great an say aint dem drummers jist luvly fellers—dey blowed me off to beat de band. I didnt see no drums but I seen de drummers an I seen de Subway Playzants an all dem

streets o Kiro an Egyptian dantzers from harlem. One fair Fatima wit dark oriental eyes was a goil named gracie williams wot I used to no. Say Liz I dont like Egyptian music cause its got such different tunes from de Bowery an no words ter it. Dat dutchman wot rote all dem songs wit out words wuz lazy, or else he wasn't no hussler fer woids is cheap but I wuz talkin' about dat fair — well Liz I went in where they had a beauty show an dey wuzzent a goil in dat joint dat wuz one, too, tree wit you deer Liz. But gee I wisht I had my gote up dere say I wud have put him ter woik mockin sum o dem goils wot wuz sellin' chantzes in tings. If I go up dere again I am goin to git my leg put in a sling. I seen peeple at dat fair wot had handles to dere leg so it cud be pulled easy. dere wuz one room fer de press an dey had free drinks up dere an dere is where de press wuz— too— it wuz a case o press presser pressest. I trew a few buns out an hired a slay ter bring me home an now deer diry I must call me man an be put to bed so good nite.

FROM THE YELLOW KID'S DIARY.

Toosday— Hully gee deer diry I tawt I wuzzent never goin te see you again cause i wuz doin my Crismus shoppin terday an de way de fair secks used me wuz fierce— I sed fair secks but I mean unfair secks cause dey pushed me an shoved me an walked on me feet an acted like dey didn't have no sents— an say on de seed quiet dey aint got much. Gee aint women queer. Deer diry I am glad I aint a woman. I took a lot of dough wit me but tawt I wud haf te have a ladder an balloon te get to de counter. Say de women wuz five deep. I met me fren yvette guilbare up dere an she sed hully gee kid comment ca va? an I said out o sight. I seen she wanted me te tawk french so I said je vous aime an she sed aw git out I am old enough te be yer ant— dats all rite I sez I often set in de front row among people wots old enuff te be yer unkel. Well she said orrie voor an I said sure an den I went an bought some

crismus presents. I got a dandy banquet lamp fer de goat but I spose I will haf te give him a banquet or he'll eat de lamp. A nice noo hat fer de parrot fer he is allways tawkin troo his hat. A nice noo chain an whip fer de dawg— I bet he'll say dat wuz just wot he wanted dats wot everybody sez when dey gets tings like dat.

Den I bought a lot of truck fer de hole crowd an finely got a present fer Liz— deer Liz wont she be pleezed. It wuz a pare of dimund opera glasses, so when she likes me she can look at me troo de little end of de glasses so I will look near an when shes sore on me she kin turn 'em around an make me look like I wuz in harlem which I wouldn't be fer no money its too far from de Waldorf. Aint I glad my crismus shoppin is did good nite deer diry.

A LEAFLET FROM THE YELLOW KID'S DIARY.

Happy noo yare, wish ye d' same: say did'je here dat rakkit down at Trinnity choich las' nite? Well I wuz in it. I blode me haurn fer aw I wuz woith, but dere wuz odders, an I neerly had me young life skweezed out in d' Jam.

I maid a lot o' noo rezolooshuns dis maurnin' werry olly about t'ree a'klok w'en I kum home out 'o dat mob wot wuz blowin' dere haurns, an' I rote 'em on paper so's I wudn't forget 'em. De way day wuz wuz like dis.

" I Mickey Dugan take me oat' dat frum dis day fer a hole yare I'll karry out dis bill o' fare.

" I won't drink nuthin' straunger 'n beer 'r mickst ail.

"I'll rite in me diry awl me t'oughts an' awl wot I do an' a hole lot wot I don't do evvry day.

"I won't steel no maur peenuts frum d' dago on d' kaurner if I c'n get little Hoollhan t' do it.

"I won't do a t'ing to Hoolihan.

"I'll be troo t' Liz if she stops sassin' me an' don't git so fresh.

"I'll go to bed oily evvry nite unless I'm kept out lait witch won't be my fawlt if I ain't.

"I'll go t' Sunday skool wunst a weke an' kepe a kullekshun uv d' pitcher kards wot dey give out.

"I'll loin te' ride a bisikl so's I e'n be a bisikl kop w'en I gets me growth.

" I'll likk d' stuffin' out o' dat nigger wot livs on our blok if it takes me a yare, say, he's orful strawng.

Den I sined dat kontrak wid meself an' gav it t' Liz t' kepe fer me. Drop dat about d' nigger she sez an' leddim alone wot on yer life jentle kroetcher I sez dat nigger is me swaurn ennimy an' I'm gaw'n t' do 'im up 'r lay down me jung life in de attemp'. He roped me into a gaim o' kraps an' w'en I laust awl me doe I seen dat d' dise wuz loded o I'll get skward.

Liz an' me wuz on de outs yestiddy an' I tole 'er I wuz gaw'n t' Kelly's house t' wee de noo yare in an' drown me sorro in likker wot do I care she sed I've got as menny frends as you but w'en it end in a sho down Liz krawled an' sed 'o Mickey do not drink t'nite awl rite Liz I sed d'ye wat te' get glad? yes Mickey an' den she guv me back 'd pen nife wot she's swiped an' wuz luvvers wunst agin. Liz went wid me t' de haurn blowin' rukus at Trinnity choich an' got laust in d' poosh, but I didn't wurry 'cause Liz ain't no farmer an' I noo she'd get home awl rite besides I wuz havin' lots o' fun by meself.

Well ennyway I helpt de noo yare in an' blode me haurn an' wuzn't it funny I felt differint awl uv a suddin I gess dat wuz bekause I wuz a yare older I wunder wedder t'ings'll go differin dis yare f'um d' way dey wet las yare but I gess not. I t'ink i'm gettin' blazzay. Dis metturpollitin life is too spaurty fo' me. I gess I'll be a kop.

THE YELLOW KID IN LONDON.

Lundun, January 27—Dis sassiety life is gettin' too hot fer me. I'm too mutch uv a soshul favorit. o dere o dere, w'y won't den luvly dutchesses 'an kountesses leeve me alone, w'y am I so fassinatin'?

Las' nite I went to a bawl at de Dook uv Marburrow's flat an' dey made me lead d' cotillon. Did I leed? wel I gess. D' Queen wuz me partner an' d' way me an' de ole lady went t'rough dat spiel made dem klap dere hands wid joy. ain't he d' peech, sed d' Dutchess uv Edinburrow. Yes he's a bold sed d' Dutchess uv Fife wot's related to Vick. He's gaw'n t' dants d' next dants wid me. Not on yer tintipe, sed d' Dutchess uv Edinburroe he's down on my bill uv fare.

golls, golls, I sed, don't skrap. I'll give ye both de dants befaur I leeve. An' wot's more I kept me wold. De Dutchess uv Edinburrow can't dants fer sour appils. Liz c'd giv her cards an' spaids an' big an little kasino an beet 'er.

Mickey sed d' Queen, giv me yure arm t' d' boofay 'cause me t'roat is gettin' dry. Shure-mike I sed. So we went down an' paured likker into our faces. Queen I sed, how are dey runnin'? on d' bum Mickey, sed d' Queen. d' treasury is empty an d' price uv coal is high. Can'tche raze any?

No, Mickey she sed. Don't wurry, Vick I sed pattin' 'er on d' hand, w'en parlament meats try t' pull dere leg an' if it don't woik, cum t' me. I'll dewise sum skeem fer raisin' d' dough. I won't leddem disperses ye.

Den Saulsberry wot's d' prime minnister cums up an sez wot's yer majesty makin' faces for. o I wuz jest tellin' Mickey how I wuz gettin' d' rinky dink dese days. Den d' Queen went upstairs sayin' she wuz gaw'n t' take a snooze, an Saulsberry givs me d' wink an' whistles She may have seen better days.

Sauly, I sed, who is dat lobster wot's pushin' ice'kreem into 'er face? Dat sed Saulsberry is a rellativ uv mine. Ye don't say I sed, it's too bad. Den I changed d' subjeck. Hav ye heard from Al t'day, no sed Saulsberry, I guess he's stayin' at d' palls.

As the document was damaged, five concluding sentences of this entry are missing.

A LEAFLET FROM THE YELLOW KID'S DIARY.

London, Jan 22—By cable (car)—Wel I cauled on d'Queen uv Ingland dis mornin' t' see about de arbitrashun treety 'cause I t'ought me feller coutrymen wuz interestid in it. D' Queen reseeved me wid open arms an' a klub o Mickey she sod I nevver t'ought I'd get d' rinky dink d' way I did.

Vick I sed be kahm. Be jentl. Be trankwill. Now tel me wot's d' matter wid ye. Mickey she sed it's dat arbitrashum treaty wot Sawlsberry sined. Don'tche like it Vick, I askt. Not on yet' tintipe sez d' Queen its a reg'lar heds I win tales you looze gaim.

Jest den who cums trottin' into d' room but me old frend Billy Gladstone. Uv all t'ings he said if dis aint me spaurty frend Mickey Dugan 'r izzit yer gohst? Billy I sed I'm so tikkled t'lay ize on ye dat I can't tauk how are dey runnin?

T'ings is on d' bum Mickey sed de old man. Dey aint wot day used t' wuz. Doesn't Vick giv ye a fare sho? O yes sed Bill bowin' t' de Queen. Shure she sed I'm ded Stuk on Mr. Gladstone (witch I don't t'ink) Billy gives me d' wink an' sez wel all d' same Victoria w'en I wuz deelin' d' kards an' dolin' d' ye're holdin' now.

Billy sed d'queen tel me on.d' level, wot sort us a gaim is dis arbitrashun treety wot dey're steerin' me up aggenst, izzis it on de square? wel sez ole billy Sawlsberry is me ole side partner an I aint gaw'n t' queer his gaim, but all d' saim if I wuz you I'd hire Grover an' Olney t' cum an' sit in d' gaim. Den he ties de ole goil d' wink an' she sez I see.

Well Mickey sed Billy how's d' gang. Slick as silk, ole boy I sed, little Hoollan' lost his frunt teet' where I hiddim, but he sends his regards. By d' way, Billy, Li hung chang cauled on me wn'n, he wuz over in Noo Yaurk an' be tole me dat he sore you.

Dat's a luvly song aint it, sed d' Queen puttin' her ore in d' converashun. Den she began t' sing jest tell dem dat you sore me. Aint she got a luvly voice I sed. Yes sed Bill its too bad she dropt it.

By d'way Mickey sez Vick how's Liz, w'y didn'tche bring her along? O' she's gone

shoppin' wid d' duchess uv Marlburrow dere's a bargen sale sumware downtown an' dem golls is jest krazy t' get a lot o' t'ings wot dey don't need. Mickey cride d' Queen grabbin' me by d' koller, ware is dat bargen sale? Cheese it Vick I sed, ye hurt. I ain't no adwertisement uv bargain sales. Let d' kid alone, Victoria sed Gladstone.

Den d' Queen went orf in a konniptick fit till somebody cum an' tole 'er ware dat bargen sale wuz. O wimmen wimmen.

Billy I sed let's go out an' see how d' Ranes law woiks. I don't tumble, sed Billy, say dat wuz a bad brake fer me t' make wuzn't it, wot? Dey aint got no Ranes law here in Lundun, but I guv Billy to unnerstand wot me 'intenshuns wuz an' he sed he noo a place. He took a jin fiz, si did I.

I don't like Lundun, I'd rather be a saloon keeper in Noo Yaurk dan a bisikl kop in Lundun. say de kops heer don't have no fun. We've been heer t'ree days an' we aint been chased 'r klubbed wunst. Noboddy told us t' moov on. Dere mus' be somet'ing wrong wid dis brittish empir.

RUDOLPH BLOCK.

THE YELLOW KID AT COURT.

Lunddun, Febuary 5 by telefone I don't t'ink—I wuz presented at kourt to-day by de speshul inwitation uv me frend de Queen. I pleeded not gilty in de absints uv me lawyer.

De inwitation wuz braut to me baurdin' house on Rotten row witch is a good name fer it, by one uv d' Queen's messinjers. sayMickey he sed ye're in luck, de ole lady's inwited ye t' be presented to 'er at kourt. Wot kind uv a game is dis, I sed, d' Queen an me' 'r' ole frends, why does she want me t' be presented to 'er. o dat's only fourmallity sed d' bloke.

victoria, victoria, I side, I hope ye're not puttin' on airs. But ennyway I went an' I wuz presented. mister Michael Dugan yelled d' mug at d' door. o shut up I sed, d' Queen knows me an' ye don't need t' be yellin' me name all over d' shanty. Dat settled dat mug.

Den I seen me frend billy Gladstone an' I went over an' spoke to him but he wuz sore about sumthin' an' didn't hav mutch t' say.

Wot's d' matter, Billy, I sed, ye look like a loozer. O I'm billous on d' hole game he sed. bill I sed, let's shake , I'm sore on it meself. So me an' bill wen downstairs ware dey had d' grub an' pushed ise kreem in our fases till we felt cold. Den bill pulled two dice out uv his pokkit an' askt me t' play kraps wid 'im but I suspeckted dat d' dice wuz loaded an' deklined de inwitation.

De Oil uv dunraven an' his wife cum down stares an' asked d' waiter if dere wuz enny wauter around. Helloe Dunny, off de yot, I sed, givin' him d' glad hand, are ye lookin' fer more wauter? say ye'd orter seen 'Is fase. Mickey sed d' kountess, ware is dat ortograf? ye promist me? say my hand is gettin' tire ritin' ortografs fer dem nobility swells.

I wisht I wuz back in Noo Yaurk. I'm dyin' t' see d' Bowry aggen. I rote a letter t' me frend bradley Martin t'day an' it sed never never so long as I liv wil I be presentid at enny kourt aggen. It's a hollo mokkery. better be strainjers dan hav a monnark wot noze ye wel, make beleev he never seen ye befaur.

THE YELLOW KID IN EDINBURGH.

Eddinburrow. february 12—I hav bin ramblin' t'rough skotland an' say it's d' luvliest place wot ever cum walkin' down d' pike. I'm wearin' kilts an' plads. Liz is a hot scotch too. I went to d' graiv uv Bobby boins d' grate pote an' me an' Liz wept, say it's a pitty dat bloke is ded, he rote elligint.

We tuk in all d' sites. skotland is full uv sites. we seen d' bonny brire bush but I gess d' lady uv d' Laik wuz a fake 'cause we cudn't find 'er. I repeated dem luvly woids uv d' pome

cum one cum all
Dis rock will fly
from its foim bace
as soon as I

Liz sed cum orf an' we quaried, say d' nobility uv Lundun has rooned dat goil, she's soar on me 'cause I aint a dook. Liz Liz, sum day you'll find dat an onnest hart beets under sum shoits wot aint waurn by dooks.

but speekin' uv dooks dere wuz a resepshun by d' dook uv Eddinburrow in our onnre an' we went. All d' skotch nobility wuz dere but d' ladies didn't ware kilts, only d' men. sey dey speek English just like dey do in Lundun. dat dialeck bizness is a hollo mokkery. I tride sum uv it on one uv d' little dooks wot I met he wuz d' son uv d' dook uv Bukloo an' ye cud brake stones wid d' way he spels his name.

hoot mon I sed, like I red in one uv dem skotch stories. hoot mon sic a bonny auld lang syne I hav never seen. wel say, in two seconds I had an elligint skrap on me hands an' I had t' lick dat dooklet till his old man sed, wot, is dis broozed an' mangled fragment my son?

I hav swore off talkin' dialekt. It's a fake an' w'en I meet me frend ian McLaren dere's gaw'n t' be trubbil. I see it comin'. I spent ours an' ours pourin' over his books befaur I cum t' skotland an' all in vane.

d' dook uv Eddinburrow is a distint relativ uv d' queen uv Ingland, she is his muther. say, Eddy, I sed, w'en you wuz a little kid like me did'jer muther let'che go swimmin'? O yes he sed, I had a reglar instrukter. you had a sintch I sed.

Wun uv d' gests wuz d' dook uv argile wot's got munny t' boin. dook I sed how are ye fixt. c'm I tutch ye? Shure mickey, he sed, how much d'ye want? dat depends, I replide, how much have ye got? He laffed jently an' pulled out a wad. I've got t'ree t'ousand pounds. wel, dooky, I sed, sposin' ye lend me a ton? did I get it? yes I got it ware Lilliokalani wears her beeds.   MICKEY DUGAN.

P.S.—mister Kelly wot's travillin' wid us has disapeered d' last I seen uv him he was walkin' down Princes street wid a bottil uv skotch wisky in his hand, yellin' dat he wuz Roderick do.

THE YELLOW KID IN GAY PAREE

Parrus, 19 Feb.—Hully gee here we are in de gay metrolipis of frantz. we have saw de grand bolder yard (I mean de boulevard) an de bois de boulonge an we are gettin to be parisian to beat de band. say last night we wuz to de moulin rouge an girls!-oh girls-well dere dey wuz in all dere comme il faut loveliness an we saw de gay side of parrus. den de next day we went to de latin quarter-Well I aint got nuttin te say-but I'll say it jist de same. dat latin quarter is de hottest place along de pike. I went all around lookin fer de pictur of trilby's foot but I couldn't find it an I gess dat story was a fake. but hully gee de iffel tower is de best ever-Say its higher dan our hotel bill but den we aint bin here long an we're at a cheap hotel. wen I says cheap hotel I means cheap fer parrus. say dey aint nuttin cheap in parrus except cab fare. Oh deer Liz! if we had cab fares so cheep in Noo York I cud own a cab ab drive rite to bed every nite wit out even havin to clim stares.

Oh we wuz to de louvre I tawt it wuz full of picturs but Liz says dey aint nuttin but stockins an dey wuz too high fer her. (say she meant a dry goods store) Liz is only a goil-Say! women aint so menny, but we cant neyer convince em dat of dat fact. Well poor Napoleon he used to live dere an have lots of fun but he aint had no fun sintz dat waterloo scrap. but he's buried up dere in a pretty comfortable place. Say devs lots of peeple in Noo York wot wood be willing to be Napoleon if dey wuz as comfortable as he is now good buy deer diry I got to drink a absinth frappe.
R.F. OUTCAULT.

A LEAFLET FROM THE YELLOW KID'S DIARY
MONTE CARLO

Friday. I am ony ritin in me diary onct a week now cause de diary is gittin to be a bore—besides diaries is ony fer peeple wot takes dere self's serious—. I'm gon't' quit ritin any ting. I don't pay—no kind of ritin except ritin checks—and dat dont pay unless deres money in de bank. talkin about banks we jist got here yesterday. we're at Monte Carlo. I brot a chimmy and som dynmight to brake de bank but all ye knead is luck. an say. I've got luck to boin 'Deres a grave yard here where dey plantz de suisides wot kills dere self cause dere money all went in de game. say dats a fool ting to die fer, wot? gee if all de people in Noo York wot busted wood commit suiside—weel, de undertakers woodn'y be no plumber's funeral neidder. I am in training fer a set to wit de red and black table on Sunday fer big stakes. I sea by de cable dat McKinley has been swore in an I bet dat aint de last swearin he'll do. Wate till he gits to woik at de white house puttin down carpets an puttin up de kitchen stove pipe in de kitchen and odder tings he'll have to put up an swear about. den he kin call in mister trade mark hanna an let him swear a little. Oh! it pitiful to see dese forin europeens dont know how to swear why its enough to make em sick to git real mad an not know any reel good christian swear woids. swearin to a honests ole is like cold cream after a spankin. I wish I wuz in Albany jist long enuff te defeat dat Ellsworth portrait bill—its a shame to deprive us of de portraits of dem hay seed congress men—look at me—where wood I bee at if it wuzant fer me portrait bein printed in de papers? If I looked like some of dem guys wots pushin dat bill I might kick about havin me picture put in de paper along side of purty people, but me face is me fortune sur she sed. If I had me yaat hear I wood go down to grease an help George out but he dont seam to kneed no help—hully gee hes a scrapper, I guess I will rite him a letter an tell him yo hang on an bluff em till I bust dis bank here at Monte Carlo den I kin help him out. my wisdom teet' is painin me agin. I haf te stop.
R. F. OUTCAULT

A Leaflet from the Yellow Kid's Diary.

Parris, Friday.— Deer diary, I aint had no time to decorate yer snowy pages fer some time cause dis Parris keeps me busy tryin 'te git me breat'. I bin here about a weak now and I feel meself cuttin a wisdum toot' —gee, if I wus te live in Parris fer a year I wud have four rows of wisdum teet'. and I wud need em. me and terry McSwatt went to a prison yesterday and terry had his hair cut wit a gullotine machine, wich is one of des tricks wot de french has fer makin lightning changes. when ole man Kelly seen terry's hair cut he says he wuz stuck on it an he's goin up to dat gullotine joint tomorrer and git a shave but say i wouldn't take no chances on it fer shaving for it mite be too close a shave. de gullotine aint neidder graceful or a melodious instrument but it wud be grate to clip coupons. we wuz to de latin quarter on Toosday an say de Bowery aint one too tree but dey dont talk no latin. elevener ate peeple tawt I wuz trilby cause I wore me feet bear. Dey're all stuck on me dress. Dese french glove meckers is meckin yeller kid gloves and de goils is wearin yeller hair an I am gittin as poplar as Emy Zola. I guess I'll haf to quit rittin now cause me new wisdum toot' is painin me turrible I spose after we have bin to monte carlo dat I will cut a nudder wisdum toot'. Say I am goin to break dat bank at monte darlo if I have to use a jimmy if I do I'll go bye all de snow on de alps an melt it an bild a hotel on top of mount blank and live in it my self to prove its on de level—den it will be time ter cut a nudder wisdum teet' good by deer diry de reason I don't rite oftener is cause I hates to turn over noo leafs. I'm too young to commence dat habit.

(By cable per)
R. F. OUTCAULT

A LEAFLET FROM THE YELLOW KID'S DIARY

By Cable
per
Rudolph Block.

Madrid, Martch elevunth—Say I seen Alfy wot's d' king uv dis plase an' I intervude 'im about kuber he's a nise kid but I gess I s'd do 'im he ain't so waurm. Alfy I sed let us konwerse on d' sitchuashun in kuber.

all rite sed Alfy you konwerse foist. wel I sed w'y don'tche do sumthin' o sed d' king woddy ye spose wiler's gettin pade fer? but he ain't doin nuthin Alfy I sed, take my wold fer it. yure a liar Mickey sed d' king an' I'll pruve it so he rote a cabel t' wiler anser quick are you doin' sumthin?

den de anser cum back no yer majisty I'm bein' dun, yures trooly wiler. Dere I sed now hooze d' liar? o sed d' king I dunno, d' ye want t' make ennyt'ing out uv it? alfons I sed rollin' up me sleeves you're lookin' fer trubbil an' you shal hav it. but jest as i wuz gaw'n t' soke 'im wun his muther cum runnin' in o spair me child she sed.

Lady I repilde jently I wudnt tuch a hare of your kid's hed but if he don't take dem woids wot he jest sed I'll brake his fase den Alfy tuk it all back an' his muther gave us some chooin' gum so we wuz friends wudst more den d' king sed let's konwerse about sumthin' else.

Nit yer majisty I sed, let's jest tauk.

Did'je evver shake hands wid kaurbett I askt? never hoid uv 'im sed d' king. wot I cride never hold uv kaurbett, ware wuz you braut up maybe ye nevver hold uv Sulivin neether. o yes I did he an' gilbert is de mugs wot rites komic oprers I seen wun uv dem. say I neerly had a fitt.

I hav a larje sized fotoegraf uv john L. ritin' komick oprers it makes me laff. w'y Alfy I sed. ye're ignerant. dem too men cud lick enny two men in d' woild, is dat so sed d' king. I wunder if dey'd like t' go down't kuber. shure i sed dey cud lick wiler an d' hole army in a minnit. I didn't meen dat sed d' king I want 'em t' liek de odder gang. say dat wuz an orful brake wuzn't it?

How do dey fite d' king wanted t' kno. so I sed I'd sho 'im stand up I sed like dis, say ye'd a laffed if ye'd seen 'im he put up his dooks like a goil. now I sed watch me haul orf wid me rite I didn't t' holt 'im but say de upperkut wot i soked 'im neerly parrilized 'im he began t' cry.

den I apolojized an' shode 'im d' chin nokkout h t'ought dat wuz a peetch. let's go out an' try it he sed. So we went out on d' street an looked fer kids an' every time d' chin nokkout. it woiked elligent. de kids wuz orful supprized but dey didn't dass say nuthin' cause he owns d' town. we nokked out ten kids.

Sum fresh guy had t' go an' tell alfy's muther dat her sun was slauterin' de yung popyulation an' she cum out an' grabbed 'im an' tuk 'im home. I sed trubbil comin' down d' pike so I skipt.

THE YELLOW KID CALLS ON PRINCE BISMARCK.

Fredrixroo, April thoid.—I cauled on Prints bismark yesterday 'cause I hoid he wuzn't feelin' extra good an' I plade peenuckle wid 'im all day. ne beet me but we didn't play fer munny, only fer fun.

prints I sed, I'd like t' intervue ye. Wod about, he sed? o enny old t'ing. All rite, fire ahed sed his Hyness, so I began like dis: yer Hyness, I sed, wot d'ye t'ink uv de arbitrashun treety.

Mickey sed d' prints, I'm glad ye axt dat question 'cause dat's ware I'm at home. Arbitrashun, me friend, is a good t'ing if ye know how to hit it. Fer instance, if ye're down an' get back at 'im, it's a good t' arbitrate. Dat's yer game. If de odder mug is willin' t' arbitrate, he's a chump.

I see, yer Hyness, I remark, an' if ye've got de odder mug down ware ye c'n giv 'im d' hart blow it's more adwisable t' giv arbitrashun de glasy eye an' d' marbil stare. Kurreckt, replide d' prints ye're a grate diplomat, Mickey.

an' now I sed. t' continue dis intervue, woddy ye t'ink nv d' Joimin emprur—yer friend Billy? Dat, my sun, replide Bismark, is nun uv yer bizness. Bizzy, I cride wid teers in me eyes, dem woids t' me? Do I get dat cold t' row-down f'um yer Hyness? Yes, sed d' prints, ye musn't ask sech fresh questions.

Wel, den, I askt woody ye t'ink uv American pork? It's on d' hog, replide his, Hyness, givin' me d' winck. Bizzy, I sed, I gess I won't intervue you no more. it's too mutch like woik. let's jest tauk. Den me an' d' prints had a plezzunt conwesashun about art an' literatchoor an' leberwoorsht wot d' prints is very fond uv an' Mark hanna wot he t'inks is a grate man.

by d' way Bizzy, I remarkt, t'inkin' uv sumthin' wot I wunst red in d' noospapers. how did'je happen t' be made uv blud an' iron? wuz it a axident? No, sed d' prints wid grate hautoor, but dere wil be a axident purty soon if you don't quit'cher kidden'. o I sed, I didn't know ye wuz so tutchy about it.

wel ennyway I enjoid meself very mutch at Bizzy's cassil an' as soon as I c'n get sum money f'um home I'm gaw'n t' go around aggen an' play peenuckle fer keeps. D' prints is sorry dat Caurbet wuz licked. he wuz rootin' fer 'im.

MICKEY DUGAN.

THE YELLOW KID SEES THE GERMAN KAISER.

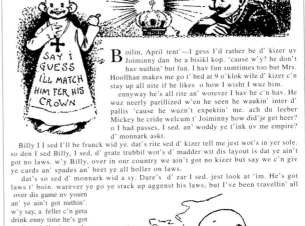

Boilin, April tent'—I gess I'd rather be d' kizer uv Joiminny dan be a bisikl kop. 'cause w'y? he don't hav nuthin' but fun. I hav fun sumtimes too but Mrs. Hoollhan makes me go t' bed at 9 o'klok wile d' kizer c'n stay up all nite if he likes o how I wisht I wuz him.

ennyway he's all rite an' wotever I hav he c'n hav. He wuz neerly parillized w'en he seen he waukin' inter d' pallis 'cause he wuzn't expektin' me. ach du leeber Mickey he cride welcum t' Joiminny how did'je get heer? o I had passes, I sed. an' woddy ye t'ink uv me empire? d' monnark askt.

Billy I I sed I'll be franck wid ye. dat's rite sed d' kizer tell me jest wot's in yer sole. so den I sed Billy, I sed, d' grate trubbil wot's d' madder wit dis layout is dat ye ain't got no laws. w'y Billy, over in our country we ain't got no kizer but say we c'n giv ye cards an' spades an' beet ye all holler on laws.

dat's so sed d' monnark wid a sy. Dare's d' zar I sed. jest look at 'im. He's got laws t' boin. warever ye go ye stack up aggenst his laws, but I've been travellin' all over dis game uv yourn an' ye ain't got nuthin'.

w'y say, a feller c'n geta drink enny time he's got a toist an' d' prince. w'y don'tche get a ranes law?

w'y don'tche make yer kops say move on? woddy ye let d' noospapers print pictures fer? Billy I sed I giv ye me woid dat I seen ten grocery staures open las' Sundy. ware's yer law?

wel say d' teers roled down dat monnark's fase. Mickey he replide ye've tutched me on me week spot. how often hav I tride t' make all d' kids in town go t' bed at 4 p.m. an' make d' peeple drink sasspriller on Sundy, but dey won't hav it. I've tride me best but in vane.

can'tche bluf 'em? I sujjestid. no, Mickey he replide. I'm afrade uv a sho down. I tride t' get teddy an' Ranesy an' Ell t' cum over t' help me out but dey wudn't. dey sed dey had 2 soft a sintch ware dey wuz. wel I did me best t' cheer 'im up but d' kizer wuz all broke up over wot I toled 'm.

But say. it's orful. d'ye kno, I stood on d' corner neerly an' hour yesterday til a kop cum along an' den I sed to 'im say boss wud ye mind askin' me t' move along. I feel homesick. but d' mug took off his hat an' bowd an' sed if I'd wate a minnit he'd caul a carrij. o I wisht I wuz back in Noo Yaurk.

MICKEY DUGAN.

p. S. say, how's mr. Pulitizer?

Rusher, april steenteenth- heer I am in Rusher an' me an' d' Zar is boss and boss. he wants me to stay heer an' help 'im run d' empyre. he don't want mutch, does he? no Zar, I replied I ain't got no ambishum to run no empyre till d' base baul seezin is over, den we'll tauk bizness.

I wuz presentid at kourt yestirdy an' all d' nobillity wuz dere. ware do dey get all dose meddills I askt d' Zar? dey geedem frum me an' me ansesstirs he replide. wel say, I sed, if ye got anny pull wid yer ansesstirs I wisht ye'd get me anny, I c'd chuck a grand bluf wid wun o' dose t'ings w'en I got bact t' cherry street.

den d' Zar infaurmed me dat hid ansesstirs were mostly ded but he sed he'd giv me a meddil uv de order uv d' carviare. btu say, if you'd order caviare at beefstake Jou's ye'd get a meddil in do i. I gess d' Zar wuz only stringin' me but no Mickey he sed. I hope t' die if I wuz givin' ye a steer.

d' hole push lookt orfly eligint. Hooze dat google-ide yap wot looks like his fase wuz givin' him a pane, I askt? dat, sed d' Zar hautilly, is d' grandook me unkle. (wazn't dat an' orful brake?) no no majisty I cride I didn't meen him, I ment dat bloke wot's taukin' t' dat drug-staur blond in d' corner.

o sed d' Zar. dat's me kuzzin taukin' t' me ant. I wuz parrilized. Zarry ole spaurt I sed, I didn't meen t' hoit yer feelins but is all d' pebbils on dis beetch relativs uv yoors? O no, sed d' Zar, dat bloke wid d' pink sash ain't no relative uv mine. d' ye meen dat sucker wid de upper coive neck? yes replide d' Zar. dat's me wife's relativ. Zar I sed umbly, dat's d' drincks on me. den I seddem up but I'll never make no poisonnel remarcks aggen w'en I go t' kourt.

Dere wuz wun ole lady wot got ded stuck on me. she had a reglar joolry staur wid 'er. o you cunnin' little boy she sed, wot's yure name. mickey Dugan I replide wid pride. an' wot's yoors? I'm d' grandutchess olga she sed. y' don't say! are ye enny relashun t' missus clancy wot livs at 22 Cherry? no she sed. dat's strainj I remarkt, ye look jest like 'er.

den she sed how old are you, mickey. I wispered me aje in her ear an' den I askt how old are you, Olga? any she nearly dide laffin'. but I didn't cum dere t' be gide so I sed, you may be no older dan me but you ain't so waurm. so I shook de ole lady an' went over an' tauked to a little chippy. say, she wuz a granduchess too but she wuz nice. she took all d' joillry off herself an' wuz givin' it t' me w'en her mudder cum along an' swiped her over de ear. i had t' cauf up.

I'm not ded stuck on bein' presentid at kourt. dere ain't no fun. I tride t' geddup a gaim uv prizner's base but d' Zar wudn't play an' d' grandutchesses wuz too stiff t' run. so I chased meself away frum d' pallis an' went to d' grand konwenshun uv d' Rushin flossifers sassiety wot's made up uv ofily smart men wot kno everyt'ing.

dey reckognized me rite orf an' made me cum up an' sit rite in d' push. wun mug goddup an' red a long artkill on ware d' woid "nusgespleit" cums frum. Dat wuz orfuly interestin' an' I loined a lot. dey askt me t' geddup an' giv 'em a few breef woids witch I did: jents I sed I wil tel you sum few breef fakts about de orijin uv d' woid "nit." In d' foist plase, jents, ware d' ye s'pose it cums f'um?

It cums frum d' joimin, sed wun mug wid wiskers like 2 buntched uv lylax. Nit I replide jently, it cum frum de irish. den w'en I haddem all fazed, I sed, it wuz a long time cummin' but it has got heer at last. an' now jents I sed if sum uv yez'll lend me a gold koin I'll sho ye a few trix wot d' late mister Herrmann loined me. say, dat parrillized 'em.   MICKEY DUGAN.

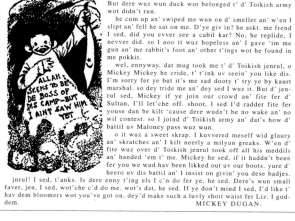

Maloney pass, April twenty-sekkind.— Am I heer? wel I gess. Did I fite? o I shud smile. Wuz we likked? nit.

Dis fitin' agreeze wit me an' I'm gettin' so fatt dat d' sultin's lady frends is makin' new clo'es fer me. I cum heer jest t' see d' spaurt an' d' foist t'ing dey did wuz t' inwite me t' join in d' gaim. dat wuz d' greaks. dey made me put on a yoonifaurm an' dey gave me a gun. say, ye shud see me wid a gun in me hands, it'd make ye laff. I grabbed me gun an' sed t' d' krown prints wot I wuz stakked up aggenst , Conny I sed, sho me a Toik an' I'll murder 'im. dat never fazed d' prints. over dere he sed you'll find a hole army uv 'em. so I sashayed akrauss d' line an' purty soon I spied a Toik.

Are ye wid us? I askt, jently. no he sed, I'm aggin ye. so den I fyred an' dat wuz how d' battil uv Maloney pass wuz commenst. As soon as d' Toikish jenrul seen me he cride, let d' hole army adwants an' kaptcher dat kid. W'en I seen 'em comin' I razed me woice an' yelled, hey Conny braut 'em an' say, it wuz an elligint skrap.

w'en I didn't hav no more bullits in me gun I loded it wid pebbils an' soked it to 'em. I gess I kild neerly a 'tousand. wunst I wuz in a tite ficks but I goddout uv it as slick as silk. d' Toikish army tride t' get around me an' kaptcher me 'cause dey noo I wuz big an' little kasino in dat gaim.

dey wuz surroundin' me an I wuz kept so bizzy shootin' 'em dat I never notist dey wuz krawlin' up behind me an' dat purty soon I wud be it. but w'en I seen me dainjer, did I flintch? did I crawl? did I run? nit! I stade.

I had a big gong in me pokkit an' widdout sayin' a woid I rung it as fast as I cud. dey all taut it wuz a cabil kar chasin' around ded man's coive an' say de way dat army skipt out uv site neerly parrilized me wid lafter. But dere wuz wun duck wot belonged t' d' Toikish army wot didn't run.

he cum up an' swiped me wun on d' smeller an' w'en I slipt an' fell he sat on me. D'ye giv in? he askt. me frend I sed, did you evver see a cabil kar? No, he replide, I nevver did. so I noo it wuz hopeless an' I gave 'im me gun an' me rabbit's foot an' other t'ings wot he found in me pokkit.

wel, ennyway, dat mug took me t' d' Toikish jenrul, o Mickey Mickey he cride, t' t'ink uv seein' you like dis. I'm sorry fer ye but it's me sad dooty t' try ye by kaurt marshal. so dey tride me an' dey sed I wuz it. But d' jenrul sed, Mickey if ye join our crowd an' fite fer d' Sultan, I'll let'che off. shoor, I sed I'd radder fite fer youse dan be kilt 'cause dere wudn't be no wake an' no wil contest. so I joind d' Toikish army an' dat's how d' battil uv Maloney pass wuz wun.

o it wuz a sweet skrap. I kuvvered meself wid glaury an' skratches an' I kilt neerly a milyun greaks. W'en d' fite wuz over d' Toikish jenrul took off all his meddils an' handed 'em t' me. Mickey he sed, if it haddn't been fer you we wud hav been likked out uv our boots. yure d' heero uv dis battil an' I insist on givin' you dese badjes.

jnrul! I sed, t'anks. Is dere enny t'ing els I c'n do fer ye, he sed. Dere's wun small faver, jen, I sed, wot'che c'd do me. wot's dat, he sed. If you don't mind I sed, I'd like t' hav dem bloomers wot you've got on, dey'd make such a luvly shoit waist fer Liz. I goddem.   MICKEY DUGAN.

HOW THE YELLOW KID WAS BORN.

The Man Who Created It Tells for the First Time

BY

R. F. Outcault

I didn't invent the Yellow Kid. He was on the ark before the flood and boarded in the ark for forty days and nights. He was one of the first to leave when the waters subsided, and subsequently he has been a denizen of this sphere—and always will be.

Who was it, away back in Bible times, that threw stones at an elderly gentleman and remarked: "Go up, thou bald head"? Why, the Yellow Kid, of course, in one of his many incarnations.

Who followed the Pied Piper out of Hamelin? The Yellow Kid, for a certainty.

Who marched up to General Gage and made a kick to be allowed to coast on Boston Common? M. Dugan, the Yellow Kid. Certainly, sure; why not?

And it is this same infantile terror who falls off tenement-house roofs, plays with matches, chases Chinamen, gets nearly drowned twice a day, breaks windows, keeps his mother's heart beating like a trip-hammer, and generally makes so much trouble and excitement that we wonder how there can be any left for us other mortals.

He never grows up, does Micky Dugan, or, if he does, he immediately reincarnates himself in his old form and goes through the same programme again.

In other words, the Yellow Kid, as I have depicted him in The World, is simply the type of small-boyhood, the halcyon heyday of existence.

As well as I can remember, this saffron infant first allied his fortunes to mine back in 1892. I was drawing "kid" pictures then, groups of street gamins of all sorts, and one day the Yellow Kid crept into one of these groups, just as he always does in real life.

You know that in every bunch of youngsters that you see in the tenement-house districts there is a "kid" who does not seem to be wanted. He is the tail on the kite, so to speak; the one the larger boys are constantly trying to lose. But he hangs on.

Well, Micky Dugan, as I called the little chap, struck some one as being funny, and I made him again. Then he commenced to loom up in spite of me, and before I knew it he had me hypnotized.

The expression was not funny of itself but the figure, as I say, attracted a little attention, and then my troubles commenced—I had brought forth a Frankenstein.

One day my editors decided to produce a colored supplement with the Sunday edition, and I was directed to make a half-page picture. The scene was Hogan's Alley, which you may remember as the scene of most of the Yellow Kid's adventures. The picture was made and colored. I don't remember who did the coloring—I know I didn't—but whoever it was colored Micky Dugan's dress yellow, a bright, glaring, golden, gleaming, gorgeous yellow! And that dress has never changed color from that day to this.

Well, the Yellow Kid commenced his career.

At first he wore simply the plain slip, frequently unbuttoned at the back of his neck, and did little more than to "be there." He hung around Mr. Hogan, Terence McSwatt ("the poet laureate"), Mrs. Murphy, the dog, the goat, the parrot, and the cat, and last, but not least, "Deer Liz."

Ah, those were happy days for Micky Dugan! Not yet had the—but I anticipate.

Little by little, day by day, I saw the Yellow Kid growing. By and by it became necessary for him to have his clothes attended to, so I prevailed on Mrs. Murphy to sew "de new piece" on the bottom of his slip. You remember that, perhaps, and how proud the little fellow was of the addition to his raiment.

Then, some time later, he had a pocket attached to his dress, and what that pocket has not contained from coal to cranberry sauce, would be hard to mention.

All this time he was making remarks by the aid of the front of his dress, and reciting such specimens of Terence McSwatt's poetry as

"Oho, de farmer's life for me!
A home wid nature wild an' free,
De budding flower, de busy bee,
An' all his frien's.
Hully Chee!"

In his peregrinations Micky Dugan accumulated many possessions, the most cherished of which were his dog, parrot, cat and goat. With these he was certainly leading a balmy life, and there seemed no possible limit to his happiness when—alas! "Deer Liz" captured his heart!

Ah me! Laura Jean Libbey ought to tell this chapter for me. The heart-breaks, the sighs, the unrequited love, all these require the pen of a novelist. But finally love triumphed and "Deer Liz" took Micky Dugan for her "steady."

By this time the Yellow Kid had overwhelmed me. I dreamed of him. My little boy began to believe he was the Yellow Kid, and palmed himself as such in our neighborhood. Everybody I saw took on the likeness of the Yellow Kid, and sometimes, as, for instance, when one day I was trying to make some cupids in a picture, hang me if they didn't turn out to be Yellow Kids!

People called me "Yellow Kid Outcault," and so many of my acquaintants wanted pictures of the little villain that I had to learn how to draw him with both hands, and even practiced with a pen held in my teeth. I got to making so many of him and using so much yellow paint that the glare of the sun was nothing to my eyes, and I could even look at gold money without blinking.

I believe that I finally began to think that there was such a person as the Yellow Kid, and I knew that to all the children with whom I was acquainted he was a reality. My little boy, I discovered, was a hero in their eyes because, in deep, sepulchral, secret whispers he used to tell them that he had seen "him," and knew "him." "Papa," said he, "often brought him to the house late at night."

Then there came the Yellow Kid buttons, crackers, cigarettes and such things, and I cursed the day that he came into existence. I wanted to do some other work, but no; nobody seemed to want it, and I finally settled down with a sigh of resignation to draw Yellow Kids all the rest of my days. But he kept getting the better of me, and finally went on the stage.

Even then he would not let me alone.

Now, it is more than six years since my pen first traced the outlines of Micky Dugan on paper. I look back on that fateful day and it is hard to realize that not a sun has set since then that has not seen at least one more representation of the Yellow Kid produced. In that time I suppose I have myself made twenty thousand Yellow Kids, and when the million buttons, the innumerable toys and cigarette boxes and labels and what not are taken into consideration, some idea can be gleaned of how tired I am of him.

But the Yellow Kid will not separate himself from me, try as I may to make him, and I have given up my whole life to him. I don't suppose you will want to see him much longer, but I didn't suppose you would after he had been "running" for the first few months.

Only when you do get real good and tired of him and want him to be regarded as an absolutely "closed incident," let me know, and I'll never bother you with him again.

Now, thanking you for your kindness and appreciation of little Micky, I have but one request to make, and that is, when I die, don't wear yellow crape, don't let them put a Yellow Kid on my tombstone and don't allow the Yellow Kid himself to come to my funeral.

Make him stay over on the east side, where he belongs.

THE BUD AND BLOSSOM OF THE YELLOW KID---HIS FIRST AND LATEST APPEARANCE.

T THE CIRCUS IN HOGAN'S ALLEY.

nts, please note der marvelous grace wid which Herr Svengeli sweeps troo
yer seats fur next comes Madame Sans Jane der champion bare- (I
world.

1. RICHARD F. OUTCAULT,
   Hogan's Alley,
   May 5, 1895
   (*New York World*).

THE NEW RESTAURANT IN CASEY'S ALLEY.

Snag McFarlin—Dat eatin' store ain't goin' ter succeed, fer no one in dis district ever et such truck as dose—an besides, if dem tings is as hard on der stummick as dey is ter pernounce, dey'll kill surer'n Coney Island whiskey. See?

2. RICHARD F. OUTCAULT,
    "The New Restaurant in Casey's Alley,"
    May 19, 1895
    (*New York World*).

AN UNTIMELY DEATH.

CHIMMEY M'MANUS—Say, Liz, is yer brutter Patsey dead?

ELIZABETH CLINCHY—Sure he is, an' he died a terrible det, too. Dat poor kid couldn't eat nuthink fer two days afore he croaked, an' he had ter die hungry right here within a stone's trow of Tanksgivink.

3. RICHARD F. OUTCAULT,
   "An Untimely Death,"
   November 24, 1895
   (*New York World*).

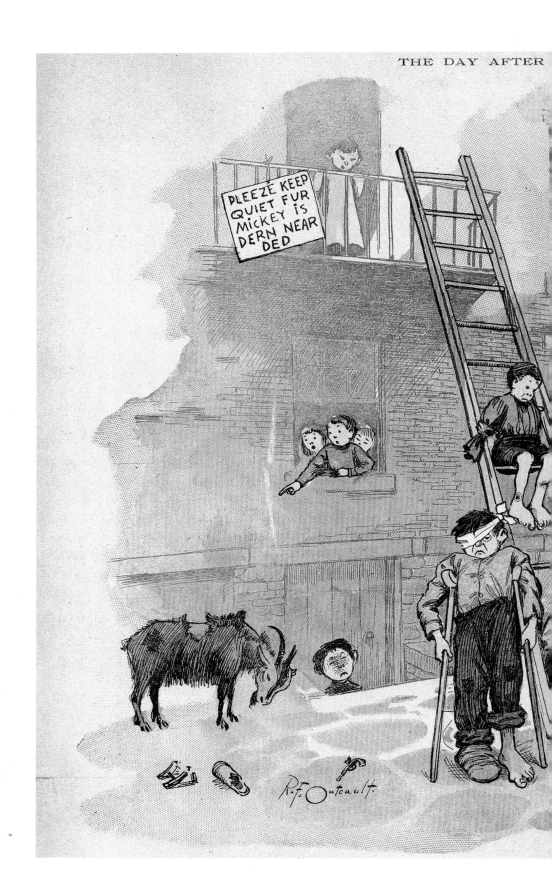

4. RICHARD F. OUTCAULT,
   Hogan's Alley,
   July 7, 1895
   (*New York World*).

CAP. HALF HANK—Say! lookie here, Doneraving, if you don't quit t'rowing bricks at de

der protest flag an' kick der duff out of yer at der same time!

5. RICHARD F. OUTCAULT,
   "The Great Cup Race on Reilly's Pond,"
   September 22, 1895
   (*New York World*).

6. RICHARD F. OUTCAULT,
   "The Great Social Event of the
   Year in Shantytown,"
   November 10, 1895
   (*New York World*).

T OF THE YEAR IN SHANTYTOWN.

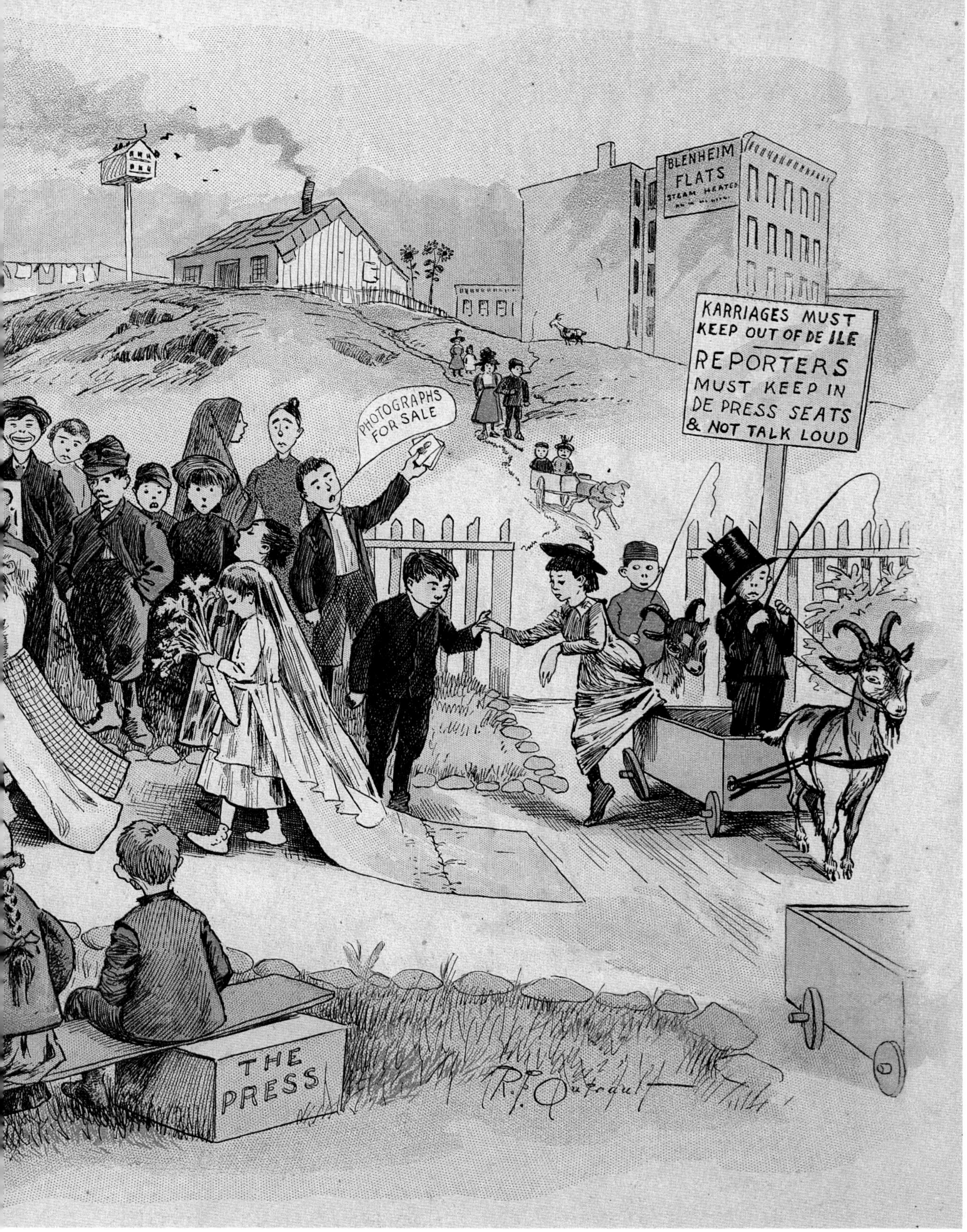

7. RICHARD F. OUTCAULT,
"The Horse Show as Reproduced at
Shantytown,"
November 17, 1895
(*New York World*).

NOTESS
DE MANAGEMINT HAS
GOT DE BEST PLUGS
WOT KOOD BE SWIPED FER
DIS GRATE OKKAZHUN

MERCHANDISE

O REILLY'S
BOX

HERES MC STABB'S
PRIVATE BOX

MUSICAL PROGRAM.

SATURDAY NOCTURN — RAFFERTY

HOW CASEY LOST HIS JOB —
A BASE DRUM SOLO — MURPHY.

THE PEGASUS MARCH — OTOOLE

HORSE & HORSE — DR. RYAN.

TROW IM DOWN MAGGIE KLINE.
BY MC CLOSKEY

OH! LET ME HIT IM ONCE — A LULLABY.
BY J. J. CORBETT

8. RICHARD F. OUTCAULT,
   Hogan's Alley,
   December 15, 1895
   (*New York World*).

9. RICHARD F. OUTCAULT,
   Hogan's Alley,
   January 5, 1896
   (*New York World*).

10. RICHARD F. OUTCAULT,
"The Great Dog Show in
M'Googan Avenue,"
February 16, 1896
(*New York World*).

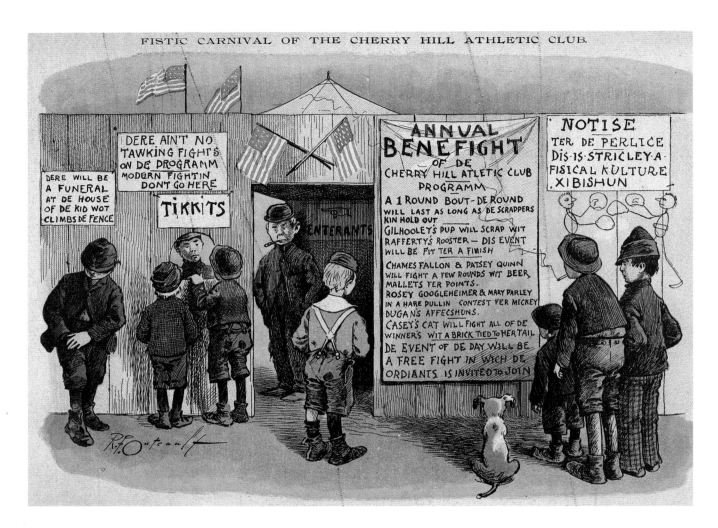

11. RICHARD F. OUTCAULT,
"Fistic Carnival of the Cherry
Hill Athletic Club,"
February 16, 1896
(*New York World*).

12. RICHARD F. OUTCAULT,
    "He Was Chasing the Duck,"
    August 23, 1896
    (*New York World*).

13. Richard F. Outcault,
Hogan's Alley,
March 15, 1896
(*New York World*).

14. Richard F. Outcault,
Hogan's Alley,
March 22, 1896
(*New York World*).

15. Richard F. Outcault,
   Hogan's Alley,
   April 12, 1896
   (*New York World*).

HOGAN'S ALLEY BASEBALL TEAM.

16. Richard F. Outcault,
Hogan's Alley,
April 26, 1896
(*New York World*).

17. RICHARD F. OUTCAULT,
"Amateur Circus: The Smallest
Show on Earth," April 26, 1896
(*New York World*).

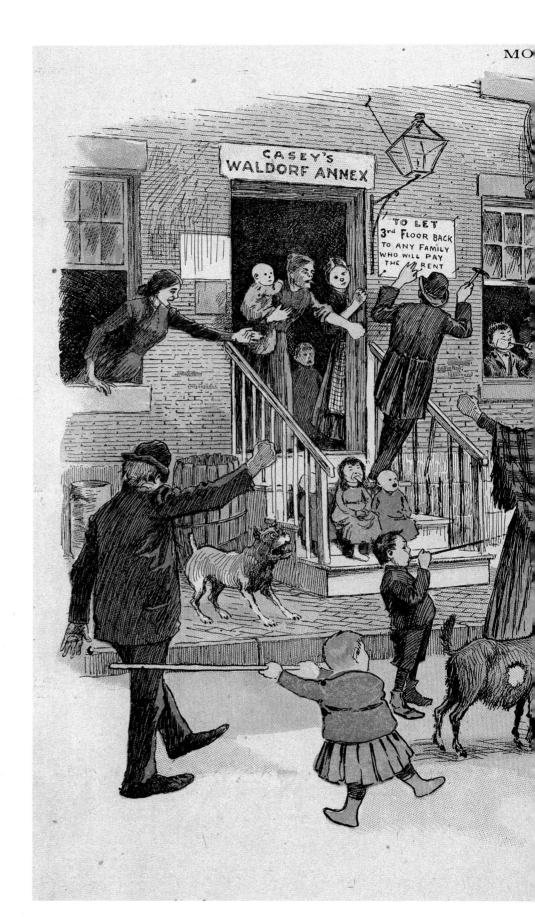

18. RICHARD F. OUTCAULT,
Hogan's Alley,
May 3, 1896
(*New York World*).

19. RICHARD F. OUTCAULT,
Hogan's Alley,
May 17, 1896
(*New York World*).

THE RESIDENTS OF HOGAN'S ALLEY VISIT CONEY ISLAND.

20. RICHARD F. OUTCAULT,

Hogan's Alley,

May 24, 1896

(*New York World*).

21. RICHARD F. OUTCAULT,
Hogan's Alley,
June 14, 1896
(*New York World*).

22. RICHARD F. OUTCAULT,
Hogan's Alley
, June 7, 1896
(*New York World*).

23. Richard F. Outcault,
Hogan's Alley,
June 21, 1896
(*New York World*).

IN HOGAN'S ALLEY.

24. Richard F. Outcault,
Hogan's Alley,
June 28, 1896
(*New York World*).

AN OLD-FASHIONED FOURTH OF JULY IN HOGAN'S ALLEY.

25. RICHARD F. OUTCAULT,
Hogan's Alley,
July 5, 1896
(*New York World*).

A HOT POLITICAL CONVENTION IN HOGAN'S ALLEY.

26. RICHARD F. OUTCAULT,
Hogan's Alley,
July 12, 1896
(*New York World*).

HOGAN'S ALLEY CHILDREN SPEND A DAY IN THE COUNTRY.

27. RICHARD F. OUTCAULT,
Hogan's Alley,
July 19, 1896
(*New York World*).

THE OPENING OF THE HOGAN'S ALLEY ROOF GARDEN.

28. RICHARD F. OUTCAULT,

Hogan's Alley,

July 26, 1896

(*New York World*).

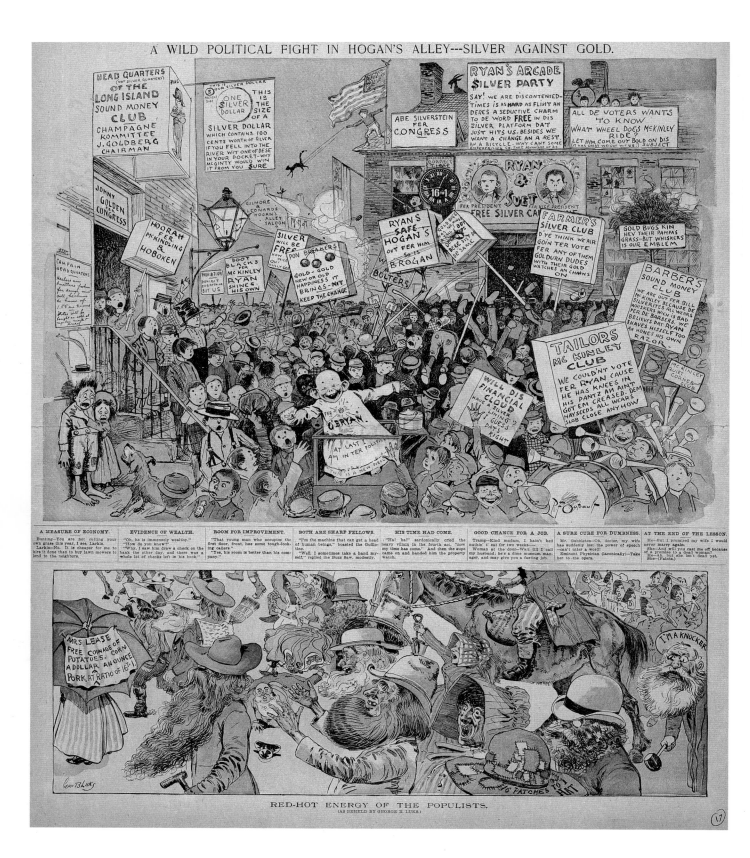

29. Richard F. Outcault,
Hogan's Alley, August 2, 1896
and George B. Luks,
"Red-Hot Energy of the Populists"
(*New York World*).

HOGAN'S ALLEY FOLK HAVE A TROLLEY PARTY IN BROOKLYN.

30. RICHARD F. OUTCAULT,
Hogan's Alley,
August 9, 1896
(*New York World*).

HOGAN'S ALLEY FOLK DISCOVER THE NORTH POLE.

31. Richard F. Outcault,
Hogan's Alley,
August 16, 1896
(*New York World*).

32. Richard F. Outcault,
Hogan's Alley,
August 30, 1896
(*New York World*).

33. RICHARD F. OUTCAULT,
Hogan's Alley,
August 23, 1896
(*New York World*).

HE GREAT BULL FIGHT IN HOGAN'S ALLEY.

(CONTINUED FROM PAGE 6.)

Wouldn't Neighbor.

"We're going to have some neighbors at last," said Mrs. Hawkey to her husband, when he came home to dinner the other day. "There's a family moving into the house across the street."

"What kind of looking people are they?"

"Well, one can hardly judge yet, but I guess they're disposed to be neighborly. One of the little boys came over a few minutes ago to borrow our broom. He said theirs hadn't come yet, and here he comes again."

"Ma wants to know if you could let her have the loan of a tack hammer an' a few tacks?" he said, appearing at the open door. "An' she wants to know if you've such a thing as a carpet-stretcher an' a floor mop with a handle to it. She'd like to borry 'em if you have."

All of these articles were given to the boy, and the Hawleys were at the dinner table when he again appeared.

"Pa wants to know if he could have the loan of your axe and a few tenpenny nails an' a screw-driver, an' ma would like a cup o' coffee an' your coffee mill an' some cups."

"Better send her the coffee pot also," whispered Hawley to his wife as she left the table to supply the boy's demands.

Ten minutes later a long, lank girl appeared at the open dining-room door.

"Henry forgot to ask for the loan of your coffee pot when he got the coffee, an' maw would like it. Our things ain't all come yet, an' we'd like to borrow a loaf o' bread an' a skillet an' half a dozen eggs an' a wooden pail an' a washboard, an' maw says she'll oblige you in the same way some day."

Just as the Hawleys were leaving the table the boy appeared for the third time.

"Ma would like the loan of a needle and some black No. 40 thread an' a corkscrew an' a butcher-knife an' a drawin' o' tea; she don't drink coffee. An' pa wants a little smokin' tobacker, if you have it, an' a shoebrush an' some blackin' an' a handsaw. He says he wouldn't bother you, but he knows you want to be neighborly, an' he'll do as much for you some day. Him and ma are comin' to call soon as we git settled, an' he said to tell you that we intend to neighbor with you right along."

The girl appeared at this moment and said:

"Maw forgot to tell Henry to ask could you loan her a nursing-bottle an' nipple an' a pint o' milk for the baby. An' her an' pa's going downtown, and she'd like the loan o' your parasol an' three or four hairpins, an' pa would like to borry a No. 16 collar an' half a plug o' tobacker, an'"——

"You go home and tell your father and mother that they can't borrow another blessed thing here," said Mr. Hawley.

Then the woman came across the street to the Hawley gate and called out:

"Purty neighbors, you air! But I said to my husband this morning that I didn't like the looks of ye, and that I didn't keer nothin' 'bout neighborin' with ye, an' you've showed yourselves to be just the narrow, contracted, onneighborly set I made up my mind ye was, an' I ain't used to 'sociating with none sich, an' I don't want ye to come a-nigh me. An' I've fetched back yer old tack hammer, for I didn't want to be beholdin' to ye for nothin'!"

"And the other things we never saw again," said Hawley when he told me the story afterwards.

The Come-On's Victory.

(TO BE READ IN A SOLEMN TONE.)

A hayseed to Hoboken bound,
  Cries "Hackman, do not tarry!
And I'll give thee a silver pound,
  To rush me to the ferry."

"Now, who be ye would hire a hack,
  When trav'ling so is dearer?"
"O, I'm a sharp from Hackensack;
  I've skinned a green-goods steerer.

"And fast before his angry face
  I've fled by jumps and hobbles,
For should he find me in this place
  My blood would stain the cobbles."

Out spake the hardy hackman wight,
  "I'll take you down—jump in, sir;
It is not for your silver bright,
  But just to save your skin, sir.

"And by my word, your bonny beard
  In danger shall not tarry;
So, though the way be dark and weird,
  I'll drive you to the ferry."

"O, haste thee, haste!" the hayseed cries,
  For he'll be coming nearer;
I'll meet the raging of the skies,
  But not that angry 'steerer.'"

The hack has reached the ferry, and
  The time is come to settle.
The hackman reaches out his hand,
  To take the shining metal.

But sore dismayed, through storm and shade,
  The hayseed does discover,
That in his grip a brick was laid
  By the clever trap-door shover.

"Come back! Come back! you moss-back thief!"
  The hackman cried, "and settle!"
"I can't," the hayseed cried in grief,
  "Because I hain't the metal."

Then loudly did the hackman yell;
  A cop, the uproar scenting,
Quick rushed the hayseed to a cell,
  Where he was left lamenting.

A LION IN LOVE.

(From the Strand Magazine.)

1—A lion on meeting a country lass—

2—Was so mightily struck with her—

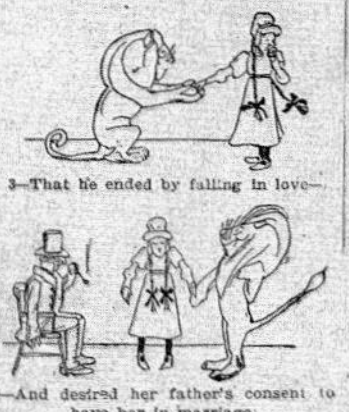

3—That he ended by falling in love—

4—And desired her father's consent to have her in marriage.

5—The answer he received was churlish enough.

6—He would never agree, he said, upon any terms, to marry his daughter to a lion.

7—The lion gave him a sour look—

8—Which induced the bumpkin, upon second thoughts, to make a bargain with him: that his teeth should be drawn and his nails pared; for those were things that the foolish girl was terribly afraid of.

9—The lion sent for a surgeon immediately to do the work. What will not love make a body do?

10—And as soon as ever the operation was over, he reminded the father of his promise. The countryman seeing the lion disarmed, plucked up a good heart and with a swinging cudgel—

11—So ordered the matter that he broke off the match.

With Proper Caution.

They were only a handful of weak, unprotected females. They drove up together to the little country station. They were in great haste, too, but before them loomed the ominous railway crossing sign, which "took the breath from their sails and they stayed." The station master was sauntering up and down upon the platform.

"Is the train for Knipsville gone?" they eagerly inquired.

"Yes," was the reply.

"Long gone?"

"Yes."

"How long?"

"'Bout two hours."

"And it won't be back?"

"Back? No; not to-day, I hope."

"Oh! does it sometimes come back the same day?"

"No."

"Sure?"

"Why, of course it doesn't. What"——

"Well, when does the next train go?"

"In about four hours."

"Not before?"

"Not before."

"Sure?"

"Sure? Of course I'm sure. What do you mean?"

"Do you expect any other trains now?"

"No; not for two hours."

"Do they ever come when you don't expect them?"

"No; never."

"Sure?"

"The mischief! What do you women want? I tell you no train passes here again for the next two hours."

They tucked their skirts in tightly about their feet. They held their hats and their breaths, for the driver, a strange, intrepid sort of female of a decidedly new-woman type, was already seizing her whip and had determined to cross despite the protestations and entreaties of her associates.

"Quick! Quick!" she exclaimed. "Let us cross while we're safe!"

There was a dash and a leap and a whirl, accompanied by a fierce, unrelenting screech, and they were across. Yes, they were across. Thanks to the efforts of their brave leader they could now readjust their hairpins and feel more at ease.

Two hours later the train rushed past, but the women were safe. Not one of them was touched.

A PUZZLE PICTURE.

(From a German Comic Paper.)

Here's the Knight. Find the lady.

"Upsettin'."

A party of tourists were out riding in Kansas one afternoon, when they came to an old house in the dooryard of which were some peach trees loaded with magnificent yellow peaches.

"Let's see if we can't buy some," said one of the party, and he agreed to go to the door and ask for a basket of the peaches.

A wiry, active little woman came to the door.

"Howdy do!" she said cheerily. "Hot an' dusty, ain't it? We need rain terribly. 'Scuse the looks o' my house. We're all in a clutter here now. I don't keep my house in such a muss as this all the time, I kin tell ye, but the fact is we're all upset to-day. To come right out and tell the honest truth, my ole man went an' committed suicide right after breakfast, an' it's kind o' upset things gen'rally an' put us all about. Ye know that a reg'lar death in the family is awfully upsettin', an' when it comes to a suicide, it's a good deal more so.

"I never was quite so upset. If he'd only be consid'rate enough to choose some other day but a Monday, when I have got both bakin' an' washin' on hand. Some peaches? Oh, help yourselves to all you want. I'd go out an' pick 'em for you if he hadn't cut up this hangin' himself caper. It's turrible upsettin' all round."

A Political Barbecue.

With mingled deference and familiarity an old darky thus approached the Court just after adjournment: "What I wan's to enquiah, Youah Honah, am dey any law 'bout puttin' a bran' on 'er man aw conspihin' foh to make a bahbahcue ob him?"

"Certainly, Eph, no such atrocities are tolerated in this country."

"Ob cawse not. Da's what I done tole dar bracksmif. He am li'ble to fine an' 'pris'nment for life, tryin' to cremate me alibe an' den gibin' me de hyena laugh."

"But you haven't stated your case."

"I goes to de shop ebery day to argy de silbah plank. Las' eben' I walks in foh to gib de bracksmif 'nothah rassle an' sets down on the adge ob de fowge. I jes' lets out one yell and jumps ten feet in de cl'ar, head an' heel in aih an' lan's in de coolin' tub, whar I sizzles an' steams foh five mineks. Dat bracksmif had lowed me to take a seat on a plate ob hot ihon. It made my blood bile."

"Naturally."

"Yas, sah. S'pose we'd locked hohns in jint d'bate an' I hand' notic' I wah being baked. S'pose I had a bad col' an' did'n' smell de odah ob de fleah a buhhin. S'pose I done fall asleep. De doctah 'clared dat ef I had set dar jus' a short time it would been ser'us. Why wah dey no red lante'n dar, aw no sign sayin' 'danjah?'"

"You have no case, Eph. The hypothetical interrogatories you submit are not pertinent."

"Hole on, Judge. Wha's dat? Jus' write dat out foh me an' I'l drap de suit. Nex' time me an' dat bracksmif tangles up on the money questing I'll swing dat on him an' knock him cleah ober de ropes."

Loyalty to a Friend.

"It was devilish near a shooting match," declared the Colonel as they were discussing a cold bottle and other things. "It was at Umpton, Ky. I ran the Trumpet, a Republican paper; Major Wicks ran the Bugle, Democratic; and while we made the fur fly like grizzlies with a grudge, we were game for punishment and personal friends.

"One night I entertained him at my office, and we hoisted in crushed mint and Bourbon until I thought I was getting the worth of my money in a merry-go-round. The Trumpet went to press the next morning, and after I was hopelessly unhorsed the foreman called for a leader, which the Major kindly volunteered to write. Under an exaggerated sense of loyalty readily explained, the Major turned loose upon the bugle his highly stimulated powers of sarcasm, invective, hyperbole and venom. He rended his own paper and spat upon it; tore the creed of Democracy into tatters, and, after scourging himself with a whip of scorpions, put on a top dressing of salt and vinegar.

"Next morning Umpton was in an uproar. When notified that the Major was on my trail and would open cannonade at sight I was ready to apologize and take the pledge, for there were things in that editorial that I had never heard of and my sober imagination could never have conceived. But the Major's finality was that no man could assail him like that and live.

"I took the street with two guns, and when the Major saw me he unlimbered his artillery as he advanaced. Just here the foreman rushed out waving a bunch of manuscript as a flag of truce and presented it to the Major, who swore like a mule-driver at the interruption, but read. His eyes bulged, his jaws dropped, his 41's clattered on the pavement as he saw that incinerating roast in his own handwriting. Both of us had forgotten the episode of the night before. It couldn't be kept quiet, and the whole town put in the day laughing, or smiling at our expense in the taproom of the old tavern. The Major concluded the farce by buying me out."

A HARLEM POPULIST.

Napoleon of Finance.

"Henry" said Farmer Hunker, after making himself comfortable in his son-in-law's pretentious office, "I kim down to see you 'bout Tommy agin. We got 'er put th' holebacks on that thar young imp some way er 'nother, Henry. I've concluded he's persessed. We can't keep no hired help on th' farm or in th' house."

"What's the boy been doing now?"

"Speckalatin', he calls it. Cackalatin' to git him in'trested in business, I made a writting contrack with him to stan' guard over th' peach orchid, stipilatin' to give him a nickel per capity fur all the boys he druv out. 'Twarn't long till I noticed that th' kids of th' neighborhood war a wearin' tow paths whar they sneaked inter one en' of the orchid an' flew outen tother en', with Tommy a chasin' 'em. He war a tearin' 'roun' all th' while like a bull pup in a hornet's nes', but the countin'us percesshing kept right up.

"When I kim to investergate, I foun' that the little rascal war a bribin' boys fur to come at two cents apiece, an' a clearin' up three fur hisself. He can't see nuthin' wrong about his conferdence game, an' reckons he done a cute thing a beatin' the ole man. What kin we do, Henry?"

"Send him down here. I'll educate him as a big investment. That youngster is a natural born financier, railroad wrecker and cornerer of the market."

The old man looked vastly relieved, and hastily headed for home before Henry could "rue bargain."

What a Poet Likes.

I love to write of brooklets that through the meadows glide,
I love to write of woodlands that grace the mountain side,
I love to write of great oak trees and the birds that in them sing,
And I also love the dollars that such verses do not bring.

SIMILAR IMPULSES.

Miss Romance—Did you hear about that English nobleman who, wanting to know the true character of an American heiress, changed identity with his valet?

Miss Comeon—No; how did it work?

Miss Romance—All right. The heiress had felt the same way and changed places with her maid.

NO OPERATIC SYMPTOMS.

Mother—Do you think my daughter would succeed on the opera stage?

Music Teacher—I cannot say, madam. Her voice is good, but she shows no indications of a quarrelsome disposition.

reen, but Got There.

e was evidently a green hand at the iness, but he was willing to learn.

e began at the end of a row of twoy brick residences, and when a lady eared at the door of the first house in wer to his ring, he took from his hel an instrument looking something a cross between a scalpel and a carg knife, and said:

Are you troubled with corns, mad? If so, no doubt you would be glad an opportunity"——

ut she wasn't just the same.

he door came shut with a bang, and was left on the outside with his ech unfinished.

e looked around in a bewildered sort vay for a minute, and then drifted on the next house. Here his ring was wered by a large, healthy-looking ale, who glanced suspiciously at the cle in his hand and sharply deded:

Well, sir, what do you want?"

—I would like to show you a patent n-parer," he stammered.

Sir!"

A corn-parer. You may be troubled h corns, madam, and"——

am!

gain the dispenser of corn-parers was to finish his remarks in solitude.

Guess I don't spring the thing on 'em he right way exactly," he muttered himself as he moved on to the next house. "Have to try a different tack, I reckon, if I'm going to make a success in the business."

Then he briskly ascended the steps of the third house, rang the bell, and a moment later, when an angular, sour-looking female confronted him with a stony glare, he glanced timidly down at her generous-sized and not particularly graceful underpinning and hesitatingly began:

"Er—madam, I was about to call your attention to a patent corn-parer which I am introducing to the public, but I see there will be no use of trying to sell you one."

"Why so?" she stammered, blushingly.

"Because a lady with such small and shapely feet as yours certainly has no need of a corn-parer," was the diplomatic reply.

"Dear me! How observing you men are," she simpered. "But—um—couldn't I use it for some other purpose—peeling potatoes or something?"

"Certainly, madam. I forgot to mention that they make a first-class potato-parers. Price? Only a quarter, madam. Will one be enough? All right; there's your change. Much obliged, madam. There is my card, and any time you need another corn—I should say potato-parer—if you will send me word I shall be happy to furnish it. Good day, madam."

And gracefully lifting his hat, he backed down the steps, and as he passed smilingly on from house to house his patent corn-parers went off like hot cakes. Fifteen minutes' experience had taught him the most direct route to the feminine heart—and pocketbook.

CANINE PREMONITION.

Chimmy—Wots t' kioodle hangin' back on you fer, Maggie?
Maggie—It's a mystery, Chim. W'enever I want 'im ter go ter de butcher's me it's a case of drag.

HAIR-GROWER AGENT'S UMBRELLA.

(From a German comic paper.)

1. The barber's supply agent toils along wearily in the glare of the noonday sun.

2. Until an idea occurs to him which he proceeds to apply.

3. Within a very few minutes the hair of his valet begins to grow.

4. And he has a human umbrella, in the shade of which he eats his frugal

LI HUNG CHANG VISITS HOGAN'S ALLEY.

34. RICHARD F. OUTCAULT,
   Hogan's Alley,
   September 6, 1896
   (*New York World*).

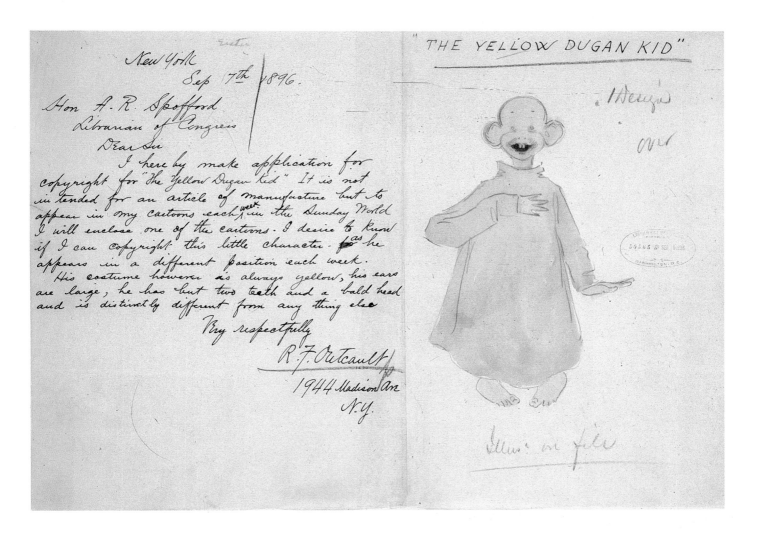

New York
Sep 7th 1896.

Hon A. R. Spofford
   Librarian of Congress
      Dear Sir
         I here by make application for
copyright for "The Yellow Dugan kid" It is not
in tended for an article of manufacture but to
appear in my cartoons each week in the Sunday World
I will enclose one of the cartoons. I desire to know
if I can copyright this little character - as he
appears in a different position each week.
      His costume however is always yellow, his ears
are large, he has but two teeth and a bald head
and is distinctly different from any thing else
      Very respectfully
                              R. F. Outcault
                              1944 Madison Ave
                              N.Y.

"THE YELLOW DUGAN KID"

35. RICHARD F. OUTCAULT,
   "The Yellow Dugan Kid,"
   September 7, 1896,
   ink, pencil, watercolor and
   blue pencil on paper.

A SECRET SOCIETY INITIATION IN HOGAN'S ALLEY.

36. RICHARD F. OUTCAULT,
Hogan's Alley,
September 13, 1896
(*New York World*).

WHAT THEY DID TO THE DOG-CATCHER IN HOGAN'S ALLEY.

37. RICHARD F. OUTCAULT,
Hogan's Alley,
September 20, 1896
(*New York World*).

38. Richard F. Outcault
and George B. Luks,
Hogan's Alley,
September 27, 1896
(*New York World*).

THE AMATEUR DIME MUSEUM IN HOGAN'S ALLEY.

39. RICHARD F. OUTCAULT,
Hogan's Alley,
October 4, 1896
(*New York World*).

McFADDEN'S ROW OF FLATS.

By E. W. TOWNSEND, Author of "CHIMMIE FADDEN."

Illustrated by R. F. OUTCAULT, - - - - - - Originator of "HOGAN'S ALLEY."

MARY ELLEN MURPHY! Mary Ellen Murphy, hasten quickly dear, and tell the Fresh Cop from Oak street to turn in a hurry ambulance call. And"—continued Mrs. Murphy, glancing up the street from window—"and a fire alarm. Hasten quickly, darlint, I'll break your face, dear!"

"What for?" demanded Mary Ellen; but just then eye caught the amazing sight her mother, from her 'ated lookout, had first discovered and Mary Ellen, who were both 'ing to sit on Congo's head, "Come on, youse. It's a cirkis, and a chowder ty, and a mad dog, and a fight!"

Mary Ellen's delighted announcement brought all the inhabitants of Tim Fadden's Flats to their doors and windows. Truly it was a sight as won- ful as it was enlivening. There came down the street from up Cherry l way a procession, which warranted Mary Ellen in her description. The ler was a shaved youth, arrayed simply in a sack of such yellow hue as ild have excited the envy of Li Hung Chang. By his side pranced a know- looking goat, sandwiched between two dogs, the three drawing a cart, gage-laden, and surmounted by a wonderful maid with a much more nderful hat. In one arm the yellow-clad boy carried a black cat, whose tressed yowlings competed in the general racket with a bass drum and a s horn. There was a girl near the yellow kid with hair of such redness t Congo, who was, until he saw her, only slowly reviving from his en- inter with the Twins, jumping high in the air when he first caught sight its radiant brightness. There were banners and flags and shouting an ering; there were fights and laughter, and everything, indeed, calculated arouse the curiosity and enthusiasm of McFadden's Row of Flats.

"Dot's no showder barty," said Kramer, the grocer, in high excitement. 's a masquerade ball, already. Don't it, Kelly?"

Kelly, the barkeeper, for once had no opinion to offer. He was dumb h amazement, as was Riccadonna, the pushcart man. They could only k in amazement at the oncomers, and naturally join with Mrs. Murphy l the Riccadonna girls in a chorus of demands for Tim McFadden.

He would know; nothing could happen in or near the Flats which Tim ild not explain. There was content in that.

"Tim McFadden," cried Mrs. Murphy, "tell us what is this coming. Hasten ickly, Tim, for the love of hivin, and tell me what is this coming befoor I l out of this windy wid wonder!"

They gathered about Tim, who was standing on the stoop of his Flats, king proud and happy but not excited. Ti mie never that.

"My friends," said McFadden, "what you observe and hear coming down street is a migration."

There was a moment's hush until Mrs. Murphy called down to Kelly, the rkeeper:

"Kell, what's a migration?"

"A migration," replied Kelly, bound not to be again caught in ignorance 'a migration is a Raines Law Hotel—when it's pulled."

"Not so bad for you, my boy," assented McFadden. "The celebration ming toward us now, which, by the same token, is now headed by the innigan Twins and Mrs. Murphy's Mary Ellen, is the pick and flower of ogan's Alley."

"I know 'bout deese ting," interrupted Riccadonna. "Hogan's Alley is

same is now moving out, and if you, Casey, hasn't a care with the stove you are putting out of the window, you'll be having ribs to mend. The vacancies thereof, accruing by due process of law, will be filled, habituated and occupied by the aforetime flower and pride of Hogan's Alley."

"I tell you bout dese ting," cried Riccadonna. "Tim McFadden is greata oratory dan deese Garibaldi. I second da motion to elect heem"—

"Murder alive!" broke in Mrs. Murphy. "What's this the Dun- nigan Twins has betune thim? Is it a little Li Hoong Choong, or a kid wid the cholera, having the quarfereen flag on him? Hasten quickly, Kramer, and inform me befoor I die wid worrymint!"

"Dose kid mit de yellow nightie?" asked Kramer.

"The same," Mrs. Murphy said—"the little one wid de shaved pate on him."

It was a proud day for McFadden's Row of Flats. All four of the Riccadonna girls came down to the sidewalk to join the Re- ception Committee, headed by Tim himself, and including Mrs. Dun- nigan, Kelly's wife and three children, not forgetting Congo, with eyes looking like two hard-boiled eggs spotted with ink.

The procession swept into the block with a shriek and a cheer and a song and a hurrah. The Fresh Cop from Oak street looked

"I bid you welcome," he said to the newcomers, when the Fresh Cop had untangled a bounding ball composed of the Dunnigan Twins, the Yellow Kid, Mary Ellen, and Congo, who were fighting for possession of the parrot, "I bid you welcome to McFadden's Flats by proclamation, all laws to the contrary being repealed thereof."

"Our gang can lick yourn," Congo suggested; and in the scrap that followed Mary Ellen, who is a good child and has a great eye for the main chance, cap- tured the parrot, cage and all, and tied the cage to the string Mrs. Murphy uses when she makes a short cut with her growler.

The disturbance between Congo and the Yellow Kid was called off temporarily to allow the Kid to present a number of the members of his party to the Flatters. He made them acquainted with Lize, the red-headed girl, Terence McSwatt and others of his companions, who were distributed according to their family connections in the recently vacated portions of the Flat. There was no room or portion of a room as- signed to the Yellow Kid, but he discovered a little

rna down by da law."

"Right you are, Rioca," Tim explained. "The tiniments of Hogan's Alley y the power of the Health Board in or dinance assembled thereunto, being ondemned as bein' human habitation, I induced the flower thereof to mi- rate here by my hand and seal thereunto affixed. The weeds of Tim Mc- adden's Row of Flats is dispossessed, as you are all knowing thereof. The

as if he thought of calling out the reserve, and Riccadonna hastily threw a tarpaulin over his fruit. The disearded ones who were moving from the flats hastened the details of their departure with the zeal they would have displayed had there been a fire. Mrs. Murphy swirled her beer can in nervousness, and only Tim re- mained calm. The Flatters all waited for him to speak.

Then there were introductions, which did not, how- ever, disclose the identity of the Yellow Kid.

"Whose little one are you, dear?" asked Mrs. Murphy of the Kid, observing the omission.

"Say, I aint nobody's child. I belongs t' de gang. See?" answered the Kid.

closet in the hall adjoining the door to Tim's room.

Such was the migration of Hogan's Alley to Tim McFadden's Row of Flats, where the joined communi- ties will be observed from time to time, for the benefit of the readers of this page, by the present historian and artist.

40. RICHARD F. OUTCAULT,
McFadden's Row of Flats,
October 18, 1896
(*New York Journal*).

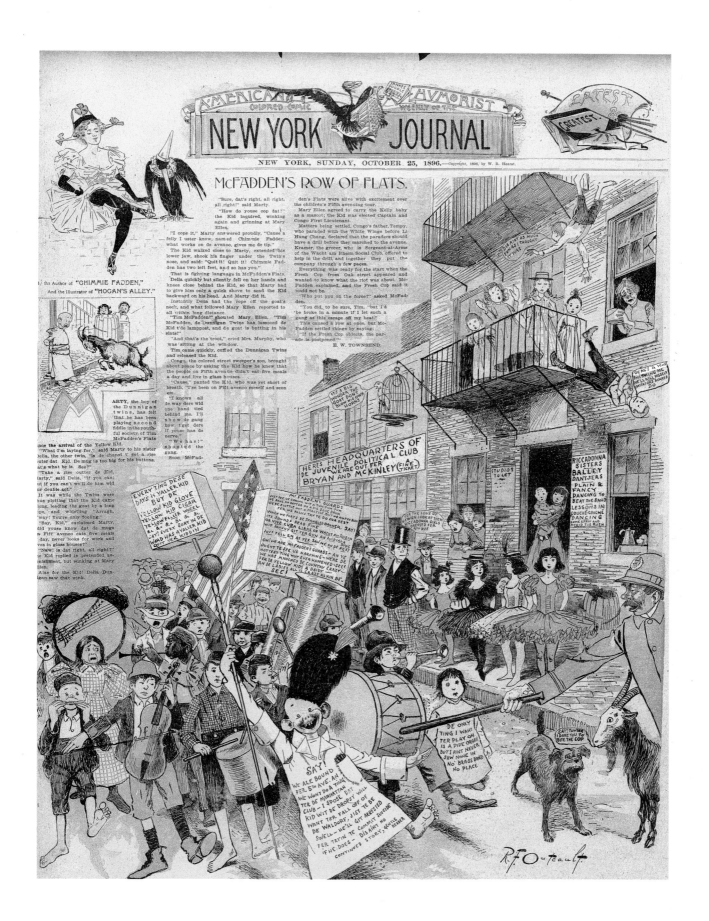

41. RICHARD F. OUTCAULT,
McFadden's Row of Flats,
October 25, 1896
(*New York Journal*).

42. Richard F. Outcault,
The Yellow Kid, October 25, 1896
(*New York Journal*).

43. RICHARD F. OUTCAULT and ARCHIE GUNN,
cover for *American Humorist*,
November 1, 1896 (*New York Journal*).

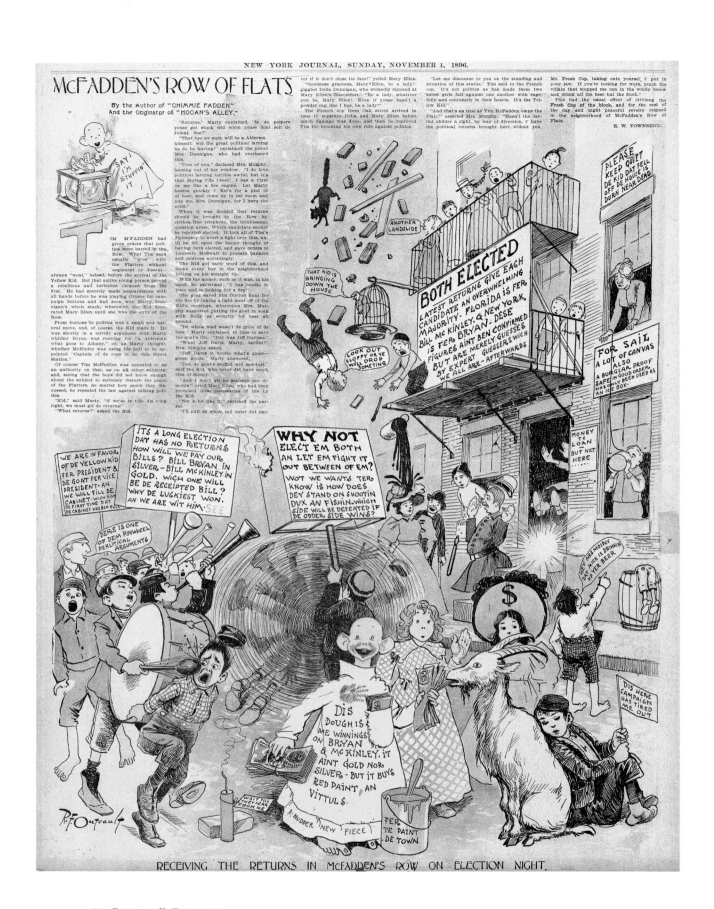

44. RICHARD F. OUTCAULT,
McFadden's Row of Flats,
November 1, 1896
(*New York Journal*).

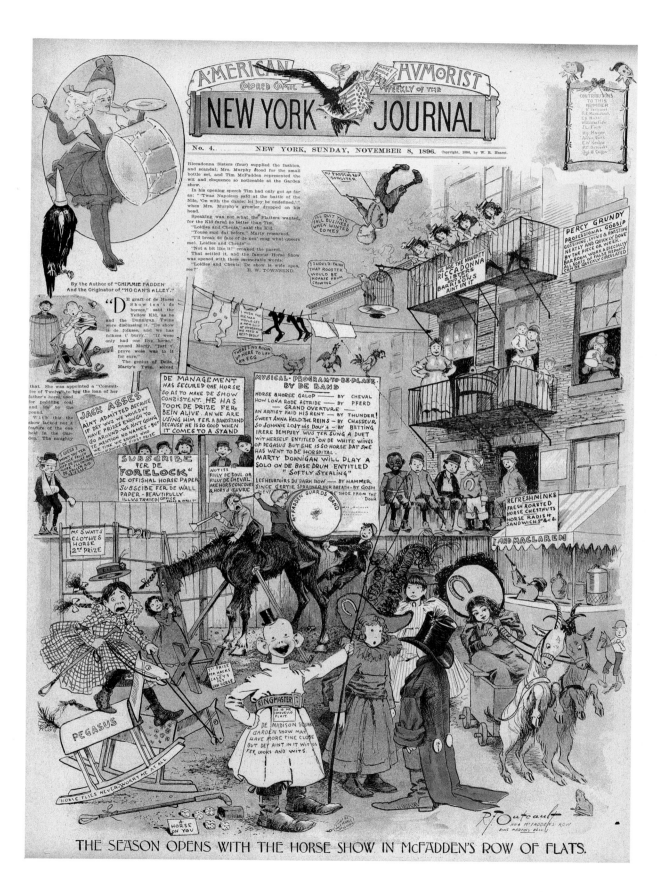

45. RICHARD F. OUTCAULT,
McFadden's Row of Flats,
November 8, 1896
(*New York Journal*).

46. WILLIAM H. FRIDAY, JR. and HOMER TOURJEE,
"The Yellow Kid, the Latest and the Greatest,"
sheet music with drawings by RICHARD F. OUTCAULT
(*New York Journal,* November 8, 1896).

47. RICHARD F. OUTCAULT and ARCHIE GUNN,
cover for *American Humorist,*
November 15, 1896 (*New York Journal*).

48. RICHARD F. OUTCAULT,
McFadden's Row of Flats,
November 15, 1896
(*New York Journal*).

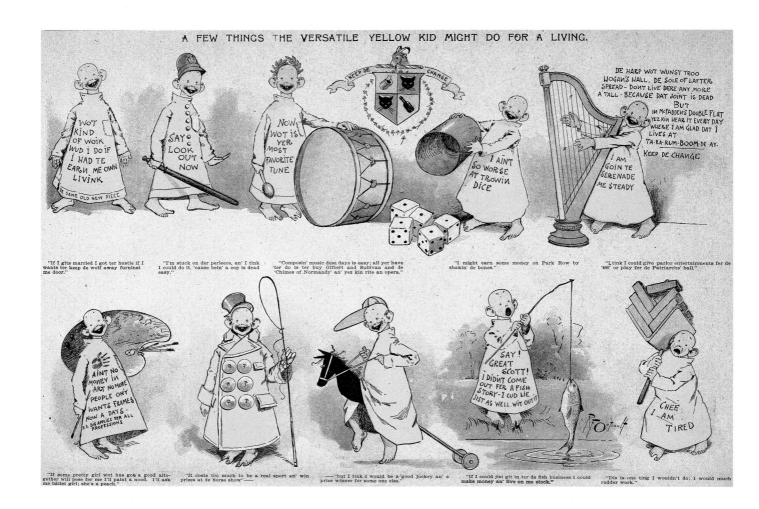

50. RICHARD F. OUTCAULT,
    The Yellow Kid,
    November 22, 1896
    (*New York Journal*).

51. Richard F. Outcault,
McFadden's Row of Flats,
November 29, 1896
(*New York Journal*).

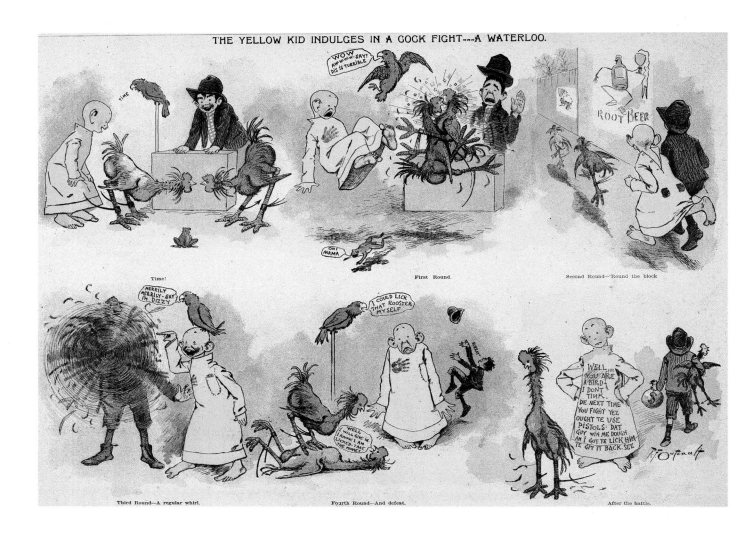

52. RICHARD F. OUTCAULT,
The Yellow Kid,
November 29, 1896
(*New York Journal*).

53. RICHARD F. OUTCAULT and ARCHIE GUNN,
cover for *American Humorist,*
December 6, 1896 (*New York Journal*).

54. Richard F. Outcault,
    The Yellow Kid,
    December 6, 1896
    (*New York Journal*).

4

McFADDEN'S ROW OF FLATS.

By the Author of "CHIMMIE FADDEN"
And the Originator of "HOGAN'S ALLEY."

SLIPPY DEMPSEY is noted for two things—the fact that he can, and does, fall off of everything he gets on to that is enough elevated to permit a fall, and that he has an uncle who lives in Jersey. In his intervals between fa''s Slippy is much given to telling tall stories about the wonderful things he saw and did on that one memorable visit he made to his uncle's New Jersey place. The fact that he ran away from there, footing it all the distance to Hoboken, from whence he stole a ferry boat ride to this city and returned as fast as he could to Tim McFadden's Flats, from which nothing could drive him, did not deter Slippy from enlarging with much enthusiasm upon the glories and wonders of Dempsey's Dell.

Thus it came about that when Tim McFadden announced that he had decided to give a Winter picnic to the Flatters, there was an immediate and delighted demand on all sides that Dempsey's Dell be made the picnic grounds.

"I've hard that much about the Dell that I'm 'terrible awful anxious to be seeing it, though I don't believe much in going to foreign parts," said Mrs. Murphy to the gossips who came to her room to discuss the affair over a can of beer.

"And Dempsey has a saloon there," said Mrs. Dunnigan, mother of the Twins, in a comforting manner.

"Sure, that's nothing to me," exclaimed Mrs. Murphy, indignantly. "It's little I care for the beer. I'll have you understand, Mrs. Dunnigan, I likes tea much more better."

Among the young folk the promised event created boundless enthusiasm. McSwatt at once composed a title for the outing as follows: "The McFadden Flatters' Skating, Tobogganing and Bear Hunting Expedition."

That bear hunting hint came from the stories told by Slippy. When he first returned from the Dell he swore that the woods thereabouts were alive with bears.

"Dere's more of 'em dan dere is cops in de Oak Street Station," Slippy asserted, solemnly.

When he found that the Flatters were all going there Slippy began to hedge on his bear stories until he reduced it to one bruin, but he did not tell that that one was a very tame and good-natured pet belonging to his Uncle Dempsey. If he had seen better if he had, for then Mrs. Murphy and many others would have been saved a sore fright. But that is anticipating.

"Dats Dunnigan refused to be much frightened about these bears until she was calmed and reassured by the Kid.

"Fear not, lady Bella," said the Kid, bravely. "Trust t' me, and heed no danger. Shouldat de bear seek t' give youse a argyment I wouldn't do a ting t' him but slay him."

"He wouldn't do a ting but chase himself t' beat de band," sneered Marty.

Mrs. Kelly became so alarmed about the bears that she threatened to keep the baby at home, which would have spoiled Mary Ellen's fun, she being engaged to "mind" the Kelly baby. But Mary Ellen restored Mrs. Kelly's peace of mind by pointing out that the Riccadonna girls (four) were sure to go in costume. "And," added Mary Ellen, "dose goils will be such a show dey would frighten de most biggest bear dat ever happened off de face of de eart."

Nothing was neglected by Tim which could add to the insurance of a good time by all the Flatters.

Skates were dug up from old trunks and borrowed from junk shops until every living Flatter, barring the parrot and the monkey, was supplied with a pair. Tim grew sentimental over the two pair he dug up for himself and Mrs. Murphy from among his most cherished belongings.

"Many's the time we've skated with these, Mrs. Murphy," he remarked as he displayed his recovered treasures to that lady.

"Well I remember it, Tim," she responded with a sigh. "It was on the pond where the Mad'son Square Gardens do be now. Do you mind?"

"I remember it well; it was before Murphy married you."

"It was; havin rest his soul" again sighed the lady. "But talking of poor Murphy always makes me as dry as a stone. Hasten quickly to Kelly's, Mary Ellen, dear, and fetch a can." "Hasten quickly, darlint"

It was a great day for the whole neighborhood when the start for the Dell was made.

There were many in the party of Flatters who had never in their lives been off Manhattan Island, and there were those among them who were not without misgivings as to the result of making so distant a pilgrimage into the unknown dangers of New Jersey. But happily the trip by ferry and steam cars was made without much incident. To be sure, the goat, Day, monkey and parrot got loose in the baggage car, and before the train hands had subdued the resulting battle there was not a piece of baggage which had not suffered severely; and the conductor had to be argued with with much sternness by Tim before he would consent to carry the Riccadonna girls in their astonishing get-ups. But these were looked upon by the Flatters as minor incidents tending to add rather than detract from the gayety of the voyage.

At the Dell Uncle Dempsey met the party with a cordial welcome. He whispered to his nephew that the bear was concealed in the woods, as Slippy had desired, and all hands began preparations at once for the principal fun—skating and tobogganing. No one noticed that Slippy quietly stole away into the woods. Soon the fun was going on at a furious gate. The young folks slid down hill to beat the Tract Building elevators, and filled the ice pond with animation and shouts of hilarity.

Dempsey's saloon supplied refreshments for the old folks, and there Tim and Mrs. Murphy renewed the sentiments of their youths until they were both so much overcome with emotion that they found skating on the ice a puzzling pastime.

While this was going on Slippy had quietly untied the pet bear and led it to the edge of the wood, when he suddenly emitted a yell of bloodcurdling character.

"It's Slippy falling out of a tree," remarked Mrs. Murphy, looking in the direction of the cry. What she saw was Slippy, apparently frightened nearly to death, running toward them, followed by a sure-enough bear. The monkey discovered this at the same time, and it and Mrs. Murphy rushed to Tim, uttering wild shrieks of alarm.

"It's Slippy falling out of a tree," remarked Mrs. Murphy, and fell in a fluffy bunch at the same moment that three or four parties of tobogganers were wrecked in fright at the same dire discovery.

Down the hill came Slippy with the bear bounding after him, and when they reached the ice the Flatters, old and young, were scattered in prostrate ranks, fearing the worst. All save the Kid. That artful youth fixed his most expansive grin on his face and boldly approached the dreadful animal with outstretched hand, remarking as he did so: "Shake, old chappie; we're glad to see you."

To the amazement of all but Slippy, the bear grinned almost as expansively as the Kid, stood upon its hind legs and extended a paw of welcome.

"I told youse I'd do it," the Kid remarked to Della, with a wink.

When all had ceased to marvel they began to be suspicious; and Slippy soon gave away the 'secret—that the Kid had put up the whole job with him.

"I could never forgive the Kid," said Mrs. Murphy, still trembling in Tim's arms. "I could never forgive him only that a fright do give me a thirst like the Desert of Sarah. Let us hasten quickly to Dempsey's, Tim, dear."

And they hastened.

EDWARD W. TOWNSEND.

McFADDEN FLATTERS' SKATING AND TOBOGGANING EXPEDITION

55. RICHARD F. OUTCAULT,
McFadden's Row of Flats,
December 6, 1896
(*New York Journal*).

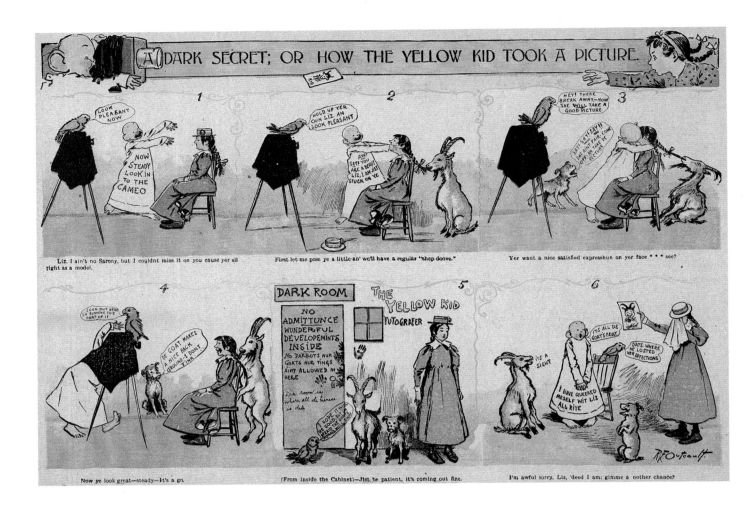

56. RICHARD F. OUTCAULT,
The Yellow Kid,
December 13, 1896
(*New York Journal*).

57. Richard F. Outcault,
McFadden's Row of Flats,
December 13 1896
(*New York Journal*).

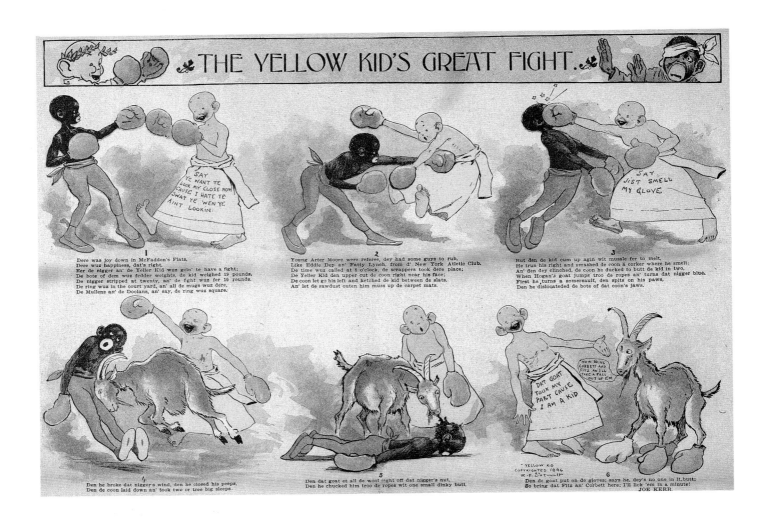

58. RICHARD F. OUTCAULT,
The Yellow Kid,
December 20, 1896
(*New York Journal*).

59. Richard F. Outcault,
McFadden's Row of Flats,
December 20, 1896
(*New York Journal*).

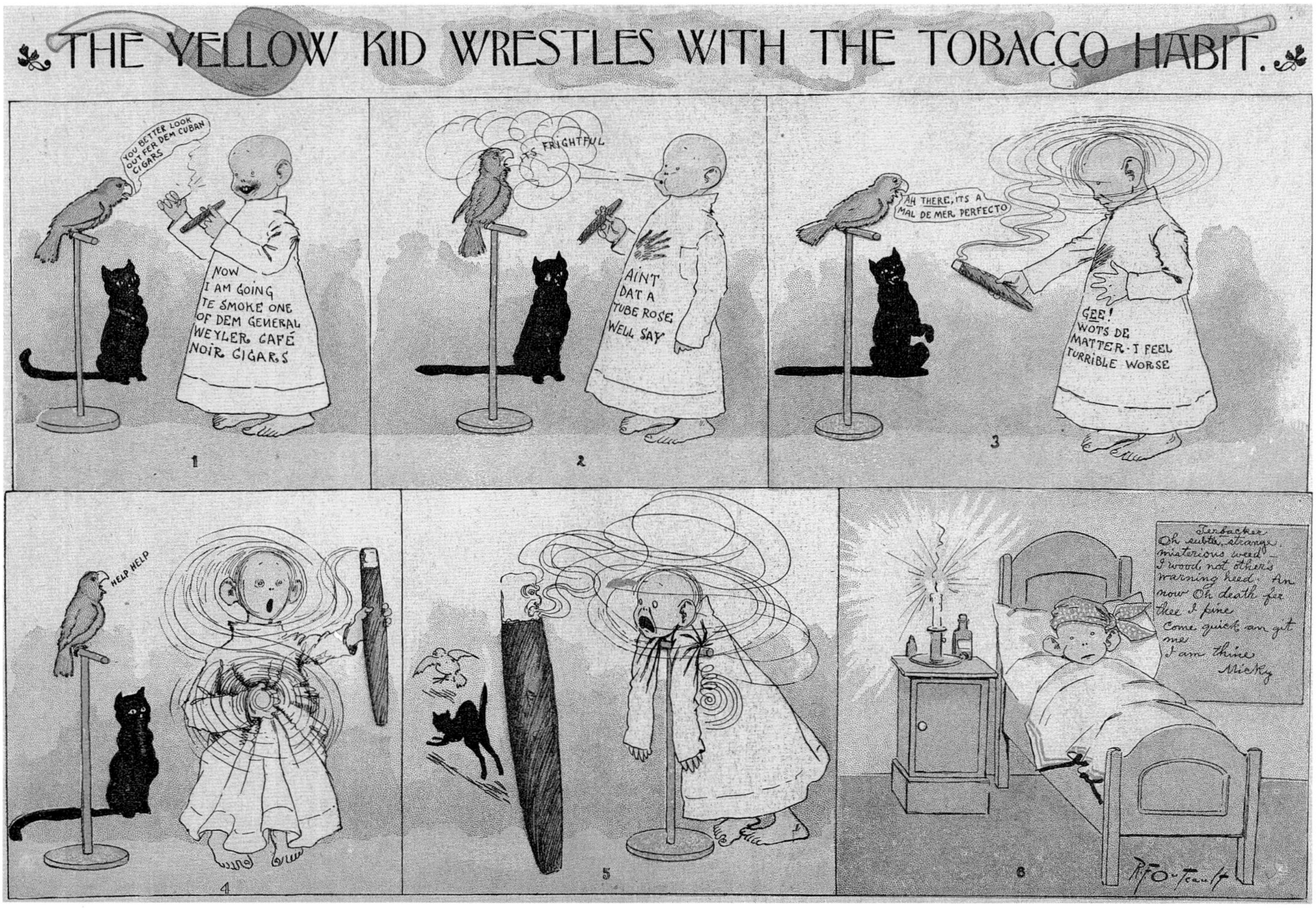

60. RICHARD F. OUTCAULT,
The Yellow Kid,
December 27, 1896
(*New York Journal*).

61. Richard F. Outcault,
McFadden's Row of Flats,
December 27, 1896
(*New York Journal*).

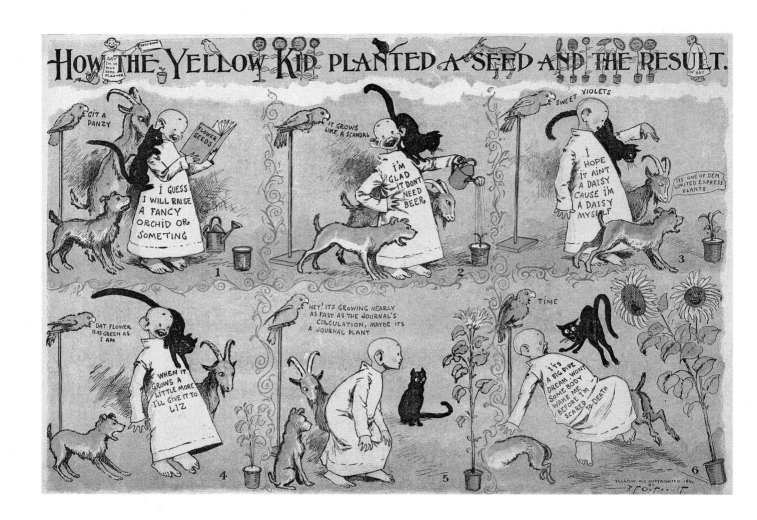

62. RICHARD F. OUTCAULT,
The Yellow Kid,
January 3, 1897
(*New York Journal*).

McFADDEN'S ROW OF FLATS.

By the Author of "CHIMMIE FADDEN,"
And the Originator of "HOGAN'S ALLEY."

A S every one knows, or should know, certainly, Tim McFadden's row of flats were, many years ago, the homes of rich and fashionable people. Not far from them, and on the very spot where this paper is printed, was, until within a couple of years, an old family mansion, once occupied by the British Governor of the Sugar House Prison, and Tory nabobs built the thick walls which, with but little change, still enclose Tim's flats. You should hear him discourse on interesting historical facts in this relation! To me, who believe we receive strong mental impulses from our inanimate environments, the facts are chiefly interesting as offering the probable explanation for the notable social bias lately observed among the Flatters. The beauties of the days when Madison was President danced and flirted in those same houses, and it is no wonder that Tim's Flatters are much given to social festivities.

These remarks are but preliminary to a statement concerning a discovery of a highly interesting character made recently by Tim. In one of the houses there is an unusually high garret, which Tim was recently investigating to see if it could not be used for lodging rooms. He had never known how the place could be lighted or aired until, at this time, he discovered some inside blinds which, once opened, flooded the old place with light. Tim was amazed, and at first a little frightened. He saw uncouth wooden figures with legs and arms in wild disorder, dust covered plaster casts of the human form in whole and in part, old frames, rugs, outlandish tables and what not.

He hastened to invite Mrs. Murphy to inspect his find, and she promptly announced her belief that Tim had disclosed a joss house. She invited the gossips to see, and then the truth was told by Mrs. Riccadonna. In her youth she had been an artist's model—there is a hint of her youthful beauty in her girls (four)—and she recognized the place at once as an artist's studio.

Of course so interesting a discovery could not be long kept from the children, and soon they were in full possession.

The Riccadonna girls took to the place as ducks take to water, and it was their suggestion that the finding of this unexpected treasure be celebrated by a studio party. They had all done a little something in the way of posing for artists, and knew the game. They said that when artists gave parties they always invited a chaperon.

"And what's a chaperoon?" asked Mrs. Murphy.

The oldest Riccadonna girl explained that a chaperon was an experienced woman who accompanied inexperienced women to teach them how to flirt and to arrange opportunities for so doing.

"Sure, then, there's none needed at our party," exclaimed Mrs. Murphy.

But all the young ladies insisted that a chaperon was needed, and that Mrs. Murphy should fill that delicate office.

The Kid was installed as Artist. No one selected or elected or suggested him; he just took the place. He announced that for the occasion he should be known as "Little Billee," and Delia as "Trilby," and the latter was dressed for the part.

Mrs. Dunnigan prepared tea for the party. Mrs. Murphy insisted upon that, saying: "I do so love a good cup of tea; I'd not have the strength to be a chaperoon without me tea, Mrs. Dunnigan."

It was supposed that the good lady was drinking tea out of her can until the cat knocked a plaster figure over on her head, and she, supposing the falling object to be, of course, Slippy Dempsey, dropped her can, and, its contents scattered, the odor of beer pervaded the apartment to an amazing degree.

The accident did not mar the occasion, however, as there was more tea—in fact, a keg of it from Kelley's—and the party went on with no regrettable incident, excepting the goat's display of artistic appetite, which Outcault has graphically explained.

The triumph of the day was achieved by Mary Ellen, but then she had the inside track, her mother being the chaperon. With that advantage she was afforded chances for tender meetings with McSwatt and Marty until she nearly drove the four Riccadonna girls insane with jealousy.

"But," explained Mrs. Murphy to Tim afterward, "it's a pity the dear child couldn't flirt all she wanted with her own mother a chaperoon to help her out."

E. W. TOWNSEND.

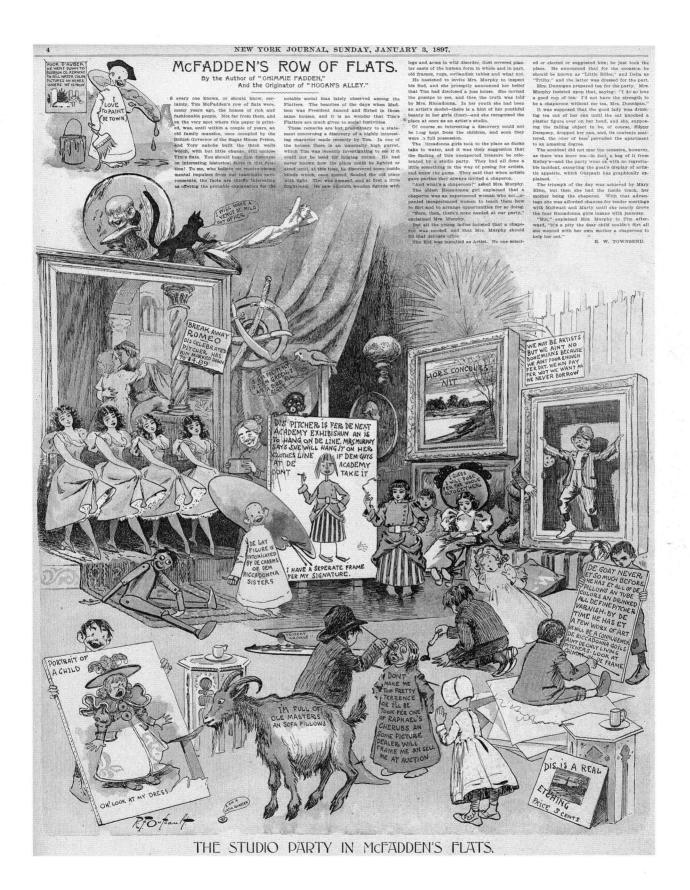

THE STUDIO PARTY IN McFADDEN'S FLATS.

63. RICHARD F. OUTCAULT,
McFadden's Row of Flats,
January 3, 1897
(*New York Journal*).

64. RICHARD F. OUTCAULT,
McFadden's Row of Flats,
January 10, 1897
(*New York Journal*).

65. Richard F. Outcault,
Around the World With the Yellow Kid,
January 17, 1897
(*New York Journal*).

66. RICHARD F. OUTCAULT,

Around the World With the Yellow Kid,

January 24, 1897

(*New York Journal*).

67. RICHARD F. OUTCAULT,
The Yellow Kid,
January 24, 1897
(*New York Journal*).

68. RICHARD F. OUTCAULT,
   Around the World With the Yellow Kid,
   January 31, 1897
   (*New York Journal*).

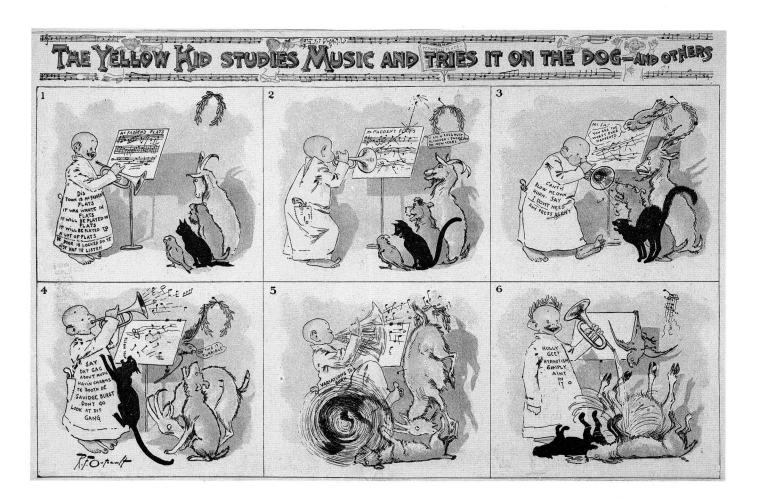

69. RICHARD F. OUTCAULT,
The Yellow Kid,
February 7, 1897
(*New York Journal*).

70. RICHARD F. OUTCAULT,
Around the World With the Yellow Kid,
February 7, 1897
(*New York Journal*).

WORLD WITH THE YELLOW KID.

BY RUDOLPH BLOCK.

n ye last. She sez if yer room very much try fly paper an' she uses.

ption in d' Kassil last nite an' cotland wuz dere. D' nobilitty Cassidy aint so orful warm. ot had names dat wuz full o' m brought a little kid wid 'im one hand.

had a lawn festerval wot wuz sez d' Queen t' me how are ye on Vick I sed, try me. I'm a scotch an' w'en I heer d' bag say I feel like I wuz Rod-

pipes an' d' Queen sashays over Mickey she yells. all rite ole t loose. Wel say, before I got t'rough wid dat Highland fling I made dem dooks

feel like dey wisht dey wuz ded. o ye dance so luvly Mickey sez d' Queen an' die dancin' wid ye. Den one o' d' duchesses wot wuz rigged up in Scotch plads cums waltzin' up an' sez won'tcher Majesty let me hav a spiel wid d' luvly boy in yeller? shure sez d' Queen, Mickey let 'er went.

wel d' way I made dat duchess dance wuz out o' site, she wuz nearly ded. Mickey sed d' Queen before you go back t' Noo Yaurk I'm gaw'n t' make ye a nite.

Liz had t' get fresh. jest because one o' dem countesses sed I wuz too cunnin' t' liv an' guv me a kiss Liz had t' stik dat hat pin o' hers in me leg where dere wuzn't no kilts. o Mrs. Cassidy I'm ded sore on kilts.

Say ye hav no idee how ignerent peeple is over heer. One o' de dooks sed he wuz a grate frend o' de pressident uv de united States is dat so I sed, dere aint no flize on Grover even if

dere is lots o' room. Wot, sez d' dook. Hooze Grover? He's d' pressident I sed.

o he sed I t'ought Andy Karneggy wuz d' pressident, Yes Mrs. Cassidy d' peeple is orfly igner- ent heer. D' kids don't no how t' play Hop scotch an' ye can't get no butter scotch in d' kandy stores dey don't even no dere own country.

D' Prints o' Wails is gaw'n t' giv a banquet t'nite an' I'm gaw'n t' be d' gest uv onner. Wuz ye ever a gest uv onner, Mrs. Cassidy, it's grate spaurt. I'm gaw'n t' spring one o' Chancy De- pew's speetches on 'em—nit, 'cause dey've all been got no grudj aggenst 'em.

I'm feelin' elligint Mrs. Cassidy an' d' rest uv us is all rite. D' coon is

gettin' sassy but I aint afrade. Hoolihan's got a biak eye wot I guv 'im. He sends his luv. Tel all d' kids dat we're havin' grate spaurt an' w'en we get to Ireland we'll send 'em all sum shamrox. I wish ye'd send me 'n' Liz sum peanuts. Ye Can't geddem heer.

send 'em care uv d' Queen kassil Balmoral Scot- land, I don't no d' number.

Rispectibly yoors trooly,
MICKEY DUGAN.

P. S. uv course Slippy Dempsy had t' go an' fall awf d' roof uv d' Kassil but he aint ded.

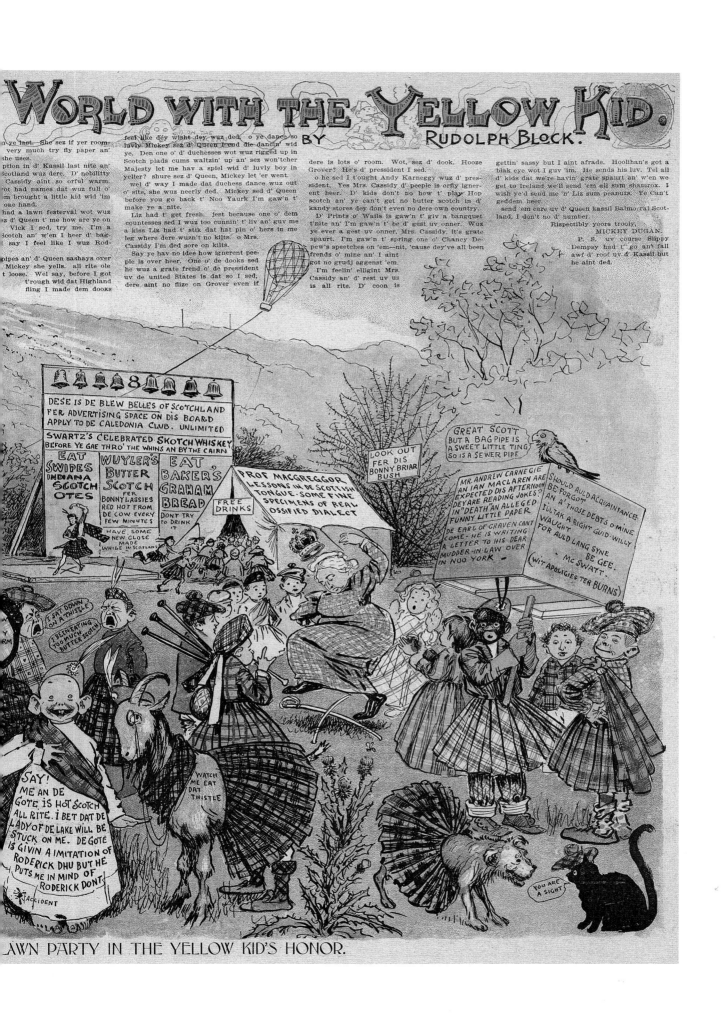

LAWN PARTY IN THE YELLOW KID'S HONOR.

71. RICHARD F. OUTCAULT,

Around the World With the Yellow Kid,

February 14, 1897

(*New York Journal*).

BLARNEY KASSIL.—Dere Mrs. Cassidy, here I am in d' land uv me ansessters and, o, wot a luvly country it aint not nit. D' hole gang wuz ded stuck on goin' t' Ireland but no sez I, no me frends, let us not go, let us goe su mware else.

bekause we got trubbils enough an' wot's d' use uv borrowin' sum uv Ireland's trubbils. But d' gang wuz stubborn an' dey went an' Liz went an' where Liz goze I go. but say, dey regret it. Shure dey regret it an' if we get out alive we wont get caut again.

De land uv me ansessters aint wot it's crakked up t' be an' I don't blame 'em fer gawn' t' Noo Yaurk witch is a sinch cumpaired wid Ireland. I cauled on yure ansessters Mrs. Cassidy an' I guv 'em yure luv an' I had an elligint scrap wid a little Cassidy boy, o how I dun him up.

foist we went t' Dublin where Mr. Kelly went out wid a soljer wot had a luvly unifaurm on an' cum home wid two soljers wot wuz carryin' him on a board. O he had a peetch. I t'ink it wuz Dublin stout but I aint shure, he never had one like dat befaur. We put him t' bed an' he sed it wuz all rite all rite but I don't know wot he ment.

Den we went t' d' laiks o' killarny. I wish we had dem laiks in Sentril Park dey're fine. D' coon went swimmin' an' d' laiks wuz full o' ded fishes d' nex day 'cause dey'd never saw a coon befaur.

We're havin' grate spaurt wid d' coon, dere aint no coons in Ireland nothin' but trubbil an' fites.

I met d' Markwiss uv Londonderry in Killarny an' he inwited me to his pallis wot's in Ulster, say I know a man wot's got his Ulster in a pallis wot belongs t' simpson but I didn't spring dat gag on d' Markwiss 'cause me an' him is grate frends. Dere aint no flize on d' nobillity uv Ireland, dey aint got mutch munny but dey've got sand.

Markwiss I sez wot's d' matter wid Ireland ennyway, wot? wel Mickey he sed Ireland is strugglin' t' be free. Hooze keepin' it back I sed. He guv me d' wink an' sez, wisper Mickey, it's d' Queen. Ye can't fool me Markwiss I sed, I'll bet d' Queen knows better. Ennyway I'm gawn' t' rite to d' Queen about it an' see wot I c'n do fer Ireland. D' Queen is me frend an' she'll do wot she can fer me. I fergot t' say in me last letter dat she wants t' be rememburd t' Mr. Cassidy.

we stopt at d' hotel waldorf witch wuzn't d' name uv d' hotel but say Mrs. Cassidy ye'd orter seen d' bil wot dat hotel keeper sprung on us. It wuz an orful nerve. we guv him enuff munny t' feed d' starvin' poor in Ireland fer ate years. Wen Slippy Dempsy seen dat hotel bil he sed o mommer I'd be afraid t' fall awf dat bil it's too high.

Den we went t' Blarney Kassil. say dat's d' funniest game wot I ever run up aggenst. If ye kiss d' stone wot's pasted up on d' top uv d' kassil where ye can't get at it ye c'n lie like a pollitishun an' noboddy gets on t' ye. I tride t' kiss d' stone but it wus no go. I neerly broke me nek.

Slippy Dempsy tride t' kiss it but he slipt an' fel. o he's a lukky boy he fel on his hed.

I red a luvly story in me gide book about d' Blarney Kassil an' de odder nite I sprung it on Liz. we went out fer a walk t' pick shamrox an' w'en we got t' d' kassil I told Liz how mutch I luvved her. Liz I sed on dis spot a grate nite wunst made luv to a prinsess wot livved in d'

Kassil. Her old man had munny t' boin an' d' nite had sum connexshun wid a match faktory but de ole man wuz ded leery on him. Me luv sed d' nite let's giv de ole man d' rinky dink.

nay nay sed d' prinsess 'cause he's me only father an' I wil never giv him d' shake. But wot'll we do sed d' nite, he wont giv his konsent to our marrij an' I luv you an' you luv me. How c'n we liv on d' same block widout his konsent? Let us fly. nit jentle nite sed d' prinsess, I cannot fly but I c'n die.

Den let's die sed d' nite an' dey went an' stood in d' shadder uv d' lonely Kassil. Jest as dey wuz gettin' dere daggers reddy t' do d' job de ole man cums out. ah ha he sed, traterous retch, I hav caut thee. An' wid dem woids he kills d' nite.

Den I waited fer Liz t' ask wot he did wid d' chippy, but Liz jest kept on chewin' gum so I had t' finnish d' tale. Dat luvly maden wuz locked up in d' Kassil til she dide an' on dis spot we're standin' now. o come awf, sed Liz. Mrs. Cassidy dat goil has no sentiment in her sole.

don'tche beleev it Liz I sed? no sed Liz, I red dat story in d' gide book meself. Goils aint so foolish. If a nite ever got stuk on me he cudn't lose me.

I gess I'll drop Liz, ever since she's stakked up aggenst de Yoorupean nobillity she's been gettin' fresh. Wel ennyway we went back to d' hotel an' I sed where's Mr. Kelly an' everyone in d' joint sez here I am. No I sez, I want Mr. Kelly wot belongs to our party. Is dis him dey sed, liftin' a bundle from under d' table. poor Kelly, it wuz him.

I wont rite no more Mrs. Cassidy 'cause I'm sleepy. We wuz gawn' t' Donnybrook but it's too olly fer d' fare an' t'ings is too quiet. I gess next week we're gawn' to Parris. I shal always hav tender memmeries about Ireland but I don't want t' go back. Yure luvly frend,   MICKEY.

P. S. Mr. Kelly sez dat story about St. Patrick is a fake.

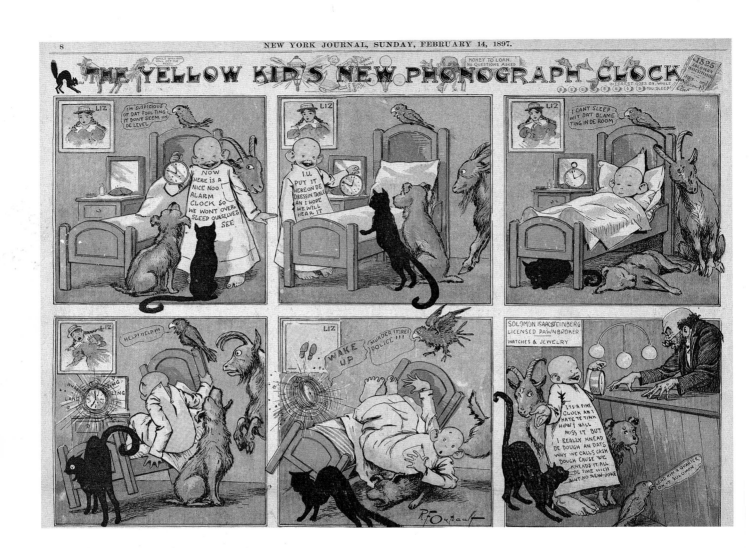

72. RICHARD F. OUTCAULT,
   The Yellow Kid,
   February 14, 1897
   (*New York Journal*).

HIGH LIFE IN PARIS--THE YELLOW KID (L'ENFANT JAUNE) TAKES AN AIRING.

73. RICHARD F. OUTCAULT,
Around the World With the Yellow Kid,
February 21, 1897
(*New York Journal*).

74. RICHARD F. OUTCAULT,
   Around the World With the Yellow Kid,
   February 28, 1897
   (*New York Journal*).

75. Richard F. Outcault,
Around the World With the Yellow Kid,
March 7, 1897
(*New York Journal*).

er billy, here we are in dis gilded hel.
hav struck dis famous pallis uv vise
ins are wun an' lost on d' glittering
s. o billy, it wuz sad t' see all dem
mmen keepin' dere eeger eye on d'

I kept my eeger eye on dat bawl

It wuz sad Befaur dat bawl begun t
happy yooth, ful uv briteness an' sun-
rate hopes fer d' fewtcher an' me wad
amber Nit. wuz I a happy yooth enny
number 6. D' bawl roled round an'
billy, I wuz a hartbroken dopy yeller
arvation givin' me d' glad hand an'
me d' winnin' smile.

r despare I sed, maybe Liz'll hav, bet-
el say, aint dat goil a peetch? She jest
on dat roolet tabil. She cudn't looze
W'en she put 'er wad on number 10,
into number 10. w'en she plade num-
wl dropt into number 28. o she had a

Liz I sed w'en all my doe wuz gawn, stake me
so's I c'n hiddem aggen. wel billy de marbil hart
an' de isy glair wot dat goil guv me froze me ded.
Foolish boy she sed, you can't play roolet fer sour
apples. go out an' play marbils wid d' kids an'
let me do d' gamblin'.

Wid a mitey effort I controled meself an' sed
nuthin but wate. tretcherous maden, I thaut to
meself. jest wate My toin wil cum I wil not
alwuz be gettin' d' rinky dink. fortchin is smilin'
on you now hartless creetcher an' you're pilin' up
dem worldly goods but remember, Liz, I thaut to
meself. remember dat evry house has a roof.

did I hav me revenj? say billy if ye cud see d'
grin on my fase at dis momint ye'd laff Liz got
playin' a sistim. she 'tought she'd found a way
t' beet d' game an' she plade dat way. wel say,
her munny went so fast it neerly boined a hole in
d' green tabil. it got woise an' woise.

I stood behind 'er an' begun t' wissl o I dunno,
you aint so waurm, dere's odder coons wot's jest
as waurm. Liz is a crool goil W'en her last pile
wuz gawn she stuck a hatpin in me leg fer revenj.
It's all yure fault she sed, you're a regler hoodoo
But me hart wuz glad. Liz wuz broke too

so I tuk 'er down an' took d' munny away
fum her Liz I sed you've got d' gamblin' feever
You'd better stay home an' play jax wid d' littl

Liz I sed let's go out in d' woods an' commit
sooside, dat's wot dey all do. If we want t' keep
in d' push we got t' get out uv it. say Liz didn't
even smile. Aint it funny d' way wimmen akts
w'en dey looze munny. Liz cride all nite. I didn't
I cauled on me frend d' Prints uv monakko wot
owns Monty karlo an' toled him uv d' hard luck
we'd run up aggents. d' Prints wuz kind an
staked me to a wad. Be wize Mickey he sed an'
keep away fum d' casino. He guv me lots uv
good adwice an' den I went back t' little casino
an' plade a nu game wot dey caul fronty-karont
I didn't no nuthin' about it but I put my munny
ware an olc lady wid a glas eye wot wuz deff put
ners.

I had a streek uv luck. Clarence, I sed to d'
mug wot runs d' game. if I win out I'll buy ye a
dimund. wel I won so fast dat I cudn't pick up d'
munny quick enuff an' dey had t' caul an assistent
wot braut a barril t' put me munny in By d'
say, Milly, I wish ye'd drop in on Corny Vander-
bilk an' ask 'im wot he wants fer dat house uv his
neer Sentril park. tel 'im I must hav it.

then I went back t' our hotell an' sed t' Liz say
I sed who laffs last laffs best An I chucked a
handful uv gold at her tribbles. Liz didn't say a
wold but she pickt up dat gold faster'n greezed
litening An put on her hat hold on, I sed, ware
r' ye gawn? I'm gawn back t' d' casino t' play
dat sistim, she sed. It's gut t' win.

chippies. I will do all d' gamblin' wot's nessessary
fer dis krowd. Say, billy, did I get square wid
dat goil? ha ha ha, wot?

wel dere's odder t'ings in Monty karlo besides
gamblin' but dey aint very hot. D' place is full
uv peeple wot's related to d' krowned heds uv
Yoorup. I tuk luncht de odder day wid one uv d'
kuzzins uv d' zar of Rusher

Grand dook I sed wil you take a messij f'um me
to yer roil kuzzin? shure mike, he sed, wot it is?
tel Nick I sed dat I'm ashamed t' look 'im in d'
fase on account uv d' way I guv 'im d' t'row down
w'en he wuz corrunated. uv all his frends wot
wuz inwited to d' saramoney I wuz de only one
wot didn't send 'im a presint.

dat's rite, Mickey, sed d' grand dook, d' Zar felt
hoit over it, too. 'cause he node you an' him wus
sutch good frends. billy, d' teers roled down my
fase. grand dook, I sed in a broken woice I had a
luvly present prepaired fer yer kuzzin. Ye no dat
luvly dimund wot I won in O'Shannessy's raffel
last yare? Kin I ever ferget it, ecksclamed d'
grand dook

I wuz gawn t' send it t' Nick t' put in 'is Frown,
but times wuz hard an' d' price uv cole wus high,
an' o grand dook, I had t' hock it D' dook looked
at me hard an' sed Mickey ye mite hav sent him
d' tikkit ennyway. Uv coürse I sed wid me hart
breakin' but fortchin wuz aggenst me. d' rote et
it up.

D' grand dook simperthized wid me never mind
Mickey he sed d' Zar has dimunds t' boin an' he'd
rather hav yure frendship dan a barril uv roobles.
He's ded eezy I sed an' den me an' d' grand dook
went carrij ridin'

De infant uv Spane has inwited us t' caul on
him. We haven't desided yet.

luv t' d' gang
MICKEY DUGAN.

P. S. Slippy Dempsey has d' mumps on d' top
uv his hed. he fel fum a roolet tabil. He wus
playin' a high game

PON THE YELLOW KID AT MONTE CARLO.

76. Richard F. Outcault,
   Around the World With the Yellow Kid,
   March 14, 1897
   (*New York Journal*).

TH THE YELLOW KID.
BY RUDOLPH BLOCK

MADRID.—deer Missus Cassidy, spane is a luvly country nit. D' klymit is on d' bum an' I don't speek d' langwij- it sounds like chineez only woise. D' goils hav ellignt black eyes but dey don't speek Inglish. little Hoolihan has a black eye too Terry McSwatt guv it to 'im.

We wuz gaw'n t' giv spane d' go-by but jest as we wuz gettin' reddy t' take in de alps I got a tellygram f'um me ole side partner Ulaylee, wot Mickey, she rote, ain'tche gaw'n t' cum down an' shake hands wid yer Ulaylee? wel wel, who c'n reesist d' pleedin' uv setch a luvly creetcher, so I telegraft back wil I cum? betcher sweet. so heer we are in a bum hotel. Madrid is littler 'n Brooklin an' it aint got so menny trolly kars.

I wuz supprised w'en I cauled on d' king. he's bigger'n me but he's a reglar softy an' I c'n lick 'im wid wun hand behind me back. but he's a nice feller an' now we're grate frends. I t'ink he's stuck on Liz.

We all went to d' pallis de odder day an' plade tag. say dem kings is funny peeple. dat little kid got mad evry time he wuz it. Terry McSwatt cauled 'im down, say majisty, he sed t' d' king. w'y don'tche take a trolly kar w'en ye're it, insted uv runnin' like d' rest uv us, wot?

dat got d' king mad, ye t'ink ye're waurm, don'tche, he sed. o I dunno sed McSwatt sarkastick like, maybe I aint so orfly waurm but you aint no vital statisticks. I seen trubbil comin' down d' pike so I sed peece peece let dere be peece.

we plade prizner's base after dat an' had fun t' boin. w'en d' king wuz caut I sed to 'im, say

Alfy I'll run ye a race fer kuba, if I beat she's free an' if you beat ye c'n keep 'er. wel d' king wuz a ded gaim spaurt, all rite he sed an' we run say dem spanyurds is grate runners. poor kuba goddit in d' neck.

Wile we wuz jollyin' d' king along who d'ye t'ink cums waltzin' into d' yard but Ulaylee she's gettin' thin Missus Cassidy, I gess it must be kuba. o Mickey she cride wid joy w'en she spotted me I'm so glad t' see ye. An' t' t'ink dat you wuz gaw'n t' giv me d' go-by, o Mickey I nevver t'ought dat uv you.

Uly me own troo luv I sed, me hart is stil in d' rite place but if me frends in Noo Yaurk noo dat I had simperthies fer spane dey'd cut me ded. our gang is solid fer poor kuba libbry. so derefaur Uly we can't hav no ofishul relashuns, see?

Uly cride an' d' luvly spannish teers roled down her face. I wud mutch rather looze ten kubas Mickey she sed dan looze yer frendship. wel I jollied 'er along an' evryt'ing wuz all rite. den we had a long conwersashun about ole times w'en Uly wuz in Noo Yaurk. she wuz orfly intrestid.

is Noo Yaurk d' same, Mickey, she sed. yes I replide, it's woise. ye don't say, how's me old frend Tommy Gilroy wot wuz mayor? wel he aint mayor no more Uly, I sed, but he's willin' t' be. o sed Uly in supprise did he get d' rinky dink? see senyoreeter I sed witch is all d' spannish I know, he aint in d' push jest now

he's a luvly dantoer ennyway sed Uly, me an' him waltzed at d' bawl, but speekin' uv bawls Mickey cum into d' pallis an' let me fix ye up a manhattin like dey giv ye in Noo Yaurk. poor Uly she's jest like odder wimmen, she t'inks she c'n make a coktale, ennyway I swallered it an' sed it wuz a luvly drink witch it wuzn't.

Wot's noo in Noo Yaurk she sed? wel I sed

dey're wolkin' on a noo entrince to d' brooklin brij, dey're kickin' about ded Man's coive, dey're tryin' hard t' refawm pollitix, dey're inwestigatin' d' trusts wot don't trust an' osker Hamerstine's got a lore soot on 'is hands.

I havn't fergottin dose t'ings sed Uly but tel me wot's happind in d' last t'ree years sints I wuzn't dere. how I laffed! Uly I sed dat's d' best gag wot ever cum down d' pike—dose t'ings is all still happenin. migh migh! sed Uly, dat beets d' band.

den d' little king begun t' holler. o I must see wot his majisty wants sed Uly, wot is it Alfy deer? I want t' dants, sed d' king. wel I sed, w'y don'tche? dere aint no ropes keepin' ye back. you don't ketch on sed Uly, we hav a little fandango in d' pallis evry day. d' kid's ded stuck on dantcin. C'n you dants, Mickey?

C'n I dants? C'n I eat? W'y Uly I alwuz dants w'en I heer musick. so dey trotted out a little band wot struck up a spanish dants. I tuk Uly fer me partner an' Liz tuk d' king. we didn't do a t'ing t' dat dants. ye're so graseful Mickey sed de infanter. dat's wot dey caul Uly heer aint I graseful too sed d' king? yes sed Liz but if yer majisty steps on my toze aggen dere'll be trubbil.

after dat we all wus toisty an' Uly sed she'd send fer sum wine. But d' hole gang held out fer beer so me an' d' king went out wid d' growler. say I'm gettin' t' like dat king. I askt 'im t' cum t' Noo Yaurk, he'd hav grate spaurt gaw'n swimmin' wid d' gang but he sed he cudn't leev till he got big enuff t' settl day kubin affare.

ye'll be sorry if ye don't cum I sed, we got a feller on our block wot c'n bend d' krab an' pick up a glas uv beer wid 'is teeth. is dat so sed d' king, I'd like t' cum.

I wont rite nuthin' more Missus Cassidy 'cause I'm sleepy. we're gaw'n to a bul fite next week wid d' king. Liz is gettin' a Karmen dres made she t'inks she'll make a mash on d' toryadoor

sinseerly yoors,

MICKEY

P. S. mr. Kelly has sined d' plej. o he had an orful one it lastid a week.

HAKES HIS TROTTERS IN OLD MADRID.

77. RICHARD F. OUTCAULT,
Around the World With the Yellow Kid,
March 21, 1897
(*New York Journal*).

PANE.—deer billy Cassidy, say tel d' fellers t' geddup a bul fite o it's grate I seen one, me an' d' king an' dook uv Veragwar who is related t' Kolumbus wot diskuvered Ameriker we all went an' had ellgint spaurt. It wuzn't no fake.

y' see it wuz like dis, Mickey sed d' king, we hav goddup a bul fite in yer onner wll ye cum? Shure Alfy I sed, hooze gaw'n t' fite wid d' bul? o d' tory doors, sed his majisty, dey get pade fer it. Wel I sed I'll go on one condishun, I want a crack at dat bul.

d' king laffed jently, Mickey he sed, as long as ye're in my kingdum ye c'n do wot ye like. witch aint no merry jest 'cause I do dat warevver I go. so ennyway we went t' d' fite, me an' me Liz, Slippy Dempsey, Terry McSwatt, little Hoolihan an' sum uv d' kids wot don't cut no ise.

wun uv dem mugs wot looks like a akter in a komic sho cums up t' me an' speeks t' me like he wuz breakin' his teet' Hooze yer frend I sed t' d' king. O sed Alfy he wants t' kno if ye'd like t' see d' bul befaur d' fite. w'y shure.

a bul, deer billy is a nobill annimil. Dem buls wot'che c'n see up in d' slauter houzes on de East rivver aint in it wid d' buls dat fite heer. Nit, billy, dey aint in d' saim class. dese buls is jentiemen wile dem East rivver buls is lofers.

I tuk a look at d' bul an' I sed t' d' king, majisty I sed I gess I wont fite t'day, 'cause me stummick has gone back on me an' me lungs is ful uv air. cum awf sed d' king, ye're a frade cat. wel billy I cudn't hiddim 'cause I wuz his gest but I dared 'im t' nock a chip orf me shoulder an' he didn't dass.

Wile d' band wuz playin' down in hot Tamalo alley in onner of our arrival his nibs d' dook uv Veragwar cums waltzin' inter our box. hello Mickey he sed hav ye cum t' see d' bul fite. o deer no I sed winkin' at d' king, I hav cum heer t' play golf. Veragwar blushed down.i' d' roots uv his wiskers an' sed dat's a hoss on me.

but'che got t' be respektful t' d' man hooze relativ diskuvered yer country, so I apolerjized an' sed I wuz only kiddin'. As a matter uv fakt, dook I sed I hav cum heer t' see d' bul fite. den we shook hands an' wuz frends aggen. say billy I wisht ye'd put sum flours on dat statchoo uv Kolumbus ware you wuz pinched last summir fer playin' bawl.

Mickey sed d' king are ye reddy fer d' fite, ledder rip I sed. so Alfy guv d' signil an' d' bul cum out. den a bloke held up a red blankit an' made fases at d' bul. say dat bul got orful mad. he cum chasin' down like a kop w'en he sees ye're playin' bawl an' he'd a kild dat bloke if he hadn't got out uv d' way.

Den anudder gy cums up an pokes d' bul in d' ribs witch d' bul didn't like fer a sent so he goes chasin' after de new bloke. den a mug cums ridin' in on a hoarse an' pokes a pole at d' bul. Gee, dat bul wuz mad. wel ennyway dey teezed d' bul til he lost his tempir an' den dey kild 'im. wot a bluddy site sed Liz. goils don't kno a good t'ing w'en dey sees it, do dey billy?

after d' bul fite we went out t' get a bite t' eat. We run akrauss Ulaylee who wuz ridin' a bisikl an' I sed hello Uly but she guv me de isy stare. o I dunno I sed you aint so waurm. but d' king sed Mickey wot's d' matter wid Uly, w'y is she soar on you, I giv it up I sed an' I don't care, dese fickel wimmen is makin' me tired.

Den Uly trots up an' sez t' me ah g'wan ye sassy t'ing I never want t' see yer mug aggen, ye aint no jentlemen. so I sed stix an' stones c'n brake my bones but names, Miss Ulaylee, c'n never hoit me. o cum orf sed d' king, wot's d' matter wid yooze 2 ye giv me a pane.

w'y yer majisty sed Uly dis kid had d' noive t' send me a kromo valentine woddy pickt up sumwares an' sined his name to it. faulse I cride, tiz faulse proud womin, perdooce yer evidents. heer it is ye little villyun she sed. o billy it wuz an orful kromo about spane an' kuber.

Uly I sed I didn't sen'je dis. onnest I didn't, hope t' die, krauss me fingers. but who did send it, who sined yer name. Uly dat's d' handritin' uv little Hoolihan an' w'en I gets home I'll push his fase in. he's jellus uv me popperlarity an' he sprung dis gag t' queer me. so me an' Uly shook hands an' it wuz all rite.

but o I didn't do a t'ing t' Hoolihan w'en we got back t' d' hotell. Hooly I sed w'y did'je try t' queer me wid de infanter? who, me? sed Hooly yes you I sed uppercuttin' 'im on d' jaw. he tride t' kraul out uv it but no. I wudn't hav it. I guv loined me an' den wid a neet rite hander I par- 'im d' haf arm jolt an' d' left hook wot Korbet rilized 'im an' drored foist blud. now wil ye be good I sed. but he wuz ded t' d' woild.

By d' way billy if ye shud run akrauss McKinley tel 'im I'm loinin' all about spannish seekrits in case uv waur. I found a impaurtint dokyoo mint in d' king's pokkit witch I cudn't reed but sent t' washington. I hope it aint a laundry tikkit yours fer keeps,

MICKEY

P. S. d' little king is ded stuk on Liz she wont do a t'ing t' d' spannish trezhury o no.

WALL STREET

I CAN SEE MY FINISH

DIS IS DE FIRST TIME I EVER PLAYED TAG WIT A BULL AN IF HE CATCHES ME, IT WILL BE DE LAST TIME AN I WILL BE IT.

R. F. Outcault

HONOR OF THE YELLOW KID.

78. RICHARD F. OUTCAULT,
   Around the World With the Yellow Kid,
   March 28, 1897
   (*New York Journal*).

79. RICHARD F. OUTCAULT,
Around the World With the Yellow Kid,
April 18, 1897
(*New York Journal*).

80. RICHARD F. OUTCAULT,
  Around the World With the Yellow Kid,
  April 4, 1897
  (*New York Journal*).

OIMINNY.—deer billy, o I dunno, joiminny aint so ollapaloosa w'en ye cum t' look at it. I'm ded stuck on it, I gess I'll stay heer an' be d' gelber knabe witch is wot dey caul me in joimin I speek joimin elligint.

we're havin' great spaurt travelin' I don't do nuthin but eat sumtimes I drink. But d' gratest nooz wot I got fer ye billy is dat I seen bizmark. he wuz orful glad

dat wuz tuff billy, how Bizzy got d' rinky dink f'um de emprur an' w'en we gets t' Boilin I'm gaw'n t' speek t' Billy about it. dat aint no way t' treet yer father's best frend, izzit? but enny- way Bizzy's havin' a purty good times an' t'ings is runnin' his way in grate shape.

he inwited d' gang t' puddup at his kassil fer a few daze but we cud only stay over nite, we're so popular an' we hav engajmints t' boin. he guv us a luvly suppir lots t' eat an' Mr. Kelly sez Bizzy noze a good t'ing in beer w'en he seez it comin' down d' pike. say billy dat beer wuz a dreem I cud die drinkin' it.

Uv kaurse little Houlihan had t' get fresh. ain'tche got enny pretzels he asked but Bizzy cauled 'im down, ah geddout he sed d'ye t'ink I'm runnin' a ranes law joint, wot? den I soked it t' Hoolihan, ware did'je leeve yer mannirs ye lofer salzstangel good enuff t' giv ye a toist? saltstangel good enuff t' giv ye a toist?

But say Bizzy wuz ded on t' Mr. Kelly, say Kelly, he sed, you seem t' be stuck on dat beer, yes sed Mr. Kelly it's grand, an' den he toled d' walter t' seddem up aggen. o dat's all rite sed Bizzy only d' next ten kegs aint as good as d' last t'ree. But ye cudn't faze Mr. Kelly. I'll take me chantces he sed.

t' see d' gang he inkwired about you an' wants t' be rememburd.

Hello mickey he sed w'en he spide me is dat you 'r izzit yer goast. it's me shure enuff Bizzy, I sed, wee gates? dat's joimin, billy, fer how are dey runnin'? o owagetzikent sed Bizzy, how's me frend Grover. he's in d' scop Bizzy I sed, Mckin- ly is runnin' d' bank now.

dat's so aint it sed Bizzy, youse mugs is alwuz changin' yer prezidents, w'y d' ye do it, o I gess it's t' keep 'em f'um gettin' moldy I sed. How's de emprur? his majisty is purty good f'um all I heer sed Bizzy but y'no me an' him don't speek as we pass by.

d' foist t'ing I noo, wun uv Bizzy's big dorgs guv an orful yel. he's got elligint dorgs grate danes he cauls 'em an' dey're as big as elefunts. we all rushed out into d' haul t' see wot wuz up an' woddy ye t'ink? Terry McSwatt had gone an' tide a growler t' d' dorg's tale an' wuz sickin' anudder dorg on it. dem dorgs wuz orful sup- prized.

ye'd orter hurd wot Bizzy sed, I wudn't rite it 'cause yer muther mite get hold uv dis letter but it wuz jest d' same wot Lumpy Dan sed d' time d' kop fanned 'im, remembur? Terry McSwatt toined pail.

wel d' next day we all went fer a carrij ride an' den we took d' trane. we went to wun uv dem luvly kassils on d' rine ware dey don't do nuthin' but enjoy demselvs an' we all baut chips an' set in d' game.

deer billy d' rine is a fake. it aint wot it's crakt up t' be. de east rivver cud giv it kards an' spades an' little kaseeno an' beet it hands down only dey aint got no kassils on de east rivver. we all rejistird at a jin mill an' den Mr. Kelly tanked up. beer aint got no effekt on him.

We had lebberwoorsht an' beer fer brekfist an' lebberwoorsht an' beer fer dinner an' lebber- woorshtwoorsht an' beer fer suppir also fer dez- zolt, nuthin' but lebberwoorsht. I don't kno wot dey put in dat game but as I don't see no dorgs heer I hav me suspishuns, Bizmark didn't dare wolk lebberwoorsht off on us.

d' peeple wot's livvin' at our hotel don't do nuthin' but sing an' eat lebberwoorsht. dere's' one mug wot I'm ded soar on he's alwuz singin'. but I guv 'im an upperkut last nite. He wuz singin' dee wokt om rine an' w'en d' game wuz finnished I sed to 'im, say mister, d'ye like t' sing?

betcher sweet I do, he sed, I'm ded stuck on it, so I sed wel w'y don'tche loin? an' den I run. me an' him are on de outs now but ennyway he don't sing no more. me an' Liz 'll spring our dooet on 'em but we're keepin' it until we've pade our bil, we don't want t' get soked too hard.

we're gaw'n t' vennis in Ittaly next but we're t'inkin' uv takin' a run up t' Boilin t' see de em- prur, he wants us t' be prezentid at kaurt (not gilty yeronner) but I'm tired uv kings an' emprurs, by d' way billy, don't ferget t' remembur me t' tom Plat w'en ye see 'im an' tel 'im Bizmark guv me a seekrit messij fer 'im.

owf weederzane, dat's wot dey say w'en dey giv ye d' go by heer.   MICKEY.
P. S. Slippy Dempsey fel into d' rine, he is ein doomkopf.

KID INVADES GERMANY.

81. RICHARD F. OUTCAULT,
   Around the World With the Yellow Kid,
   May 2, 1897
   (*New York Journal*).

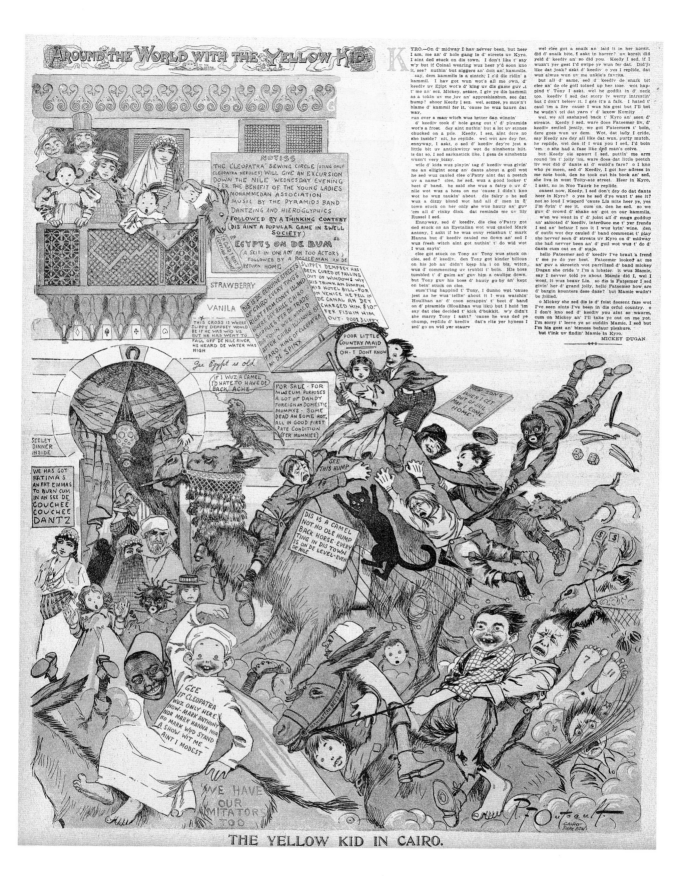

82. RICHARD F. OUTCAULT,
Around the World With the Yellow Kid,
May 9, 1897
(*New York Journal*).

83. RICHARD F. OUTCAULT,

Around the World With the Yellow Kid,

May 16, 1897

(*New York Journal*).

84. Richard F. Outcault,
The Yellow Kid,
May 23, 1897
(*New York Journal*).

85. RICHARD F. OUTCAULT,
Around the World With the Yellow Kid,
May 30, 1897
(*New York Journal*).

86. RICHARD F. OUTCAULT et al.,
cover for *American Humorist*,
October 3, 1897
(*New York Journal*).

SAY, maybe ye t'ink I didn't went t' clondike rite away —wel I gess! W'en I hoid all about d' gold wot wuz layin' loose I didn't do a t'ing but hustle an' now I'm livin' on d' korner uv Easy street an' Velvet avenyoo.

Chilkoot pas aint no worse dan d' korner uv d' bowry an' Canal street w'en dey're layin' car trax an' it didn't faze us woith a cent.

I got a dazey clame staked out all I got t' do is t' sit on d' ground an' pelt d' gang wid rox an' d' foist t'ing y' kno dey're all covered wid gold like a pawnbroker's sine.

I'm gettin' tired uv gold. it's a reg'lar chesnut here nuthin' but gold. I aint gaw'n t' stay heer mutch longer d' site uv all dis gold givs me yeller feever.

MICKEY DUGAN.

I HOPE ILL FALL IN A GOOD CLAIM

THE ALL DAY REAL ESTATE CO. NEW & SECOND HAND LAND FOR SAIL

NUGGET'S HOTEL EVERY THING IN NUGGETS

HULLY GEE DIS BEATS OLE MONTE CARLO YOU CANT LOSE NUTHIN BUT YER LIFE AN YE STAND TO WIN A BIG HEAP OF GOLD

NOT MUCH GOOD

MANY MEN'S CLAIM

DIS IS DE GOTE'S KLAIM

MY! MY! I AM SURPRISED DAT DERE AINT MORE WIMMIN UP HERE WHERE ALL DIS GOLD IS AT

CORNED BEEF

87. RICHARD F. OUTCAULT, *The Yellow Kid,* September 25, 1897 (*New York Journal*).

88. RICHARD F. OUTCAULT,
The Yellow Kid,
October 10, 1897
(*New York Journal*).

89. Richard F. Outcault,
The Yellow Kid,
October 17, 1897
(*New York Journal*).

90. RICHARD F. OUTCAULT,
The Yellow Kid,
October 24, 1897
(*New York Journal*).

THE YELLOW KID LOSES SOME OF HIS YELLOW.

91. RICHARD F. OUTCAULT,
The Yellow Kid,
October 31, 1897
(*New York Journal*).

HOW THE GOAT GOT "KILT ENTIRELY!"

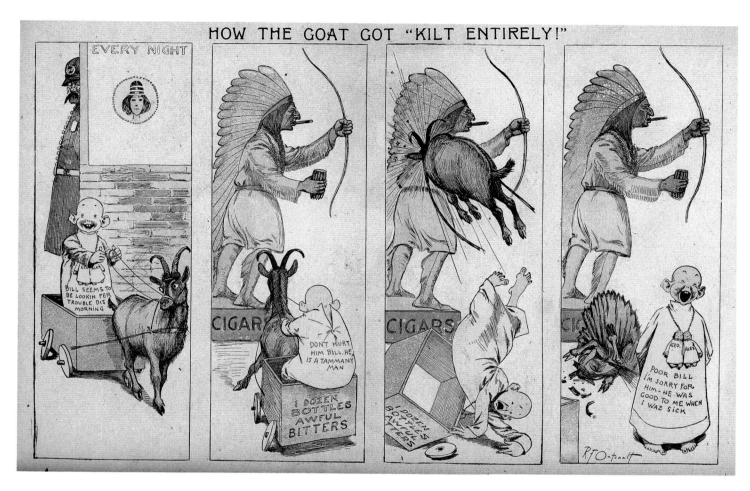

92. Richard F. Outcault,
The Yellow Kid,
November 14, 1897
(*New York Journal*).

THE CROWD GETS UP AN ELECTION BONFIRE

93. RICHARD F. OUTCAULT,
   Ryan's Arcade,
   November 7, 1897
   (*New York Journal*).

94. RICHARD F. OUTCAULT,
Ryan's Alley,
November 21, 1897
(*New York Journal*).

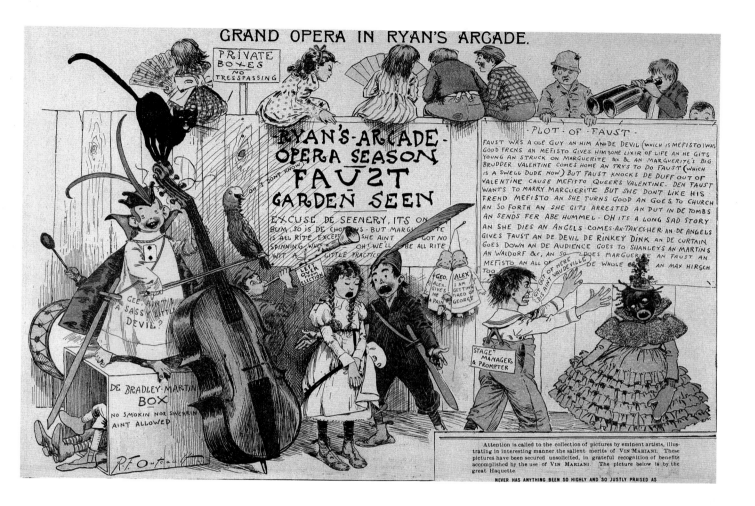

95. Richard F. Outcault,
Ryan's Arcade,
November 28, 1897
(*New York Journal*).

96. RICHARD F. OUTCAULT,
Ryan's Arcade,
December 5, 1897
(*New York Journal*).

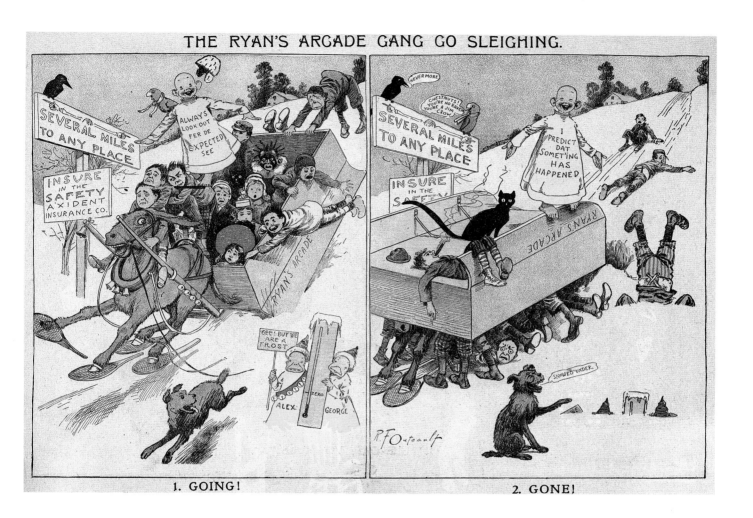

97. RICHARD F. OUTCAULT,
Ryan's Arcade,
December 12, 1897
(*New York Journal*).

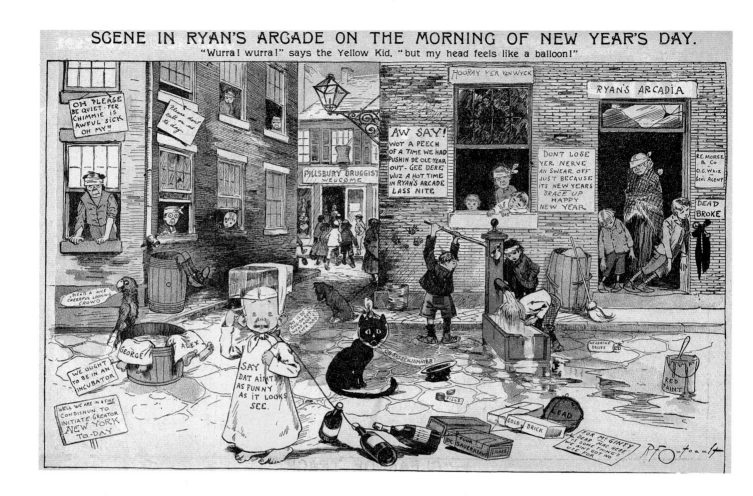

98. Richard F. Outcault,
Ryan's Arcade,
December 26, 1897
(*New York Journal*).

99. RICHARD F. OUTCAULT,
The Yellow Kid,
January 2, 1898
(*New York Journal*).

100. RICHARD F. OUTCAULT,
The Yellow Kid,
January 9, 1898
(*New York Journal*).

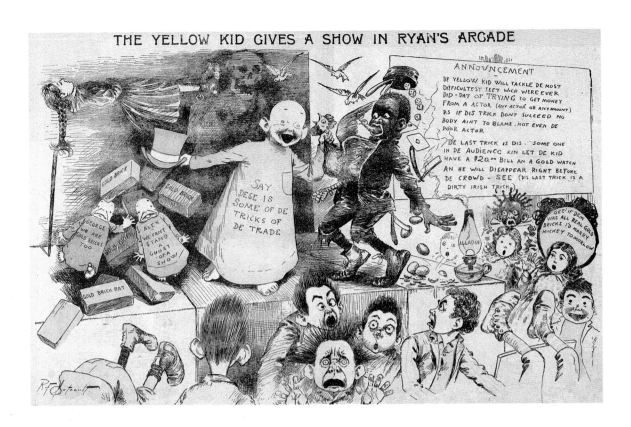

101. Richard F. Outcault,
Ryan's Arcade,
January 16, 1898
(*New York Journal*).

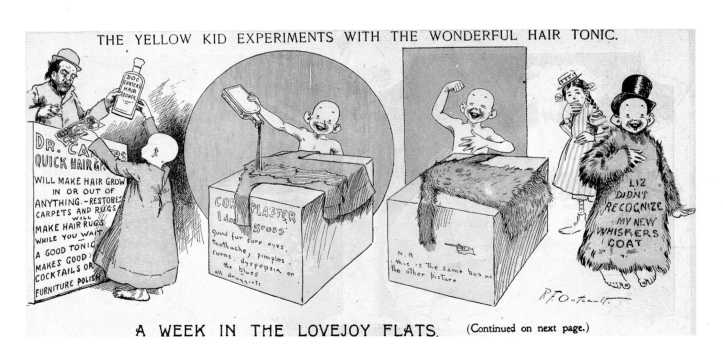

102. Richard F. Outcault,
The Yellow Kid,
January 23, 1898
(*New York Journal*).

103. Richard F. Outcault,
The Casey Corner Kids' Dime Museum,"
May 1, 1898
(*New York World*).

104. WILLIAM H. FRIDAY and HOMER TOURJEE,
"The Dugan Kid Who Lives in Hogan's Alley,"
sheet music with drawing by
RICHARD F. OUTCAULT?, (1896).

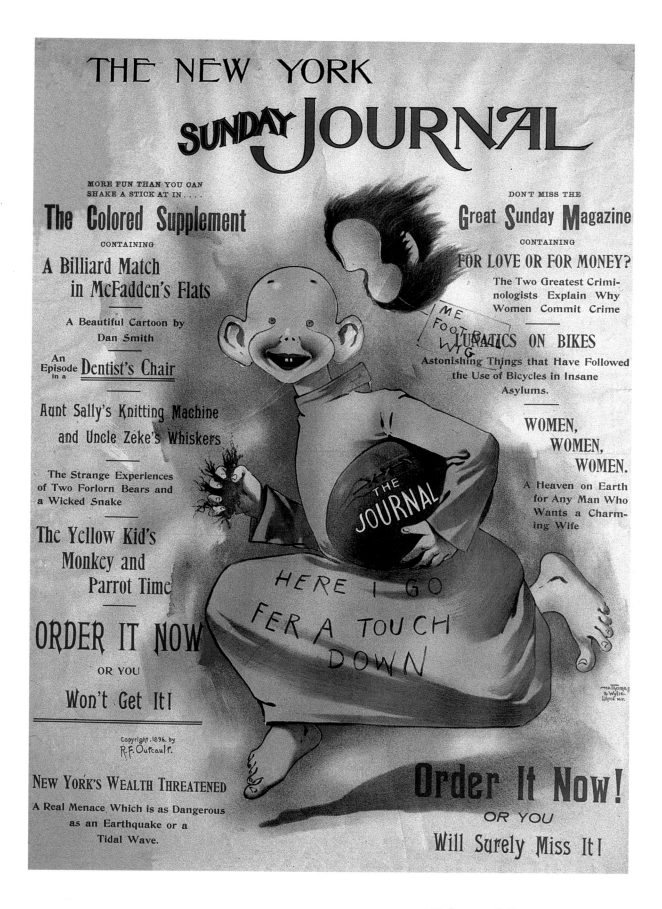

105. Richard F. Outcault,
poster for the *New York Journal,
American Humorist,* late 1896.

106. RICHARD F. OUTCAULT
and ARCHIE GUNN,
poster for the *New York Journal,
American Humorist,*
October 1896.

107. Richard F. Outcault
    and Archie Gunn,
    poster for the *New York Journal,
    American Humorist,*
    November 8, 1896.

108. RICHARD F. OUTCAULT,
poster for the *New York Journal*,
Around the World With the Yellow Kid,
January 18, 1897.

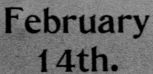

109. RICHARD F. OUTCAULT,
poster for the *New York Journal,
American Humorist,*
February 1897.

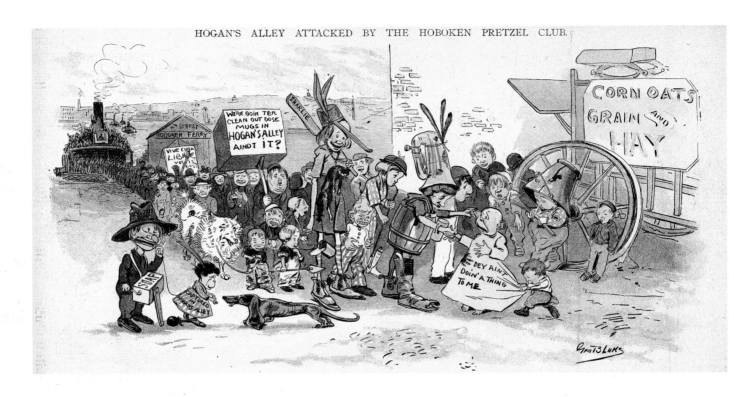

110. GEORGE LUKS,
    "Hogan's Alley Attacked
    by the Hoboken Pretzel Club,"
    May 31, 1896
    (*New York World*).

TRAINING FOR THE FOOTBALL CHAMPIONSHIP GAME IN HOGAN'S ALLEY.

111. George B. Luks,
Hogan's Alley,
October 11, 1896
(*New York World*).

112. Anonymous,
The Yellow Kid,
February 2, 1898
(*New York Journal*).

113. Rudolph Dirks,
"First, the Anti-cartoon Bill. Then,
Perhaps This," February 20, 1898
(*New York Journal*).

114. Rudolph Dirks,
cover for *American Humorist*,
March 27, 1898
(*New York Journal*).

115. CARL ANDERSON,
      "The Bill Poster and the Kid,"
      January 24, 1897
      (*New York Journal*).

116. RICHARD F. OUTCAULT,
box lid for McFadden's Row of Flats
"Yellow Kid" Puzzle, ca. 1897.

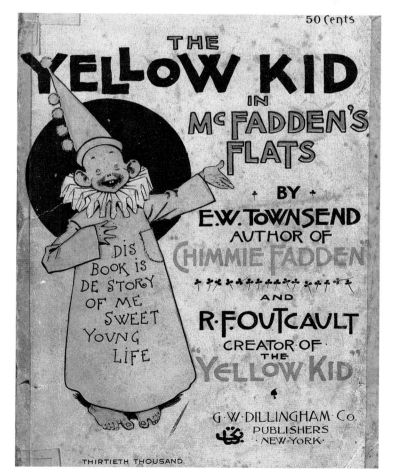

117. RICHARD F. OUTCAULT?,
cover for *The Yellow Kid in McFadden's Flats*,
by E. W. TOWNSEND and R. F. OUTCAULT
(New York: G. W. Dillingham Co., 1898).

118. RICHARD F. OUTCAULT,
Buster Brown,
July 7, 1907
(*American Examiner*).

119. Richard F. Outcault,
Buster Brown,
November 3, 1907
(*American Examiner*).

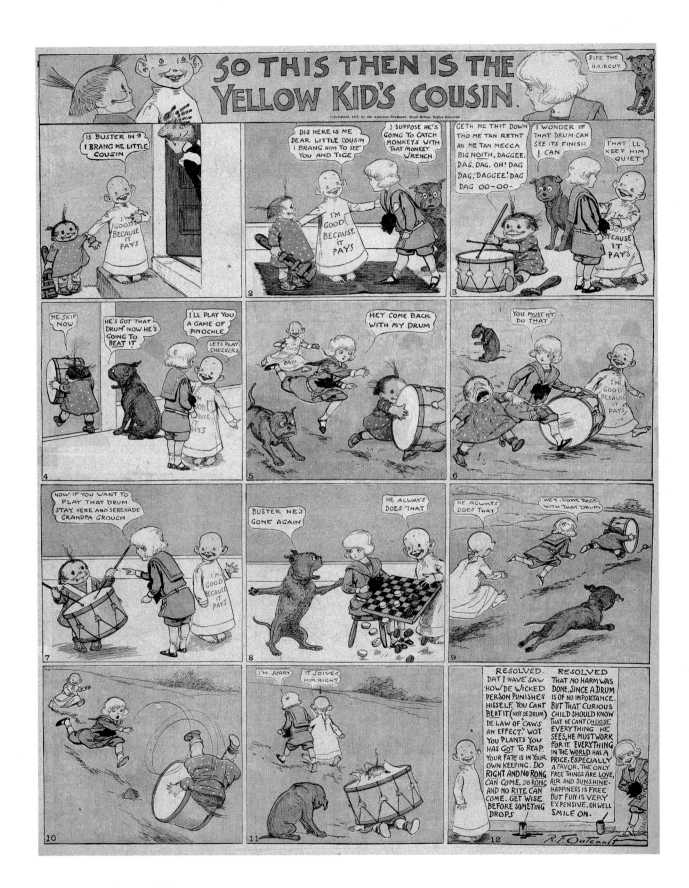

120. RICHARD F. OUTCAULT,
Buster Brown,
March 27, 1910
(*American Examiner*).

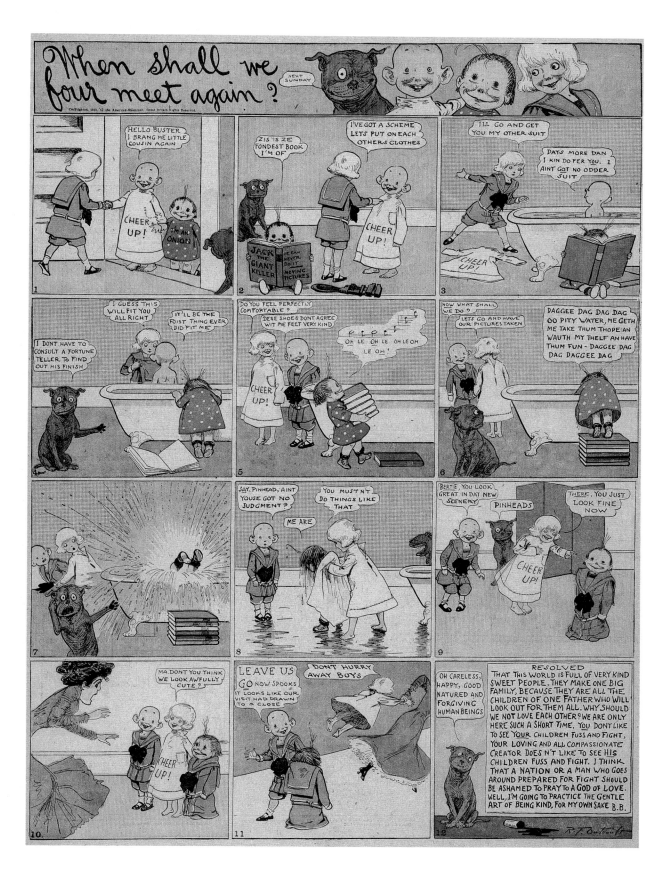

121. RICHARD F. OUTCAULT,
Buster Brown,
April 3, 1910
(*American Examiner*).

122. Richard F. Outcault,
  The Yellow Kid, pen and ink with watercolor
  wash, signed and dated May 12 1907.

Further Reading

Alland, Alexander Sr. *Jacob A. Riis, Photographer and Citizen*. Millerton, N.Y.: Aperture, 1974.

Allen, Irving Lewis. *The City in Slang*. New York: Oxford University Press, 1993.

Alexander, DeAlva Stanwood. *Four Famous New Yorkers: The Political Careers of Cleveland, Platt, Hill and Roosevelt*. 1923. Reprint, Port Washington, N.Y.: Ira J. Friedman, 1969.

Barrett, James Wyman. *Joseph Pulitzer and his* World. New York: Vanguard Press, 1941.

Barth, Gunther. *City People: The Rise of Modern City Culture in Nineteenth-century America*. Oxford: Oxford University Press, 1980.

Beer, Thomas. *The Mauve Decade: American Life at the End of the Nineteenth Century*. New York: Alfred A. Knopf, 1926.

Berger, Arthur Asa. *The Comic-stripped American*. New York: Walker and Company, 1973.

Blair, Karen. *Clubwomen as Feminists: True Womanhood Redefined, 1868-1914*. New York: Holmes and Meier, 1980.

Boyer, Paul. *Urban Masses and Moral Order in America, 1820–1920*. Cambridge: Harvard University Press, 1978.

Brown, Charles H. *The Correspondents' War: Journalists in the Spanish-American War*. New York: Charles Scribner's Sons, 1967.

Brown, Henry Collins. *In the Golden Nineties*. Hastings-On-Hudson, N.Y.: Valentine's Manual, 1928.

Carlson, Oliver and Ernest Sutherland Bates. *Hearst, Lord of San Simeon*. New York: Viking Press, 1937.

Cheape, Charles W. *Moving the Masses: Urban Public Transit in New York, Boston, and Philadelphia, 1880–1912*. Cambridge: Harvard University Press, 1980.

Davis, Allen *Spearheads for Reform: The Social Settlements and the Progressive Movement, 1890–1914*. Oxford: Oxford University Press, 1967.

Davis, Allen F. *Silver Cities: The Photography of American Urbanization, 1839-1915*. Philadelphia: Temple University Press, 1984.

DeForest, Robert W. and Lawrence Veiller, eds. *The Tenement House Problem*. 2 vols. New York: Macmillan, 1903.

DeHaven, Tom. *Funny Papers*. New York: Viking, 1985.

Drudy, P. J., ed. *The Irish in America: Emigration, Assimilation and Impact*. Cambridge: Cambridge University Press, 1985.

Du Maurier, George. *Trilby*. New York: Harper and Brothers, 1894.

Erenberg, Lewis A. *Steppin' Out: New York Nightlife and the Transformation of American Culture, 1890–1930*. Westport, Ct.: Greenwood Press, 1981.

Ewen, Elizabeth. *Immigrant Women in the Land of Dollars: Life and Culture on the Lower East Side, 1890–1925*. New York: Monthly Review Press, 1985.

Ewen, Stuart. *Captains of Consciousness: Advertising and the Social Roots of the Consumer Culture*. New York: McGraw Hill, 1976.

Gilbert, Douglas. *American Vaudeville, Its Life and Times*. New York: Whittlesey House, 1940.

Gilfoyle, Timothy J. *City of Eros: New York City, Prostitution, and the Commercialization of Sex*. New York: W.W. Norton, 1992.

Gosnell, Harold F. *Boss Platt and His New York Machine: A Study of the Political Leadership of Thomas C. Platt, Theodore Roosevelt, and Others*. 1924. Reprint, New York: Russell and Russell, 1974.

Goulart, Ron. *The Encyclopedia of American Comics.* New York: Facts on File, 1990.

Hammack, David C. *Power and Society: Greater New York at the Turn of the Century.* New York: Russell Sage Foundation, 1982.

Harris, Neil. *Cultural Excursions: Marketing Appetites and Cultural Tastes in Modern America.* Chicago: University of Chicago Press, 1990.

Hess, Stephen and Milton Kaplan. *The Ungentlemanly Art: A History of American Political Cartoons.* New York: Macmillan, 1968.

Koenig, Louis W. *Bryan: A Political Biography of William Jennings Bryan.* New York: G.P. Putnam's Sons, 1971.

Horn, Maurice, ed. *The World Encyclopedia of Comics.* New York: Chelsea House, 1976.

Isman, Feliz. *Weber and Fields, Their Tribulations, Triumphs and Their Associates.* New York: Boni and Liveright, 1934.

Kasson, John F. *Amusing the Million: Coney Island at the Turn of the Century.* New York: Hill and Wang, 1978.

Katz, Harry L. and Sara W. Duke. *Featuring the Funnies: One Hundred Years of the Comic Strip.* Washington, D.C.: Library of Congress, 1995.

Keating, P. J. *The Working Classes in Victorian Fiction.* London: Routledge and Kegan Paul, 1971.

Kroeger, Brooke. *Nellie Bly, Daredevil, Reporter, Feminist.* New York: Times Books, 1994.

Lane, James. B. *Jacob A. Riis and the American City.* Port Washington and London: Kennikat Press, 1974.

Lott, Eric. *Love and Theft: Blackface Minstrelsy and the American Working Class.* New York: Oxford University Press, 1993.

Lund, Michael. *America's Continuing Story: An Introduction to Serial Fiction, 1850–1900.* Detroit: Wayne State University Press, 1993.

Lundberg, Ferdinand. *Imperial Hearst, a Social Biography.* New York: Modern Library, 1937.

Marschall, Richard. *America's Great Comic Strip Artists.* New York: Abbeville Press, 1989.

Marvin, Carolyn. *When Old Technologies Were New: Thinking about Electric Communication in the Late Ninetenth Century.* New York: Oxford University Press, 1988.

Mayer, Grace M. *Once Upon a City.* New York: Macmillan, 1958.

McFarland, Gerald W. *Mugwumps, Morals, and Politics, 1884-1920.* Amherst: University of Massachusetts Press, 1975.

Milton, Joyce. *The Yellow Kids: Foreign Correspondents in the Heyday of Yellow Journalism.* New York: Harper and Row, 1989.

Moran, James. *Printing Presses.* Berkeley: University of California Press, 1973.

Morgan, H. Wayne. *America's Road to Empire: The War with Spain and Overseas Expansion.* New York: Alfred A. Knopf, 1965.

Morris, Lloyd. 1951. *Incredible New York: High Life and Low Life of the Last Hundred Years.* New York: Random House, 1951.

Mott, Frank Luther. 1944. *American Journalism: A History of Newspapers in the United States through 250 years, 1690 to 1940.* New York: Macmillan Co., 1944.

Nasaw, David. *Children of the City: At Work and at Play.* Oxford: Oxford University Press, 1985.

Nasaw, David. *Going Out: The Rise and Fall of Public Amusements.* New York: Basic Books, 1993.

Olson, Richard D. "'Say! Dis is Grate Stuff': The Yellow Kid and the birth of the American comics." *Syracuse University Library Associates Courier,* 28, 1: 19–34, 1993.

Painter, Nell Irvin. *Standing at Armageddon: The United States, 1877–1919.* New York: W.W. Norton, 1987.

Peiss, Kathy. *Cheap Amusements: Working Women and Leisure in Turn-of-the century New York.* Philadelphia: Temple University Press, 1986.

Pogel, Nancy and Paul P. Somers, Jr., "Editorial Cartoons." In *Concise Histories of American Popular Culture,* edited by M. Thomas Inge, 119–128. Westport: Greenwood Press, 1982.

Pollack, Norman. *The Populist Response to Industrial America.* Cambridge: Harvard University Press, 1962.

Pratt, Julius W. *Expansionists of 1898: The Acquisition of Hawaii and the Spanish Islands.* Baltimore: Johns Hopkins University Press, 1936.

Press, Charles. *The Political Cartoon.* Rutherford, N.J.: Fairleigh Dickinson University Press, 1981.

Price, Richard G. G. *A History of Punch.* London: Collins, 1957.

Riis, Jacob A. *How the Other Half Lives: Studies Among the Tenements of New York.* 1890. Reprint with 100 photographs from the Jacob A. Riis collection, the Museum of the City of New York, and a preface by Charles A. Madison. New York: Dover Publications, 1971.

———. *The Making of an American.* New York: Macmillan, 1902.

Sante, Luc. *Low Life: Lures and Snares of Old New York.* New York: Farrar, Straus, Giroux, 1991.

Schudson, Michael. *Discovering the News: A Social History of American Newspapers.* New York: Basic Books. 1978.

Seitz, Don C. *Joseph Pulitzer, His Life and Letters.* Garden City: Garden City Publishing, 1927.

Smith, Page. *The Rise of Industrial America.* New York: Penguin Books, 1984.

Snyder, Robert W. *The Voice of the City: Vaudeville and Popular Culture in New York.* New York: Oxford University Press, 1989.

Swanberg, W. A. *Citizen Hearst.* New York: Charles Scribner's Sons, 1961.

———. *Pulitzer.* New York: Charles Scribner's Sons, 1967.

Townsend, Edward W. *Chimmie Fadden, Major Max, and Other Stories.* New York: Lovell, Coryell and Company, 1895.

——— and R. F. Outcault. *The Yellow Kid in McFadden's Flats.* New York: G. W. Dillingham, 1897.

Trachtenbertg, Alan. *The Incorporation of America: Culture and Society in the Gilded Age.* New York: Hill and Wang, 1982.

Waugh, Coulton. *The Comics.* New York: Macmillan, 1947.

Werner, M. R. *Tammany Hall.* Garden City: Garden City Publishing. 1932.

Winkler, John K. *William Randolph Hearst, a New Appraisal.* New York: Hastings House, 1955.

Wittke, Carl. *The Irish in America.* 1956. Reprint, New York: Russell and Russell, 1970.

GRAND CONGRESS of
A Galaxy of Wit & Humor

BY WAY OF CELEBRATION.

ORDINARILY, combining the best creations of the greatest comic artists would be about the same thing as putting lambs, lions, cats and dogs into a cage and asking them all to please be quiet. Some of them would be quiet, because there would be nothing left of them. Then the survivors would fight it out for the supremacy, and there would be mighty little sleep in the neighborhood.

But to-day the Sunday World accomplishes a hitherto impossible feat, made possible only by the joy which the comic artists feel in the increase of its Funny Side to eight pages. They are willing to dwell in harmony here, as you see them, and for this reason we are able to present the greatest comic creations of the last decade, the things that have made you not only laugh once, but watch for them week after week. In them, from the Brownies to the latest invention, you see what you have laughed at for years. That the Sunday World has been responsible for many of them—in fact, the great majority—you will admit after you have looked at them. Under the able directorship of Hon. George W. Peck the Funny Side will doubtless furnish you with many more humorous surprises.

GEE!
I'M SO BUSY
I HAVN'T
GOT TIME
TO DO
ANYT'ING
OR
ANYBODY

R.F. Outcault

J.K BRYANS THE SILHOUETTE

THE MAN FROM BROOKLYN.
(Bargain day at the Stores.)
One of the best things by T.E. Powers that has appeared in the N.Y. World.

T.E. POWERS

THE FLUFFY DUFF SISTERS, Created in the Sunday World, 1900 by BRYANS

"THE YELLOW KID." THE MOST POPULAR HUMOROUS CREATION OF THE CENTURY. THE YELLOW KID WAS FIRST PRODUCED IN THE "WORLD" IN 1895." by R.F. OUTCAULT.

R.F. OUTCAULT THE YELLOW KID MAN

W. F. MARRINER

THE ROLY POLYS. ONE OF THE WORLDS GREATEST SUCCESSES. First Presented in 1898.

PAUL WEST CREATOR OF THE ROLY POLYS

ENGELS

ONE OF THE GREAT CARTOONS OF C.G. BUSH THAT APPEAR IN THE N.Y. WORLD.

PLATT'S FAREWELL TO CROKER

CHAS. G. BUSH. THE WORLD'S NOTED CARTOONIST.

TYPES OF KIDS Drawn by Marriner in the Sunday World. Their quaintness has made him famous.

DR W. DENSLOW THE FATHER Goose Man

"FATHER GOOSE," W.W. Denslow's Popular Creation, as he appeared in the SUNDAY WORLD